T. E. Lawrence
by Augustus John, 1919
(no. 238)

T.E. LAWRENCE

JEREMY WILSON

NATIONAL PORTRAIT GALLERY
PUBLICATIONS

Published for the exhibition at the National Portrait
Gallery, London: 9 December 1988–12 March 1989
Exhibition organisers: Robin Gibson and Honor Clerk
Exhibition designer: Martyn Bainbridge
Catalogue text copyright © N. Helari Ltd
Published by the National Portrait Gallery, St. Martin's
Place, London WC2H oHE, 1988

British Library Cataloguing in Publication Data
Wilson, Jeremy
 T.E. Lawrence.
 1. World War 1. Arabian campaign. Lawrence,
 T.E. (Thomas Edward), 1888–1935 –
 Catalogues, indexes
 I. Title   II. National Portrait Gallery
 Great Britain
 940.4ʹ15ʹ0924

 ISBN 0-904017-85-0
 ISBN 0-904017-86-9 Pbk

Catalogue edited by Gillian Forrester and John Vice
Designed by Visible Edge, London
Printed by BAS Printers Limited,
Over Wallop, Hampshire

Front cover:
Centre: T.E. Lawrence by Augustus John (no. 115)
 © Vivien John;
bottom left: T.E. Lawrence by Flight Lieutenant
 Smetham, 1928 (no. 288);
top left: T.E. Lawrence by Gillman & Co, Oxford
 (detail), *c.*1900 (no. 15);
top right: T.E. Lawrence by William Roberts,
 1922–3 (no. 257);
bottom right: T.E. Lawrence by unknown
 photographer, 1925–6 (no. 274).
Back cover: T.E. Lawrence by Augustus John, *c.*1929
 (no. 296).
Spine: T.E. Lawrence by Augustus John, 1919 (no. 175)

The First World War had a devastating effect on the lives of many young Britons who survived its slaughter but few emerged from it to find their lives transformed in such an extraordinary way as did T.E. Lawrence. Qualified for service with Military Intelligence in Cairo by a series of events arising from his primary interest in archaeology, his natural taste for adventure and strong sense of moral responsibility involved him in one of the most bizarre episodes of the war. A unique rapport with the Arabs and intense conviction of the rightness of their cause made him a natural adviser and later a leading figure in their fight against the occupying Turks. Both mentally and physically shattered by his wartime experiences, he returned to England, disillusioned and unsure of his future to discover, as we can see now, that he had become one of the earliest victims of the age of the media. Alternately seduced and appalled by the welter of publicity which surrounded his wartime exploits, his attempts to seek a future for himself in privacy only compounded press speculation about his activities. A complex character living in an age still unaware of Freudian analysis, he never succeeded in reconciling himself with the heroic persona which he had created. It is nevertheless perhaps as much for his post-war achievements that he should really be remembered today: his part in the diplomatic negotiations which led to the settlement in the Middle East, *Seven Pillars of Wisdom*, *The Mint*, his translation of the *Odyssey*, and his work on sea-rescue craft for the RAF.

This celebration of Lawrence's life and achievements falls within the centenary year of his birth and is the latest in the series of major biographical exhibitions organised by the National Portrait Gallery over the past twenty-two years. Previous great historical figures have included Boswell, Pepys, Richard III, Thomas More and, most recently, Handel. With no specialist knowledge of Lawrence when we started planning the exhibition, we were soon to find that he made an ideal subject through the sheer volume of visual material available. Lawrence's patronage of artists, especially for the illustrations for *Seven Pillars of Wisdom*, is one aspect of his life that is often overlooked, and he can be regarded as one of the few important private patrons in Britain this century. Apart from telling the story of Lawrence's life in as visually interesting manner as possible, the exhibition also reassembles as many of the original illustrations for *Seven Pillars* as have ever been seen together since they were first exhibited at the Leicester Galleries in 1927.

We were extremely fortunate in securing both as consultant on the exhibition and writer of the catalogue the author of the forthcoming authorised biography of Lawrence, Jeremy Wilson, at a time when he was in the throes of putting the final touches to his own work. His knowledge of Lawrence and the documentary sources is encyclopaedic and the exhibition and catalogue would have been infinitely poorer without his participation. To him and indeed to Nicole Wilson and the team of research assistants we owe a great debt of gratitude. We must also thank A.W. Lawrence and the Trustees of the *Seven Pillars of Wisdom* Trust for their assistance and permission to display and publish material within their copyright. Our gratitude is also due to Charles Grosvenor for his assistance in tracing portraits in private hands and for letting us plunder his iconography, and to Hugh Leach for letting us plunder his house to decorate the exhibition and for much sensible advice and encouragement.

To these and to the many lenders and enthusiasts, especially those listed here, our thanks: the Warden and Librarian of All Souls College, Oxford, St. John Armitage, Dr James Allan, Arthur MacGregor, Dr Nicholas Penny and Dr Jon Whiteley of the Ashmolean Museum, Oxford, Nicolas Barker, Richard Benson-Gyles, Jack Flavell and the staff of the Bodleian Library, Oxford, Colonel Forty of the Bovington Tank

Museum, Colonel Bradfer-Lawrence, Malcolm Brown, Jonathan Cape Ltd, Dr Lionel Dakers, Jack Easton, Mrs Michiko Helstrip, Penelope Hughes-Stanton, Janet Barrington, Jane Carmichael, Christopher Dowling, Angela Weight and their colleagues at the Imperial War Museum, the Librarian, Jesus College, Oxford, Christopher Kennington, Christopher Matheson, Peter and Barbara Metcalfe, Dr Rupert Chapman of the Palestine Exploration Fund, John Powell, Michael Bott of Reading University, Sarah and John Roberts, Marinel Fitzsimon of the Royal Society for Asian Affairs, Arthur Russell, Judith Russell, Emma Smith, John and Eve Sims, Carola Stuart of the Wessex National Trust and Mrs Joyce Knowles.

At the National Portrait Gallery our thanks go to Joanna Rickards for so efficiently handling her last task as Gallery Exhibitions Officer, to Gillian Forrester, Sarah Kemp, Carole Patey, Roger Sheppard, Tessa Cruickshank, Terence Pepper and John Adamson who were most heavily involved in the often difficult preparations for the exhibition and John Vice and Jennifer Ramkalawon who undertook valuable research for the catalogue. Special thanks are due to Martin Shirley of Visible Edge and Paul Gumn of BAS Printers for their untiring efforts on the catalogue and to Martyn Bainbridge for his impressive setting for the exhibition. It has been a great pleasure to work with them.

Robin Gibson and Honor Clerk

A number of people have contributed substantially to this catalogue, and I take this opportunity to thank them:

All but one of the introductory essays are drawn from a previously unpublished short biography of T.E. Lawrence which I wrote in 1986 with Ian Wood, my research assistant during the two preceding years. The work of writing and revision was shared almost equally between us, and in particular Ian wrote the first draft of the sections titled 'International Diplomacy' and 'The Last Years'. Our original intention was to produce a concise, informative, and accurate introductory account of Lawrence's life, and as the materials for this exhibition were assembled it became clear that just such a text was needed to provide a biographical context for the exhibits. Some modifications to the draft have been necessary so as to avoid excessive duplication between the section introductions and the catalogue descriptions. This adaptation was carried out largely by John Vice and Martin Rowe, who were also research assistants for parts of the authorised biography.

As the exhibition contains many exhibits relating to Lawrence's *Seven Pillars of Wisdom* I have added a further introductory essay, adapted from the text of a talk I gave in May 1985 to the Oxford Bibliographical Society. I would also like to acknowledge contributions to the enormous task of compiling individual catalogue entries. Outlines were drafted by Honor Clerk and Robin Gibson of the National Portrait Gallery. My responsibility has therefore been to provide the body of the entries. The text for exhibits connected with the Arab Revolt was researched and drafted by Vincent Landon and Martin Rowe, and for the most part edited by Jonathan Law; my direct contribution to this section has been very slight. John Vice helped enormously by preparing outline drafts for much of the post-war period. In addition, Vincent Landon researched biographical notes for almost all the portraits shown in the exhibition and prepared the maps for the two stages of the Arab Revolt.

Jonathan Law copy-edited all the section introductions and most of the catalogue entries. Here, as in the biography, I gladly acknowledge the many improvements he has suggested.

It would be impossible to list here all the people who have contributed to the background research that lay behind this catalogue and indeed a large part of the exhibition. A much fuller list is given in my biography *Lawrence of Arabia*, to which this catalogue is an illustrated companion. Special thanks, however, are due to Dr. Lilith Friedman and to my father, Professor Clifford Wilson, for all their help. Finally, I must thank Robin Gibson, Honor Clerk, and the staff of the National Portrait Gallery for their enthusiasm, encouragement, patience, and constructive criticism.

Jeremy Wilson

Exhibits are arranged in chronological sequence, except those relating to the writing and production of *Seven Pillars of Wisdom* which are grouped together in a separate section.

Dates of exhibits in parentheses denote the original date of copyprints, facsimiles and other reproductions.

Sizes of exhibits are given in centimetres only, height before width; for books the spine height only is given.

All otherwise unacknowledged quotations from T.E. Lawrence's letters are from those held in the Bodleian Library, Oxford. Some letters quoted in the catalogue appear in *The Letters of T.E. Lawrence*, selected and edited by Malcolm Brown and published by J.M. Dent Ltd, 1988. Lawrence's original spelling of place-names in quotations from his writings has been retained. Transliteration of Arabian names on the whole follows current usage. Place of publication of works cited is only included when this is not London. References to Lowell Thomas, *With Lawrence in Arabia* refer to the English edition, 27th impression. For a complete bibliography of works by and on Lawrence, see Philip M. O'Brien, *T.E. Lawrence: A Bibliography*, St Paul's Bibliographies, 1988.

The following abbreviations have been used throughout the catalogue:

IWM   Imperial War Museum
NPG   National Portrait Gallery
NPR   National Photographic Record
PEF   Palestine Exploration Fund
RA   Royal Academy (when the date only is given, this refers to the Summer Exhibition of that year)

The following abbreviations have been used for published works:
Biographers (Graves)
Biographers (Liddell Hart)
   T.E. Lawrence to his Biographers Robert Graves and Liddell Hart, 1963
Crusader Castles, I, II
   T.E. Lawrence, *Crusader Castles, I. The Thesis, II. The Letters*, Golden Cockerel Press, 1936
Friends
   T.E. Lawrence by his Friends, ed. A.W. Lawrence, 1937
The Golden Reign
   C. Sydney Smith, *The Golden Reign*, 1940
Grosvenor
   C. Grosvenor, *An Iconography: The Portraits of T.E. Lawrence*, Pasadena: Otterden Press, 1988
Home Letters
   The Home Letters of T.E. Lawrence and his Brothers, Oxford, 1954
Letters
   The Letters of T.E. Lawrence, ed. D. Garnett, 1938
Oriental Assembly
   T.E. Lawrence, *Oriental Assembly*, ed. A.W. Lawrence, 1939
Revolt
   T.E. Lawrence, *Revolt in the Desert*, 1927
SPW 1926
   T.E. Lawrence, *Seven Pillars of Wisdom*, privately printed, 1926
SPW 1935
   T.E. Lawrence, *Seven Pillars of Wisdom*, 1935
The T.E. Lawrence Puzzle
   The T.E. Lawrence Puzzle, ed. S.E. Tabachnick, University of Georgia, 1984

The following abbreviations are used for exhibitions:
Leicester Galleries 1921
   London, Leicester Galleries, *Exhibition of Arab Portraits by Eric H. Kennington*, October 1921
Leicester Galleries 1927
   London, Leicester Galleries, *Exhibition of Paintings, Pastels and Woodcuts illustrating Col. T.E. Lawrence's Book "Seven Pillars of Wisdom"*, 5–21 February 1927

YOUTH

1888-1910

Thomas Edward Lawrence was born on 16 August 1888 in Tremadoc, Caernarvonshire. When he was still very young his family moved to Scotland and then, in the autumn of 1891, to Dinard in Brittany, where Ned, as his family called him, attended a French school.

In the spring of 1894 the family moved to Langley Lodge, a house on a secluded private estate in the New Forest. There were now four sons: Bob, aged eight; Ned; Will, aged four; and Frank, born the previous year. They stayed there for the next two and a half years, the boys being schooled by a governess, and enjoying three summers of outdoor life.

When Ned was seven the Lawrences moved to Oxford so that their sons could receive a more formal education. They settled down at 2 Polstead Road and in September 1896 the two oldest boys enrolled at the City of Oxford High School.

At school, Lawrence's interests and personality began to emerge. He was athletically built and interested in gymnastics, but only five foot five inches tall. Perhaps as a result he was strong-willed and unconventional. He disliked organized games, preferring activities involving endurance; he often took long walks and cycle rides, and went for periods without food or sleep. His contemporaries found him aloof, but the fact that he enjoyed canoeing and cycling expeditions with his friends shows that he was a sociable and well-liked boy, if somewhat independent.

In his teens he demonstrated this independence forcefully by running away from home. It seems that he served for a short time as a boy soldier in the garrison at St. Mawes in Cornwall. He was quite unprepared, however, for the rough company he found in the ranks of the Royal Garrison Artillery, and had to be bought out by his father. His rebellious gesture had come to an inglorious end.

At school his work was sound, especially in English and Scripture. When he was seventeen he took first place in English in the Oxford Senior Locals. After this result he wrote, 'I wonder whether there is any profession in which a knowledge of one's own tongue is of the slightest use'.[1]

By now, however, his real passion was for medieval history. Encouraged by his father, he had for the past few years collected brass rubbings and salvaged fragments of old pottery from local building sites. Lawrence had also made friends with the Ashmolean Museum staff in Oxford. He rearranged the museum's collection of brass rubbings and presented several of the more interesting fragments of local pottery he had found.

Throughout his childhood he spent much of his time reading. As he read more widely about the history of the Middle Ages, he lost interest in mathematics, which was to have been his main subject, and decided to switch to history even though this would delay university entrance for a year. He took special coaching during these extra months from the historian L.C. Jane.

By the time he left school Lawrence had cycled many miles in England and Wales in search of fortifications and other traces of medieval society. In the summer of 1906 he extended these travels to Brittany, staying in Dinard with a French family he had known ten years before.

The Lawrences had become well established in Oxford, and in 1900 a fifth son, Arnold, had been born. They were living a quiet, conventional life supported by a modest private income. They attended church regularly on Sundays and kept on good terms with neighbours and many other acquaintances.

The parents' respectability, however, was not all that it seemed. Lawrence's father, whose real name was Thomas Chapman, had a legal wife and four daughters in Ireland.

T. E. Lawrence
Photograph by Gillman and Co, c.1900
(detail, no. 15)

1. T. E. Lawrence to his mother, 24.8.1906,
Home Letters, p. 31.

Lady Chapman (seated, back left) and her
oldest daughter Eva (far right) with members
of the Ogle family at South Hill.
Photograph by courtesy of R. Benson-Gyles

The marriage had been unhappy, and he had fallen in love with a Scots girl called Sarah, who was working for the family as the daughters' governess. At Thomas's expense, she moved to secret lodgings in Dublin, where a child was born in December 1885. Soon afterwards the liaison was discovered and the couple eloped to Wales under the name 'Lawrence'. As Mrs Chapman refused to grant her husband a divorce, Thomas and Sarah were forced to live as husband and wife in name only.

Lawrence wrote that he knew of his illegitimacy before he was ten; but, whatever the case, it was a gradual discovery which, through his being too young to grasp its implications, seems to have been unmarked by any personal crisis. Furthermore, the disgrace of illegitimacy was offset by the happiness of family life and the loyalty Lawrence felt towards his brothers. While the shadow of this secret must have influenced Lawrence at many stages of his life, neither he nor his brothers suffered any of the stigma or problems of upbringing commonly linked with illegitimacy. It is possible, however, that when thinking about a future profession Lawrence consciously avoided any career that might have been jeopardised if the truth were uncovered.

By October 1907, when he entered Jesus College, Oxford as a Meyricke Exhibitioner to read Modern History, he may well have been hoping to become a professional archaeologist. E. T. Leeds, who joined the Ashmolean staff a few months later, has recorded that Lawrence was already very knowledgeable about medieval pottery. There was no undergraduate course in archaeology at Oxford, and Lawrence's natural choice was a degree in History with special reference to the medieval period. This would prepare the way for a B.Litt. thesis on an archaeological topic – a typical path for an Oxford student wanting to train in archaeology.

Much has been written about Lawrence's behaviour at the University, but this was no more eccentric than that of many contemporaries. More unusual was the decision to live at home – he lived in college rooms only during his first summer term. As a result, he never participated fully in college life, and this must have reinforced his natural tendency to solitude at a stage when most students learn to mix freely.

He had few casual friendships: those who knew him well did so because they shared his interests. Some were undergraduates like himself, but others were older men: Charles Bell and E. T. Leeds at the Ashmolean, Charles ffoulkes, University lecturer on armour and medieval subjects, and L. C. Jane, who continued to give him unofficial coaching right up to his final examinations.

One college friend was Vyvyan Richards, who soon found himself involved in Lawrence's plans (inspired by William Morris) to print fine books on a hand press in a timbered hall. Earlier, when discussing this project with another student, Lawrence had contemplated setting up the press in a windmill on a headland washed by the sea. He admired Morris as a craftsman and above all as a writer. Years later he still described Morris as the writer whose work gave him the most pleasure.

In October 1908 Lawrence began his second year at Jesus. He was now living at home, but since he needed a place for quiet study away from the bustling household a two-room bungalow was built for him in his parents' garden. In this private refuge he would work and read, often late into the night, and indulge his taste for romantic historical fiction. The cloth-covered walls were hung with brass rubbings of medieval knights in armour, and his prize possession was a replica of the British Museum's bronze head of Hypnos, the Greek god of sleep.

In retrospect, the most remarkable facet of Lawrence's university career was a growing emphasis on mental and bodily fitness. During the summer vacations of 1908 and 1909 he travelled thousands of miles in France and Syria. The object of both these journeys was to study military architecture. He had decided during his first year to take advantage of a new University regulation and submit a short thesis as part of his final examination. The subject he chose required visits to medieval castles in Britain and France as well as the crusader castles in the Middle East. This level of research went far beyond the kind of effort envisaged when the thesis option was introduced.

Perhaps as an extension of his interest in chivalry and military affairs he joined the newly formed Officers Training Corps (as did many other undergraduates) and

Fougères
Photograph by T. E. Lawrence, 1907
Photograph by courtesy of Liddell Hart Centre for
Military Archives, King's College London
(not exhibited)

learned about uniforms, drill, rifle-shooting and army procedures. Later he wrote about two opposing forces in his personality, one sentimental and comfort-loving, the other Spartan and self-denying. This conflict is evident throughout his life. He once sent his mother a letter from France filled with quotations from romantic poetry, followed two days later by another containing an arid technical description of the Château at La Hunaudaye. Although the technical details were, as he stated, for himself the two letters are so different that it is hard to credit that they were written by one hand to the same recipient.

Much of the time in his second year at university was taken up with course-work. Then, during the summer of 1909, he made his planned visit to the crusader fortresses of Syria and Palestine to gather material for his thesis. This journey would take him for the first time into a non-European civilisation. With the slender means at his disposal, he would have to rely on local hospitality, speaking Arabic and living in the same way as the native population. He would have to travel in high summer, not on roads, but along rough mule tracks on foot. This was by no means an impossible challenge, but it called for considerable fortitude and stamina, and was not without risk.

Lawrence left England in mid-June 1909. Turkish Government passes had been arranged through the Foreign Office to guarantee safe conduct in Ottoman territory. He worked hard at his Arabic during the voyage and arrived at Beirut on 6 July. There he was reassured when told that the walking tour which had seemed so dangerous to friends in Oxford was not particularly exceptional.

He spent the next three weeks travelling through northern Palestine, and sent home long descriptive letters filled with biblical allusions to the places he had visited. After this he set off into the interior, less frequented by European travellers. He seems to have adapted without difficulty to native diet and customs, putting up cheerfully with blisters, flea-ridden bedding and other unavoidable discomforts.

On the whole his journey was remarkably successful. He saw some of the greatest castles of the Middle East, visiting the Crac des Chevaliers, 'I think the finest castle in the world'[2], just after his twenty-first birthday. However, the end of the journey was marred by illness, exhaustion and shortage of money. Though armed with a revolver, he had been attacked and robbed, and could not summon up the energy to tackle his last planned journey down to Petra. On 24 September he wrote from Aleppo to Sir John Rhys, the Principal of Jesus College, apologising in advance for missing the beginning of term : 'Some 37 out of the 50 odd castles were on my proposed route and I have seen all but one of them : many are quite unpublished, so of course

2. T. E. Lawrence to his mother, 29.8.1909,
Home Letters, p. 105.

I have had to make many plans, drawings and photographs. Even now I am exceedingly sorry to leave the two castles in the Moabite deserts unvisited. I would go to them certainly, only that last week I was robbed and rather smashed up. Before I could be fit for walking again (and it is very hard physically in this country) the season of rains would have begun'.[3]

He returned to Oxford in mid-October, bringing with him some Hittite seals for the Ashmolean to add to the collection presented by the Keeper, D.G. Hogarth in 1895. At Leeds' suggestion Lawrence told Hogarth about his journey. Hogarth was impressed, since he knew the difficulties of much of the country Lawrence had travelled through.

During his last year at Jesus Lawrence was preoccupied with the approach of final examinations and the preparation of his thesis. Nevertheless he found time during the autumn of 1909 to keep an eye on the excavations for a new underground bookstore at the Bodleian Library, bringing several finds to the Ashmolean. At Christmas he helped Leeds prepare a talk on medieval pottery and made the lantern-slides to illustrate it.

At about this time, Lawrence fell in love with a girl called Janet Laurie whom he had known since childhood. She was one of the few women he had got to know at all well. His education had been at a boys' school and a men's college, and his mother did not usually encourage girls to visit their house. However, she made an exception for Janet, who regularly came to Polstead Road. Many years later Janet told one of Lawrence's biographers that he had suddenly proposed to her one evening, without warning or obvious courtship. In her surprise, she had burst out laughing and turned him down. The matter was never mentioned again.

Final examinations were held in June, and a few weeks later Lawrence learned that he had been awarded First Class Honours. The result owed a great deal to his thesis on military architecture. Despite this success his private tutor L.C. Jane was to write: 'I should not call him a scholar by temperament, and the main characteristic of his work was always that it was unusual, without the effort to be unusual'.[4] The thesis was remarkable not only for the scope of Lawrence's research but also for its direct challenge to the orthodox view, as set out in Professor Oman's *Art of War in the Middle Ages*. Lawrence, who thought this book was 'altogether futile', sought to dismiss the theory that European military architects had taken their ideas from the Byzantine castles of the East.

With First Class Honours, Lawrence did not hesitate to embark on the next stage of an archaeological career, a postgraduate B.Litt. thesis. During the summer he decided on a subject: a study of the origins and development of medieval pottery in England. The only remaining problem was finance, and this was solved with the help of D. G. Hogarth, who recommended him for a junior research fellowship at Magdalen.

Lawrence spent the summer and autumn partly in Oxford and partly in France. He could relax, since his immediate future as an archaeologist seemed secure.

3. T. E. Lawrence to Sir John Rhys, 14.9.1909,
Letters, p. 81.
4. L. C. Jane to Robert Graves, 26.7.1927.

1

KILLUA CASTLE, CLONMELLON,
COUNTY WESTMEATH, IRELAND
By an unknown photographer

The Chapman family originally came from
Hinkley in Leicestershire but settled in
Ireland in the sixteenth century. One of
Lawrence's ancestors, Benjamin Chapman,
was granted the castle and estates of Killua as
recognition for services in Cromwell's army.

The Chapman baronetcy was created in
1782, and in March 1914 Lawrence's father
was the seventh to receive the title. He was
listed thereafter in *Debrett* as Sir Thomas
Robert Tighe Chapman, but used the name
'Thomas Lawrence'.

Although the family title was usually cited
as Chapman of Killua, Thomas Lawrence did
not inherit Killua castle itself. The last
Chapman to live there was Sir Montagu
Richard, the fifth baronet, who died in 1907.
The house was subsequently inhabited by his
widow, and when she died in 1920 it was sold.

There is no record to suggest that T. E.
Lawrence ever visited Ireland, but in the
early post-war years he dreamed of owning
land there, and hinted in letters that he
might one day buy Killua itself.

J. M. Wilson

2

SOUTH HILL, DELVIN, COUNTY
WESTMEATH, IRELAND
By an unknown photographer

William Chapman, Lawrence's grandfather
(1811-89), was the younger son of Sir
Thomas Chapman of Killua (1756-1837), the
2nd Chapman baronet. William Chapman
enjoyed considerable wealth and social
standing and became High Sheriff of County
Westmeath. He lived at South Hill in Delvin,
and it was there that Lawrence's father,
Thomas Chapman, grew up.

It was to this house that Lawrence's
mother came, a generation later, as a
governess to Thomas Chapman's daughters.

The Charity Sisters of Jesus and Mary

3
THOMAS ROBERT TIGHE CHAPMAN
(THOMAS LAWRENCE)
Photograph by Hills and Saunders (c. 1864)

Thomas Robert Tighe Chapman was the second of four children (three sons and a daughter). He attended the Royal Agricultural College at Cirencester, but was not attracted by farming as a career. His elder brother died in 1870, and as the oldest surviving son he continued to live at South Hill after his marriage in 1873 to Edith Rochfort-Boyd. They had four daughters: Eva (b. 1876), Rose (b. 1878), Florence (b. 1880) and Mabel (b. 1881).

The marriage was not a happy one. Within a few years Mrs Chapman developed an extremely bitter personality and became fanatically religious. Judging by surviving accounts she may have been suffering from some kind of mental illness. Thomas Chapman was unable to cope with the situation and began to drink heavily.

In later years, after he had left Ireland and assumed the name 'Lawrence', he was remembered as a gentle and unassuming man, evidently well-used to filling his days with enjoyable pastimes, especially out-of-doors. He was a good shot, a keen cyclist and an experienced amateur photographer. As he had a modest private income he chose to follow no career. This enabled him to spend a great deal of time with his children. His sons regarded him, above all, as a friend.

Private Collection

Provenance: From an album purchased from the surviving daughters of Sir Thomas Chapman at South Hill, Co. Westmeath, 1955.
(not illustrated)

4
SARAH LAWRENCE
By Sonia Mervyn, c. 1936

Little is known about the background of Lawrence's mother Sarah. She was herself an illegitimate child, born in Sunderland on 31 August 1861 to Elizabeth Junner. Sarah's father was almost certainly John Lawrence, a ship's carpenter, the eldest son of Thomas Lawrence in whose house Elizabeth Junner worked as a servant.

Sarah received a good education on the Isle of Skye where she lived in the household of a relative who was a minister of the Episcopal Church of Scotland. Through hard work and ability she was able to take a position in 1879 as governess to the daughters of Thomas Chapman.

In 1884, having left this employment, she gave birth to Chapman's first son, Montagu Robert (these were both Chapman family forenames). At that time she was living in rented rooms in Dublin, but shortly afterwards the couple left Ireland together, adopting the surname of Sarah's natural father. They moved to Tremadoc in Caernarvonshire.

By all accounts Sarah Lawrence was practical and strong-willed, running her household with an unobtrusive dominance over Thomas Lawrence and their children. Those who knew her described her as a small, likeable yet remarkably forceful woman: once she had made up her mind it was pointless to oppose her.

The artist of this hitherto unrecorded portrait was a friend of Sarah Lawrence in her later years.

Mrs Valerie Gatty, niece of the artist

Oil on canvas, 51 × 41
Provenance: Given by the artist to the sitter; returned by Dr M. R. Lawrence to the artist after Sarah Lawrence's death.

6
T. E. LAWRENCE'S BIRTHPLACE,
WOODLANDS, TREMADOC, WALES
By an unknown photographer

Thomas Chapman and his companion Sarah
may have moved to Tremadoc because there
were regular sailings to Ireland from nearby
ports. In the first years after his separation
from Edith Chapman, Thomas had to concern
himself with the administration of his affairs
in Ireland. His father was still alive, and it
was finally agreed that his younger brother
Francis should take over the family estates
while Thomas lived abroad as a 'remittance
man'. This arrangement was formalised in an
indenture dated 12 March 1888 under which
Thomas Chapman assigned his life interest in
the estates to Francis Chapman in exchange
for an annuity of £200 p.a. After this,
Thomas Lawrence had no further need to
visit Ireland, although he did so occasionally.

Thomas Edward, his second son, was born
at Tremadoc in the early hours of 16 August
1888. When the baby was thirteen months
old the family moved to Kirkcudbright in
Scotland. Although he had little Welsh blood
(his mother's grandfather came from Wales)
and never lived in Wales again, Lawrence's
Welsh birthplace would later entitle him to
a restricted Exhibition worth £50 a year at
Jesus College, Oxford.

Gwynedd Archives

5
SARAH LAWRENCE
By an unknown photographer (c. 1910)

J. M. Wilson

Provenance: the collection of Theodora Duncan;
identified by A. W. Lawrence as a photograph of his
mother.

7
LOCK OF T. E. LAWRENCE'S HAIR
1890

This lock of Lawrence's hair was given in 1939 by his mother to Miss Eva Dugdale, sister of Thomas Hardy's second wife, who had met Lawrence at Max Gate, Hardy's Dorset home. Mrs Lawrence wrote: 'I am sending you a lock of dear Ned's hair cut off when he was almost two years old. You remember he had a very thick head of hair.'[1]

Dorset Natural History and Archaeological Society

1. S. Lawrence to Miss Dugdale, 6.3.1939, Dorset County Museum.

11.5 × 4.8
Provenance: Given by Sarah Lawrence to Miss E. Dugdale, 6 March 1939; bequeathed, 1972.
(not illustrated)

8
THE FOUR OLDEST LAWRENCE BROTHERS
By an unknown photographer (1893)

In 1893 the Lawrence family moved for some weeks from Dinard to Jersey, so that the child Sarah was expecting would be born outside France. In this way the baby, if a boy, would not be liable for French military service.

Frank Lawrence was, therefore, born at St Helier, and given 'Helier' as a middle name. Later, like his elder brother Ned, he would qualify for a closed Exhibition at Jesus College, Oxford. Whereas Ned took advantage of his Welsh birthplace, Frank was able to obtain an award reserved for candidates born in the Channel Islands.

The photograph shows (left) Montagu Robert Lawrence, born in Dublin in 1885; (centre top) William George Lawrence, born in Kirkcudbright, Scotland, in 1889; (centre bottom) Frank Helier Lawrence, born in St. Helier, Jersey, in 1893; (right) Thomas Edward Lawrence, born in Tremadoc, Wales, in 1888.

Bodleian Library, Oxford (MS.Res.c.54)

9
VELVET SUIT WORN BY T. E. LAWRENCE AS A CHILD
c. 1891-3

The suit worn by T. E. Lawrence in the group photograph (no. 8).

Lawrence would later tell his biographer Liddell Hart that the family had very little money. The evidence, however, suggests that Lawrence exaggerated their poverty, intending perhaps to draw a contrast between the Lawrence fortunes and the wealth of his father's legitimate family in Ireland. In reality Thomas Chapman retained substantial capital in addition to his annuity from the Chapman Estates. This gave him an income equivalent to a good professional salary. It was more than sufficient to pay for clothes, private day-schooling, a governess, maids and family holidays.

Museum of Costume, Bath

Jacket: 61 chest; breeches: 58.4 waist
Provenance: Given by Dr M. R. Lawrence, 1964.

11

BECK FIELD CAMERA BELONGING TO THOMAS LAWRENCE

Lawrence's father was a keen amateur photographer. He taught his sons how to use a camera and to process plates and prints. Lawrence in particular shared this interest; during his university years he helped prepare slides for his friend E. T. Leeds of the Ashmolean, and took many photographs of medieval churches and castles. He often used this camera of his father's.

His skill must have been considerable, because a few months after he graduated from Oxford he took over responsibility for photography and processing at the British Museum's Carchemish excavations in Syria.

The camera is constructed from mahogany, brass and aluminium, and used 16 × 12cm plates. It is fitted with a 7.27in lens by Taylor, Taylor & Hobson.

Museum of the History of Science, Oxford (69-183(30))
Main camera body: 20 × 20 × 6
Provenance: Given by A. W. Lawrence, 1969.

10

SARAH LAWRENCE WITH HER FOUR OLDEST SONS AT LANGLEY LODGE
Photograph by ? Thomas Lawrence (1894-5)

After two and a half years living in Dinard on the coast of Brittany the Lawrence family returned to England in April 1894. On 1 May they took up a furnished tenancy of Langley Lodge, a substantial house between the eastern border of the New Forest and Southampton Water. The rent, two guineas a week, covered use of the house, kitchen garden, paddock, coach house and stabling. Lawrence's father was skilled in field sports and took out fowling and fishing licences in the Forest at the then considerable cost of £20 per season.

The Lawrence brothers spent three summers at Langley, enjoying open air pursuits. They often played with children from the Laurie family, whose father was agent for a neighbouring estate. Both he and Mr Lawrence sailed, and the boys were sometimes taken to the foreshore at Lepe where they could see yachts racing in the Solent as well as passing naval and merchant ships.

From left to right: Ned, Will, Frank (in his mother's arms) and Bob.

Bodleian Library, Oxford (MS.Res.c.54)

12

OXFORD HIGH STREET LOOKING EAST FROM CARFAX
Photograph by Henry Taunt (1907)

Oxfordshire County Council Library Services

13

2 POLSTEAD ROAD, OXFORD
Photograph by Michael R. Dudley

The Lawrences moved from Langley Lodge to this house in north Oxford in the summer of 1896, so that their children could receive a good education at a modest cost. That autumn Bob and Ned were enrolled at the City of Oxford High School for Boys.

2 Polstead Road, a semi-detached red-brick house built about six years previously, was to remain the family home until after the First World War.

14

CITY OF OXFORD HIGH SCHOOL FOR
BOYS, GEORGE STREET ENTRANCE
By an unknown photographer

The City of Oxford High School for Boys was
opened in 1881. It had been founded by the
Oxford City Corporation and the University,
and was intended to give pupils 'the best
education . . . both for those who will leave
for business or the English Civil Service, at
about the age of fifteen, and those who will
stay on . . . and enter the university.'[1] In
Lawrence's time there were about 150
pupils, the majority fee-paying, and his
parents paid £8 a year for tuition. By 1896
the school already had an enviable academic
reputation; half the boys in Lawrence's year
went on to study at Oxford University.

Oxfordshire County Council Library Services

1. *Reminiscences 1881-1981 – City of Oxford High School
– Oxford High School*, Oxford, 1981, p. 22.

15

THE FOUR OLDEST LAWRENCE
BROTHERS
Photograph by Gillman and Co., Oxford
(*c.* 1900)

From left to right: Ned, Bob, Frank and
Will.

Bodleian Library, Oxford (MS.Res.c.54)

16

T. E. LAWRENCE WITH MEMBERS OF
THE KERRY FAMILY, OXFORD
By an unknown photographer (*c.* 1900)

The Kerry family were friends of the
Lawrences at Oxford, and their son Arthur
was a year younger than Lawrence. This
photograph includes (front row left to right):
Arthur H. G. Kerry (b. 1889), his younger
brother Harold, and Lawrence. At the right
in the back row is A. F. Kerry, Arthur's
father, who taught at the City of Oxford
High School. The lady at the right end of the
middle row is probably A. F. Kerry's wife
with their youngest son Godfrey in her lap.
When Lawrence revisited France in 1906 for
the first time since his infancy, the Kerrys
accompanied him on the voyage out from
Southampton.

John Kerry

Provenance: By descent.

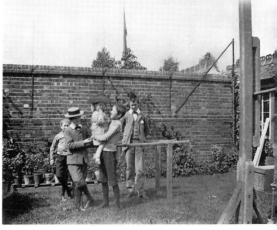

17

CITY OF OXFORD HIGH SCHOOL FOR
BOYS
School photograph (1901)

T. W. Chaundy wrote in *T. E. Lawrence by his
Friends*: 'At school the Lawrences first began
to impress my awakening consciousness by
the regularity with which new members of
the family appeared, in seemingly
inexhaustible supply: each in a dark blue-
and-white striped jersey that became almost
a uniform, the softness of the wool matching
a certain gentleness of speech and fairness of
face. Out of this prolonged family Lawrence
ii gradually became distinct by a spareness of
body and a pithy energy of speech.'[1]

This 1901 photograph includes the four
oldest Lawrence brothers. Ned, almost
thirteen, is in the fourth row from the back,
fourth from the left; Bob is in the fifth row
from the front, fifth from the right; Will is
at the left end of the second row from the
front, and Frank is at the left end of the front
row. Bob is wearing a suit, but the other
three are identifiable by their Breton striped
jumpers. All four went on to Oxford
University: Bob and Will to St. John's
College, Ned and Frank to Jesus College.

Oxfordshire County Council Library
Services

1. *Friends*, p. 41.

18

THE FIVE LAWRENCE BROTHERS IN
THE GARDEN OF 2 POLSTEAD ROAD,
OXFORD
Photograph by ? Thomas Lawrence (1902)

In the Lawrence family physical fitness was
considered to be important. Sarah Lawrence
later recalled that when they lived in France
Ned was sent three times a week to a
gymnastics class in St Malo. This photograph,
taken at 2 Polstead Road during the summer
of 1902, shows that the garden was equipped
with a set of parallel bars. The baby in Ned
Lawrence's arms is probably his youngest
brother Arnold Walter, born at Oxford in
1900. The other children shown are (left to
right): Frank, Will, and Bob.

The photograph was sent by Sarah
Lawrence to the Chaignons, the French
family who had been their landlords in
Dinard. The two families continued to
correspond with each other for several years.
In 1905 Lawrence would stay with the
Chaignons on the first of his holidays in
France.

Dr Maurice Larès

Original inscribed on reverse: *Bob 16 years/Will 12½
years/Ned 14/Frank 9½*.
Provenance: Original sent by Sarah Lawrence to the
Chaignon family of Dinard; given by their descendants
to the present owner.

19

POKERWORK SCREEN AND PENCIL BOX
By T. E. Lawrence and ? W. G. Lawrence,
1903-4

At the turn of the century pokerwork was a
popular craft. Special 'Poker Machines' were
sold which consisted of a spirit lamp,
bellows, and one or more heated points,
specially shaped for different types of work.

Numerous small wooden objects such as
boxes and screens were sold with designs
marked out for pokerwork decoration. The
design on the small box exhibited is typical
of such commercial pieces, and may have
been worked by Lawrence as a gift for his
brother Will. The screen is decorated with
designs from Lawrence's collection of
medieval brass rubbings. A note by M. R.
Lawrence states that it was worked when
'Ned was confined to the house with a
broken fibula at the age of sixteen, and also
after an attack of scarlet fever.'[1] There is a
second very similar screen by Lawrence in a
private collection, and a wooden chest
decorated with pokerwork at Clouds Hill.

Museum of Costume, Bath

1. Note in the Museum of Costume, Bath.

Wooden screen: 2 panels, 77.5 × 24.8 each; box:
39.8 × 13 × 7
Box inscribed on lid: *WGL/1903*
Provenance: Given by Dr M.R.Lawrence, 1964.

20

'PLAYGROUND CRICKET'
'By Lawrence ii'
O.H.S. Magazine, July 1904

This is the earliest piece of writing that can
definitely be ascribed to Lawrence, although
a companion piece titled 'Playground
Football' and signed 'Goalpost' had appeared
in the March 1904 issue of the *O.H.S.
Magazine*, and was written in a very similar
style. Lawrence wrote:

'Playground cricket has no handbook, so
I think that some hints to youngsters who
aspire to gain honours in this subject will be
acceptable . . . a cap will not do for the ball.
It can however be a stone, or a piece of
wood: I have even seen a potato used with
success. One man bats, another forty or so
bowl . . . The stumps deserve mention. A
wooden wall was improvised for wicket-
keeper, and 3 stumps were chalked upon it,
in white and blue. These having slightly faded
a second pair in white was applied to the
first, coinciding in width but not in height;
consequently six inches of blue overtop the
white bails. The profound wisdom which
dictated this may not appear at first sight, but
the fact is that when big boys are bowling the
blue is counted as the top; when big boys are
batting the stumps do not extend beyond the
white. That shows our wisdom.
Unfortunately some facetious individual (we
would duck him if we could find him) has
added four more white stumps, and four
more bails, which slightly disconcert the
batsmen, but greatly improve the chances of
the bowler . . . The bat is indescribable. A
mass of willow, slightly rotten in places, and
resembling a mop at the bottom. The handle
is said to be cane, but one player who has had
a most extensive and varied acquaintance
with canes, both at home and abroad,
declares that no cane *ever* stung like this bat,
so it must be of some foreign substance. The
balls go, some into the side windows of the
school, some through those of the factory,
others again attach themselves to the
windows opposite.'

A. J. Flavell

Printed pamphlet bound into volume, 35

21

CANON ALFRED CHRISTOPHER
Photograph by Hills and Saunders (1910)

Sarah Lawrence wrote in *T. E. Lawrence by his
Friends* that Ned 'was for many years a
constant worshipper at St. Aldates Church
and taught in the Sunday School there twice
every Sunday. He had the great privilege of
Canon A. M. W. Christopher's gospel
teaching from his early years till he left
Oxford in 1910. After the Canon retired
from St. Aldates [in 1905], all the boys went
to a class for students which he held in his
house every Sunday during term.'[1]

Canon Christopher (1820-1913) was a
prominent evangelical preacher, and
Lawrence's early letters show that he
received a deeply religious upbringing.
Although he had ceased to be a churchgoer
before the First World War, he retained
some form of belief, writing in later life
'Hungry time has taken from me year by year
more of the Creed's clauses till now only the
first four words remain.'[2]

This photograph was taken shortly before
Canon Christopher's ninetieth birthday, in
the garden of his house, 4 Norham Road,
Oxford.

The Reverend J. S. Reynolds

1. *Friends*, p. 27.
2. *The Mint*, Part II, Chapter 18, p. 149.

Literature: J. S. Reynolds, *Canon Christopher of St.
Aldates, Oxford*, Abingdon, 1967, ill. fp. 350.

22

BRASS RUBBING OF WILLIAM
VISCOUNT BEAUMONT AND LORD
BARDOLF, 1507, FROM WIVENHOE,
ESSEX
By T. E. Lawrence, 1905

Lawrence's father had a keen interest in
church architecture, and it was probably
through this that Lawrence was introduced
to medieval brasses. His schoolfriend C. F.
C. Beeson recalled: 'At the age of fifteen he
was well versed in monumental brasses and
had acquired a fine series of rubbings from
churches in eastern and southern counties.
Cut out and pasted on the walls of his
bedroom were life-size figures of knights and
priests with Sir John d'Aubernon and Roger
de Trumpington, a Crusader, in pride of
place. Under his tuition my first brass was
rubbed at Wytham in October 1904; and
from that date onwards throughout the
following school years we made excursions
by cycle to nearly every village in the three
counties and to many places farther afield.

'It was no collector's hobby. There were
experiments in the technique of rubbing with
different grades of heelball and paper,
assisted by friendly advice from shoemakers
and paper-hangers whose shops supplied our
raw materials. There was much searching in
libraries for the histories of those priests and
knights and ladies, which narrowed into a
study of armour and costume.'[1]

The rubbing exhibited is one of several
made by Lawrence during a cycling tour of
East Anglia with his father in the summer of
1905. The canopy and supercanopy were
omitted from the rubbing, because they are
mutilated. There are further examples of
brass rubbings by Lawrence at the Ashmolean
Museum, Jesus College, Oxford, and
Clouds Hill.

The Visitors of the Ashmolean Museum,
Oxford

1. *Friends*, pp. 52-3.

Heel-ball on paper, 181 × 76.5
Signed and dated in ink, br.: *E./Lawrence 1905*
Provenance: Given to the Oxford Architectural and
Historical Society Collection, Ashmolean Museum, by
T. E. Lawrence.
Literature: Mill Stevenson, *A List of Monumental Brasses
in the British Isles*, London, 1926, p.142; R. P. Graves,
Lawrence of Arabia and his World, 1976, ill. p.10.

23

CITY OF OXFORD HIGH SCHOOL FOR
BOYS, SIXTH FORM
Photograph by T. E. Lawrence (1907)

This photograph was taken by Lawrence
during his last summer at school. The
circumstances were subsequently explained
by one of his classmates, T. O. Balk (seen at
the left of the middle row): 'The photograph
of the VIth form 1906-07 was taken in July
1907 on the small lawn in front of the school.
Ned Lawrence was the prime mover in
making the record of a very pleasant year. He
persuaded the Head to give his consent and
also the time needed to arrange the group
and to photograph it. He used his own . . .
camera fixed on a tripod and was able to take
the photograph himself by connecting the
camera by means of a length of rubber tubing
to his cycle pump which he kept carefully
out of sight as he stood in the group . . . I
always think when I look at the group, that
the Head's expression reveals his
considerable doubt of the likelihood of the
success of T.E.'s scheme.'[1]

That year Lawrence sat the Oxford Senior
Locals. He was placed in the First Class, and
only twelve candidates received higher total
marks. He did particularly well in English
(equal first) and Religious Knowledge (equal
third). Despite this academic success
Lawrence would look back on his school
years with distaste: 'In my case they were
miserable sweated years of unwilling work:
and when after them I suddenly went to
Oxford, the new freedom felt like heaven.
I don't think men ever work as hard as boys
are made to work . . . nor do I think the
miseries of grown-up feelings are as bad as
those of boys.'[2]

Oxfordshire County Council Library Services

1. T. O. Balk, in *O.H.S. Magazine*, April 1966, pp. 36-7.
2. T. E. Lawrence to D. Knowles, 14.7.1927.

24
JESUS COLLEGE, OXFORD
Photograph by J. Valentine (1880s)

Lawrence entered Jesus College Oxford in October 1907 to study History. He was eligible for a closed award by virtue of his Welsh birthplace, and won a Meyricke Exhibition worth £50 a year. His family obtained special dispensation which enabled him to live at home, but a schoolfriend, E. F. Hall was also at Jesus, and Lawrence used his room as a base in central Oxford.

Lawrence took very little part in undergraduate life except in the summer of 1908, when he lived in College for one term. It was then that he made friends with Vyvyan Richards and A. T. P. Williams, later Bishop of Winchester. It was with Richards that Lawrence shared his interest in William Morris and fine printing.

Oxfordshire County Council Library Services

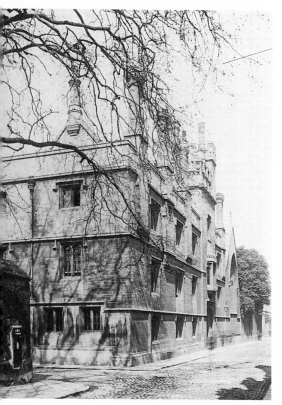

25
CHARLES FRANCIS BELL
By an unknown photographer, c. 1920
Vintage print

C. F. Bell (1871-1966) became Assistant Keeper at the Ashmolean Museum in 1896, the year that the Lawrence family moved to Oxford. Bell was particularly interested in medieval ceramics. When Lawrence began to bring fragments of pottery into the Ashmolean for identification he consulted Bell, and they frequently used to discuss medieval art and architecture.

In 1909 Bell was appointed head of the Fine Art Department and after this their contacts were less frequent. In questions of artistic taste their judgments were very different. Bell had firm views on the work of contemporary artists, and as a result Lawrence was discouraged from his original intention of presenting all the portraits and illustrations he had commissioned for *Seven Pillars of Wisdom* to the Ashmolean. Eventually two of them, Augustus John's oil portrait of Feisal (no. 98) and charcoal sketch of D. G. Hogarth (no. 50) were presented to the Museum after Bell had retired.

The Visitors of the Ashmolean Museum, Oxford (1970/36)

15 × 8.5
Provenance: Given by Miss J. B. Shaw, 1970.

26
EDWARD THURLOW LEEDS
By an unknown photographer, c. 1922
Vintage print

E. T. Leeds (1877-1955) met Lawrence soon after joining the staff of the Ashmolean Museum as Assistant Keeper in March 1908. He shared Lawrence's interest in medieval archaeology, and the two quickly became friends. Leeds and C. F. Bell introduced Lawrence to D. G. Hogarth at the beginning of 1909, when Hogarth came to the Ashmolean as Keeper. When Lawrence worked at the British Museum's Carchemish excavations in Syria between 1911 and 1914 he wrote regularly to Leeds, sending news for Hogarth about progress on the dig and details about antiquities he had purchased for the Ashmolean. As a result Lawrence wrote more letters to Leeds than to anyone else outside his own family during the pre-war years. The correspondence, which is often very light-hearted, is one of the most important biographical sources for the years 1911-14.

Lawrence kept in touch with Leeds after the war, and was delighted when he succeeded D. G. Hogarth as Keeper of the Ashmolean in 1928.

Lewis J. Leeds

Oval, 13.7 × 9.5
Provenance: By descent.
Literature: T. E. Lawrence, *Letters to E. T. Leeds*, ed. J. M. Wilson, Whittington Press, 1988, ill. pl. 24.

27
BEAKER WITH MOULDED FACE
English, 15th century

Lawrence's interest in medieval archaeology
began while he was still at school. He
collected pottery fragments unearthed in
Oxford building-site excavations, and used to
offer the workmen a small reward for
interesting pieces. Ashmolean records show
that he presented his better finds to the
Museum. The *Annual Report* for 1906 states:
'During the past year the considerable
disturbance of the ground for the foundations
of new buildings in the city, at Hertford
College, Jesus College, St. John's College, in
High Street and in the Cornmarket on the
sites of the Civet Cat and Leopold Arms, has
produced many remains of pottery and glass
of the sixteenth and seventeenth centuries.
Owing to the generosity of Mr. E. Lawrence
and also C.F.C. Beeson, who have by incessant
watchfulness secured everything of antiquarian
value, finds have been added to the local
antiquities collection in the Museum.'[1]

This beaker was found at 7 Cornmarket
Street in 1907, on the site of the curiosity
shop known as the Civet Cat.

The Visitors of the Ashmolean Museum,
Oxford (M.177)

1. 'Annual Report of the Ashmolean Museum for 1906'
in *Oxford University Gazette*, 30.4.1907, pp. 552-6.

Glazed earthenware, 9.75 h.
Provenance: Given by T. E. Lawrence, 1907.

28
BALUSTER JUG
English, 14th century

Found during excavations in Cornmarket
Street, Oxford, at a depth of 27 feet.

The Visitors of the Ashmolean Museum,
Oxford (M.8)

Glazed earthenware, 39.8 h.
Provenance: Given by T. E. Lawrence, 1908.

29
WINE BOTTLE
English, 16th/17th century

E. T. Leeds of the Ashmolean was interested
in early wine bottles, and Lawrence
occasionally helped him to collect examples
and to research the origins of those which
bore Oxford innkeepers' stamps. By 1914
Leeds had been able to establish the sequence
of wine bottles made in Oxford between the
sixteenth and eighteenth centuries. His
conclusions provided a basis for dating wine
bottles that is now used throughout the world.

The bottle exhibited here was given by
Lawrence to Ernest Barker of St John's
College, a family friend and also one of his
history tutors. It is said to have been
excavated at Oxford Castle.

After the war, when Lawrence was
elected to All Souls College, he discovered
a cellar full of empty wine bottles dating
from the eighteenth and early nineteenth
centuries. He and Leeds spent three evenings
during the winter of 1920 examining them by
candle light and collecting a specimen of each
type. This set was subsequently presented by
the College to the Ashmolean.

Nicolas Barker Esq.

Glass, 15 × 10.6
Provenance: Given by T. E. Lawrence to Sir Ernest
Barker, *c.* 1904-5; by descent.

30

T. E. LAWRENCE'S CYCLING TOUR OF FRENCH CASTLES, 1908

Based on a map belonging to Lawrence now in the Bodleian Library.

In 1907 new regulations were introduced by the Oxford examiners in Modern History allowing students to submit a supplementary thesis on some question related to one of the special subjects they had chosen to study. His original intention was to offer 'Military History and Strategy' as a special subject, and to submit a thesis on medieval military architecture (it was for this reason that he began to read the works on military strategy referred to in *Seven Pillars of Wisdom*).

In the summer of 1908 he set off on a long cycle tour of France to see more medieval castles and make plans, drawings and photographs for the thesis. He would experience no difficulty with the language, and during earlier cycling holidays he had worked out the minimum requirement of spare clothing he needed to carry. His father provided sufficient money to pay for lodging at modest country hotels.

The route was carefully planned in advance with the help of Murray's *Handbook for France* and works on medieval French architecture such as Viollet-le-Duc's *Dictionnaire Raisonné*. Lawrence crossed to Le Havre in mid-July, and cycled via Château Gaillard and Gisors to Coucy. There he turned south, covering the 500 miles to Avignon in ten days – a considerable achievement given the state of French country roads at the time. Shortly afterwards he caught his first glimpse of the Mediterranean, and wrote home lyrically, 'I felt that at last I had reached the way to the South, and all the glorious East; Greece, Carthage, Egypt, Tyre, Syria, Italy, Spain, Sicily, Crete. . . Oh I must get down here, – farther out – again!'[1] Later he suffered from bouts of malaria, which he thought he had contracted on this journey while sleeping out on the Rhône delta.

His route on the return journey northwards was a long one, involving large detours to visit castles, while trying at the same time to avoid hilly roads.

1. T. E. Lawrence to his family, 2.8.1908, *Home Letters*, p. 66.

31

FRENCH CASTLES

Photographs by T. E. Lawrence (1907-8)

(i) Fougères (August 1907)

When Lawrence first visited Fougères in 1906 he made a plan, but he had no camera. Afterwards he wrote home: 'Inside the castle is all destroyed; it is nothing but a shell, though a glorious one. No finer exterior exists I am certain . . . I shall certainly return there next year for another examination, and I shall bring a camera with me: Father's one if possible: it is a paradise for a photographer.'[1] He went back, therefore, to take photographs in 1907.

1. T. E. Lawrence to his mother, 24.8.1906, *Home Letters*, p. 29.

Literature: *Crusader Castles* II, ill. fp. 23.

(ii) Mont St Michel, the cloisters (August 1907)

Lawrence visited Mont St Michel in 1906, 1907 and 1908. His first impressions were mixed: 'The insides of the buildings on the Mont are lovely; the outside is decidedly badly proportioned, with its dumpy spire, and flat masses of unrelieved masonry. I was horrified with the exterior.'[1] In August 1907 he brought a camera to photograph architectural details, and the following summer he visited again, with his brother Will.

1. T. E. Lawrence to his father, 20.8.1906, *Home Letters*, p. 23.

Literature: *Crusader Castles* II, ill. between pp. 40-41.

(i)

(ii)

(iv)

(iii)

(v)

(iii) The Tour César, Provins (July 1908)

Lawrence visited Provins during his 1908 tour, and wrote that he found there 'a most puzzling xii [century] keep, and the remains of town walls. I was in and around them for hours, and came to the conclusion that the architect was making experiments when he built them . . . the keep would have been almost incapable of defence, and yet in spirit it is half a century ahead of its time. It ranks with Château Gaillard in importance for my thesis.'[1]

1. T. E. Lawrence to his mother, 23.7.1908, *Home Letters*, p. 61.

Literature: *Crusader Castles* II, ill. between pp. 48-9.

(iv) Crussol (July 1908)

Lawrence visited Crussol on the way south, describing it in a letter home as 'a fine xii c. castle on a 500 feet precipice over the Rhone'.[1] He told her that he had spent the night there, but omitted to mention that it was a roofless ruin.

1. T. E. Lawrence to his mother, 2.8.1908, *Home Letters*, p. 64.

Literature: *Crusader Castles, passim.*

(v) Hautefort (August 1908)

Hautefort, the castle of Bertrand de Born, was visited on Lawrence's return journey from the south of France. He wrote to C. F. C. Beeson that the castle had been 'burnt, so the butler assured me, by the English under Chas I. and only rebuilt in the xvii cent: quite so: the gateway is supposed to be B. de Bornish, but that's all rot: at least if so he was an astonishing anachronism. It may be xiv cent.'[1]

1. T.E. Lawrence to C.F.C. Beeson, 16.8.1908, *Letters*, p. 61.

Literature: *Home Letters*, ill. fp. 176.

Liddell Hart Centre for Military Archives, King's College London.

Provenance: given by A. W. Lawrence to B. H. Liddell Hart, 1938; acquired 1973.

32

LETTER FROM T.E. LAWRENCE TO HIS MOTHER
Laigle, 28 August 1908
Facsimile

After seeing the castles planned for his 1908 tour Lawrence intended to go to Brittany. On the way he visited Chartres Cathedral. The letter he wrote home is one of the most revealing to have survived from his youth. 'I expected that Chartres would have been like most French Cathedrals spoilt by restoration, so I slipped out before breakfast to "do" it. What I found I cannot describe – it is absolutely untouched and unspoilt, in superb preservation, and the noblest building (for Beauvais is only half a one) that I have ever seen, or expect to see. If only you could get an idea of its beauty, of its perfection,

Statue of Philosophus, Chartres Cathedral: photograph by T. E. Lawrence

without going to look at it! Its date is late xiith and early xiii cent. It is not enormous; but the carvings on its 3 portals are as fine as the best of all Greek work. Till yesterday I would put no sculptors near the Greeks of the Vth cent. Today the French of the early middle ages *may* be inferior, but I do not think so: nothing in imagination could be grander than that arrangement of three huge cavernous portals, (30 odd feet deep), of gigantic height, with statues everywhere for pillars, bas-reliefs for plain surfaces, statuettes and canopies for mouldings. The whole wall of the cathedral is chased and wrought like a Florentine plaque, and by master hands! You may think the individual figures stiff – the details coarse – everything is hard and narrow I admit, but when you see the whole – you can conceive at once the frame *and* the picture, then you must admit that nothing could be greater, except it were the Parthenon as it left the hands of Pheidias: it must be one of the noblest works of man, as it is the finest of the middle ages. One cannot describe it in anything but superlatives, and these seem so wretchedly formal that I am half tempted to scratch out everything that I have written: Chartres is Chartres: – that is, a gallery built by the sculptors to enclose a finer collection than the Elgin Marbles. I went in, as I said, before breakfast, and I left when dark: – all the day I was running from one door to another, finding in each something I thought finer than the one I had just left, and then returning to find that the finest was that in front of me – for it is a place absolutely impossible to imagine, or to recollect, at any rate for me: it is overwhelming, and when night came I was absolutely exhausted, drenched to the skin (it had poured all day) and yet with a feeling I had never had before in the same degree – as though I had found a path (a hard one) as far as the gates of Heaven, and had caught a glimpse of the inside, the gate being ajar. You will understand how I felt though I cannot express myself. Certainly Chartres is the sight of a lifetime, a place truly in which to worship God. The middle ages were truer that way than ourselves, in spite of their narrowness and hardness and ignorance of the truth as we complacently put it: the truth doesn't matter a straw, if men only believe what they say or are willing to show that they do believe something. Chartres besides has the finest late xvi and early xvii bas-reliefs in the world, and is

beautiful in its design and its proportions. I have bought all the picture post-cards, but they are of course hardly a ghost of the reality, nothing ever could be, though photography is best for such works. I took a photo myself of Philosophus, a most delightful little statuette, about 18 inches high: if not fogged, (I forgot to lock my camera, and somebody has fiddled with it), it may give one an idea of how the smallest parts of the building are finished with as much care as the centre-posts of the main doorways, and if Philosophus were of Greek marble there would be photographs of him in every album, between the Hermes of Praxiteles and the Sophocles of the Lateran. He is great work. I also tried to take a photo. of the masterpiece, the Christ of the south portal, but that cannot be worth looking at. I expect I will burn my photos. of Chartres as soon as they are visible. Yet perhaps with care and time, one would get something worthy from a photograph. We must return there (I would want assistants) and spend a fortnight in pure happiness.'

Bodleian Library, Oxford (MS.Res.c.13)

Literature: *Home Letters*, pp. 79-81.

33

POSTCARD FROM T. E. LAWRENCE TO MADAME CHAIGNON
Granville, 31 August 1908

At the end of the 1908 tour Lawrence had planned to stay for a time with the Chaignon family at Dinard. On 31 August, however, he sent them this postcard warning them that his plans had changed: 'Granville 31/8/08. I got a telegram to Falaise yesterday saying that my brother "Will" would meet me in Granville tomorrow to ride to St. Michel and St. Malo. I do not of course know how long we shall be, or how much of Brittany we are to see. I am afraid however that now it will be impossible for me to stay with you as I had hoped: May we come to dinner? both of us? Will write again if we delay at St. Michel. E.L.'

Private Collection

13.7 × 9
Reverse shows La Grande Porte at Granville
Provenance: Given by descendants of Mme Chaignon.
Literature: M.Larès, *T. E. Lawrence, La France et les Français*, Paris, 1980, ill. p.47.

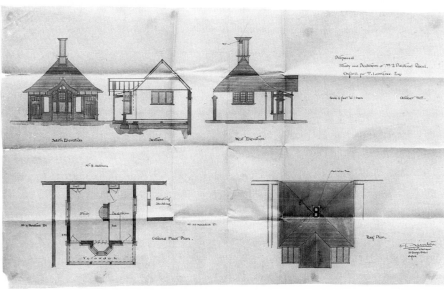

34

BUNGALOW IN THE GARDEN OF
2 POLSTEAD ROAD, OXFORD
Photograph by Michael R. Dudley

By 1908 there was no longer enough room
in the family home at Polstead Road for all
five of the boys to live and study. Lawrence
moved into College during the summer
term, and that autumn a two-room bungalow
was built for him at the foot of the garden.
It had its own coal grate, electricity, water,
and a telephone to the house.

This arrangement gave him a great deal of
independence during the months that he
worked for his final examinations. He hung
the walls with green cloth for quietness, and
preferred to study or read far into the night.
A letter to his mother written just after
Finals conveys something of the atmosphere
he created for himself in the bungalow: 'You
know, I think, the joy of getting into a
strange country in a book: at home when I
have shut my door and the town is in bed –
and I know that nothing, not even the dawn
– can disturb me in my curtains: only the

slow crumbling of the coals in the fire: they
get so red, and throw such splendid
glimmerings on the Hypnos and the brass-
work. And it is lovely too, after you have
been wandering for hours in the forest with
Percivale or Sagramors le desirous, to open
the door, and from over the Cherwell to look
at the sun glowering through the valley
mists. Why does one not like things if there
are other people about? Why cannot one
make one's books live except in the night,
after hours of straining? . . . if you can get
the right book at the right time you taste joys
– not only bodily, physical, but spiritual also,
which pass one out above and beyond one's
miserable self, as it were through a huge air,
following the light of another man's thought.
And you can never be quite the old self
again.'[1]

1. T. E. Lawrence to his mother, late August 1910,
Home Letters, pp. 110-11.

35

BUILDING NOTICE AND ARCHITECT'S
DRAWINGS FOR BUNGALOW IN THE
GARDEN OF 2 POLSTEAD ROAD,
OXFORD
Facsimiles of original documents (1908)

Oxford City Council

36
CHARLES MONTAGU DOUGHTY
By Eric Kennington, 1921

Lawrence first consulted Doughty's *Travels in Arabia Deserta* in 1908 when he conceived the idea of making a walking tour to visit crusader castles in Syria. At D. G. Hogarth's suggestion, he wrote asking Doughty's advice, and he met the famous traveller on at least one occasion before the First World War.

When Lawrence returned to England after the war he immediately renewed his acquaintance with Doughty, and he was subsequently responsible for having *Travels in Arabia Deserta* reprinted (see no. 195). Finding that Doughty was in financial straits, Lawrence also helped to raise funds and present one of Doughty's manuscripts (*The Dawn in Britain*) to the British Museum. During the same period he commissioned the Kennington portrait exhibited here, in the hope that it would eventually come to the National Portrait Gallery.

Lawrence was reluctant to show Doughty his own *Seven Pillars of Wisdom*, and was not surprised when Doughty offered little comment. The two continued to correspond, however, until Doughty's death in 1926. Lawrence took a day's leave from the RAF to attend the funeral.

National Portrait Gallery (NPG 2113)

Pastel, 48.3 × 36.8
Signed and dated br.: *21/Eric H. Kennington*
Provenance: Commissioned by T. E. Lawrence; given by him to the National Gallery, Millbank and transferred to the National Portrait Gallery, 1926.
Literature: A. J. Arberry, *British Orientalists*, 1943, ill.
Exhibitions: Leicester Galleries, 1921 (5).

37
T. E. LAWRENCE'S WALKING TOUR IN SYRIA, 1909

Soon after returning from his 1908 cycle tour of French castles, Lawrence discussed his proposed thesis with C. F. Bell at the Ashmolean. Bell suggested that a much more interesting study could be written comparing the castles of medieval Europe to those of the Crusaders, in order to determine whether certain architectural features had their origins in Europe or the East. Lawrence was intrigued by the idea, which he could put into practice by changing his special paper from 'Military History and Strategy' to 'The first three Crusades'.

By the beginning of January 1909 he had decided to make a tour of the major crusader castles, few of which had been adequately planned or described. He intended to travel on foot, relying on the hospitality of local villagers; he therefore learned a little colloquial Arabic. Since there would be no picture postcards for sale he also took lessons in drawing from the architectural illustrator E. H. New.

He left England on 18 June 1909 and spent nearly three months in Syria. The journey proved to be a turning point in his life: he was fascinated by the people and the places he visited, and even before he went home to England he had decided to go back as soon as he could find a pretext for doing so.

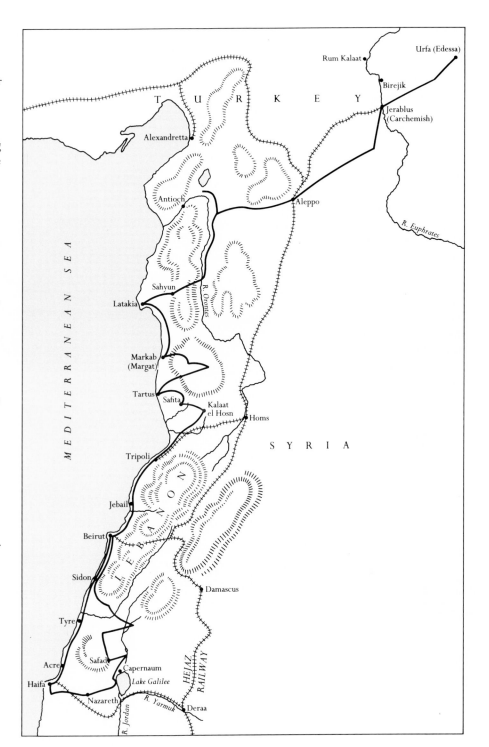

38
SYRIAN CASTLES
Photographs by T. E. Lawrence (1909-11)

(i)   (ii)   (iii)   (iv)

(i) Kalaat el Hosn, the great talus, looking
east (August 1909)

Lawrence spent his twenty-first birthday at
Kalaat el Hosn (also known by its French
name, the Crac des Chevaliers). He
described it in a letter home as 'the finest
castle in the world: certainly the most
picturesque I have seen – quite marvellous:
I stayed 3 days there, with the Kaimmakam,
the governor: a most civilised-French-
speaking-disciple-of-Herbert-Spenser-Free-
Masonic-Mohammedan-Young Turk: very
comfortable — .'[1]

1. T. E. Lawrence to his mother, 29.8.1909, *Home
Letters*, p. 104.

Literature: *Crusader Castles*, ill. fp. 47.

(ii) Safita from the east (August 1909)

The next castle Lawrence visited after Kalaat
el Hosn was Safita: 'a *Norman keep, with
ORIGINAL battlements*: the like is not in
Europe: such a find.'[1]

1. T. E. Lawrence to his mother, 29.8.1909, *Home
Letters*, p. 104.

Literature: *Crusader Castles*, ill. fp. 37.

(iii) Markab, looking east on the southern
face (August 1909)

Lawrence reached Markab (also written
Margat) in late August 1909, and found 'a
castle about as big as Jersey I fancy: one
wanted a bicycle to ride round it.'[1] He later
noted beside this photograph: 'A sort of
beehive, underneath is a sheikh's tomb.'[2]

1. T. E. Lawrence to his mother, 29.8.1909, *Home
Letters*, p. 105.
2. Annotation on the typescript of his Oxford thesis,
Crusader Castles, fp. 49.

Literature: *Crusader Castles*, ill. fp. 49.

(iv) Urfa castle, the moat (1909 or 1911)

Lawrence visited Urfa on the walking tour in
1909 'and found there the only 2 beaked
towers in all N. Syria.'[1]. He took a small
number of photographs (shortly afterwards
his camera was stolen). In 1911 he revisited
Urfa and took more photographs, for his
projected book on crusader castles. It is not
certain on which visit this view of the moat
was taken. A note in the 1911 diary for 15
July records photographing the eastern half
of the south side of the moat from the bottom
with a wide angle lens. Lawrence added:
'This makes complete my photographs of the
moat, all but the N. side.'[2]

1. T. E. Lawrence to his family, 22.9.1909, *Home Letters*,
p. 108.
2. *Oriental Assembly*, p. 8.

Literature: *Crusader Castles*; *Home Letters*, ill. fp. 240.

(v) Aleppo, entrance to the citadel

On his 1909 tour Lawrence reached Aleppo
with some relief: it was 'European, with a
decent hotel: much washing, for I hadn't had
a bath for ten days (or any other kind of
wash!)'.[1] He revisited Aleppo on many
occasions, since it was the closest major city
to the British Museum's Carchemish
excavations where he worked from 1911 to
1914. This photograph may date from one of
these later visits.

1. T. E. Lawrence to his family, 22.9.1909, *Home Letters*,
p. 106.

Literature: *Crusader Castles* II, ill. between pp. 60 and 61.

(vi) Birejik (July 1911)

(vii) Birejik from the West bank of the
Euphrates (July 1911)

Lawrence almost certainly took both these
photographs during a walking tour of Syrian
castles made after his first season at
Carchemish in 1911. His diary for 22 July,
written at Birejik, noted: '[at 4 p.m.] went
out to the top of the hill, and photographed
the town walls etc. from the S. The castle
would be behind this hill a little to the L.
Then went down into the valley and up hill
again. Took the N. half of the castle from the
N.E., in the shade against the sun: and the

(v)

(vi)

(vii)

(viii)

39
HEAD OF HYPNOS
Replica of Greco-Roman sculpture
(4th century BC)

Lawrence returned to England from his 1909 walking tour in Syria on board the RMS *Ottoway*. He was by this time keenly interested in classical and medieval sculpture, and when the ship called in at Naples he took the opportunity to see the bronze collection in the National Museum. Afterwards he visited a local foundry which produced replicas. Most were too expensive, but he managed to buy a slightly imperfect cast of Hypnos, the god of sleep. It was a freehand copy of the Hypnos in the British Museum, itself a Roman copy of a Greek work dating from the fourth century BC.

Lawrence took the bronze back to Oxford and gave it a place of honour in the bay window of his study in the bungalow. He later wrote: 'I would rather possess a fine piece of sculpture than anything in the world.'[1]

The whereabouts of Lawrence's copy is unrecorded.

British Museum Shop (by courtesy of the Trustees)

1. T. E. Lawrence to his family, 16.3.1916, *Home Letters*, p. 315.

33 × 39 × 21.5

S. half of the castle (both landward side) also from the N.E., a little further on than the one before, and under the same disadvantage of light. This finished my films loaded.'[1] Exhibit no. 38 (vii) is included in the published edition of *Crusader Castles*, but may have been added by Lawrence when he was revising the work for publication in 1911. His letters contain no reference to a visit to Birejik in 1909.

1. T. E. Lawrence's diary 1911, *Oriental Assembly*, p. 24.
Literature: *Oriental Assembly*; (vi): *Home Letters*, ill. fp. 257; (vii): *Crusader Castles*, ill. pl. 20.

(viii) Rum Kalaat, the Euphrates front (July 1911)

Lawrence reached Rum Kalaat on July 24th 1911, noting in his diary: 'The place is enormous, a town rather than a fortress'.[1]

This is one of a series of photographs he took that day. He wrote: 'Then on to the mouth of the valley and took [a photograph] of the Euphrates front. This has a little domed building like a *weli* in the foreground. Felt sleepy, so went to cave, and slept till 2 p.m.'[2]

1. *Oriental Assembly*, p. 28.
2. *ibid.* p. 30.
Literature: *Oriental Assembly*, pp. 28-33; *Home Letters*, ill. fp. 257.

Liddell Hart Centre for Military Archives, King's College London

Provenance: Liddell Hart papers; acquired 1973.

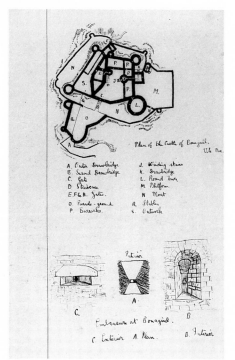

40
GROUND PLAN OF THE CHATEAU DE BONAGUIL
By T. E. Lawrence after Viollet-le-Duc, 1908

Although Lawrence visited Bonaguil in August 1908, he had done some research on the fifteenth century castle in advance, and noted that there was a long description with plan and bird's-eye view in M. Viollet-le-Duc's *Dictionnaire Raisonné de l'Architecture Française du XIe au XVIe Siècle* (vol 2, Paris, 1859, pp. 165-7). When he saw the castle, therefore, he did not stop to make plans. He commented, however, that it was 'most interesting: provision is made everywhere for canon: and at the same time the old methods were not out of date. It is so perfect that it is almost ridiculous to call it a ruin: all the vaults, stairways and some of the roofs are perfect.'[1]

The plan exhibited is traced from Viollet-le-Duc, p. 165.

The Curators of the Bodleian Library, Oxford (MS.Res.c.52)

1. T. E. Lawrence to his mother, 16.8.1988, *Home Letters*, p. 73.

Pen and ink, 20.3 × 12.7
Provenance: Given by A. W. Lawrence.
Literature: *Crusader Castles* II, ill. fp. 54.

41
BIRD'S EYE VIEW OF THE CHATEAU DE BONAGUIL
By Cyril Frederick Cherrington Beeson after Viollet-le-Duc, 1908

It was not until the spring of 1909 that Lawrence began to take drawing lessons; before this he relied on the artistic skills of his friend C. F. C. Beeson. When Lawrence had to put together the plans and drawings which accompanied his thesis, submitted to the Examiners in March 1910, Beeson helped by tracing material from published sources.

Beeson mischievously put his own initials at the bottom of this bird's eye view of Bonaguil, traced from Viollet-le-Duc.[1] He also showed Lawrence, top right, arriving at the castle on his bicycle. Lawrence hatched over the offending initials (centre, bottom) and replaced them with his own, but finally decided not to use the drawing in the thesis.

The Curators of the Bodleian Library, Oxford (MS.Res.c.52)

1. M. Viollet-le-Duc, *op. cit.* (40, above), p. 167.

Pen and ink, 20 × 12.5
Signed br.: *T.E.L.* and inscribed with title
Provenance: Given by A. W. Lawrence.
Literature: *Crusader Castles* II, ill. between pp. 54 and 55.

42
B.A. THESIS, *THE INFLUENCE OF THE CRUSADES ON EUROPEAN MILITARY ARCHITECTURE – TO THE END OF THE XIIth CENTURY*
By T. E. Lawrence, 1910

This is the copy of Lawrence's undergraduate thesis submitted to the Examiners in March 1910. For a time, Lawrence intended to enlarge the thesis and have it published as a book; with this in mind he began to make extensive marginal annotations. It was found, however, that the cost of reproducing all his maps and illustrations would be prohibitive.

The thesis was published in a limited edition in 1936 under the title *Crusader Castles*. In 1988 a new edition, edited by Denys Pringle, was published by Oxford University Press.

Lawrence's second typed copy of the thesis, which also has marginal annotations, is now at the Houghton Library, Harvard.

Principal and Fellows, Jesus College, Oxford

Paper bound typescript with MS annotations and photographs, 26.5 × 20.5
Provenance: Given by Sarah Lawrence.
(not illustrated)

43
FOLIO OF MAPS DRAWN FOR *THE INFLUENCE OF THE CRUSADES ON EUROPEAN MILITARY ARCHITECTURE*
By T. E. Lawrence, 1910

Private Collection

Bound folio of drawings in ink and crayon, 64.2 × 53
Provenance: Given by A. W. Lawrence.

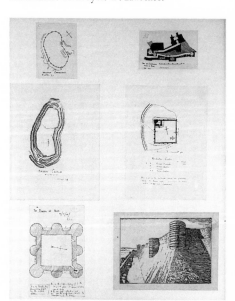

44
JANET LAURIE
By an unknown photographer, 1914
Vintage print

The Laurie family were neighbours when the Lawrences lived at Langley Lodge between 1894 and 1896. Both families had children of similar ages, and they became friends. When the Lawrences moved to Oxford, they continued to see the Lauries.

Janet Laurie went to school in Oxford and often visited the Lawrence home. As they grew older Ned and Will both developed a deep attachment to her. Ned's affection was obvious to friends such as E. F. Hall, who occasionally entertained her with Lawrence in his rooms at Jesus. Shortly before her death she told Professor John Mack, one of Lawrence's biographers, that Lawrence had proposed to her in 1910, but that she had rejected him. Later, she seriously considered marrying Will, whose affection for her remained so strong that he bequeathed her all his possessions when he died in 1915. Lawrence remained in contact with Janet for many years. She married Guthrie Hallsmith in 1919.

Private Collection

Oval, 9.4 × 6.2
Provenance: By descent from the Laurie family.

45
T. E. LAWRENCE, OXFORD UNIVERSITY
OFFICERS TRAINING CORPS
Detail from a photograph by ? Edgar Francis
Hall (1910)

When Lord Haldane became Secretary of State for War in 1905 he undertook an important series of army reforms. One of his initiatives was to start an Officers Training Corps at British universities. Lawrence was among the first to volunteer for the Oxford University OTC which was formed in October 1908.

Little is known about Oxford OTC training at that date, but his later comments suggest that nothing he learned proved of significant value to him during the war. He must, however, have practiced rifle shooting.

This photograph was taken during the OTC camp held on Salisbury Plain in the summer of 1910, which Lawrence attended after taking his final examinations.

J. M. Wilson

46
SIGNALS SECTION OF THE OXFORD
UNIVERSITY OFFICERS TRAINING
CORPS
By an unknown photographer (1909-10)

This group photograph was probably taken during the 1910 summer camp. Lawrence (front row left) was a member of the signals section, which he may have joined because its duties included a good deal of cycling. The semaphore signallers in the back row are spelling out: 'O.U.A.V', presumably standing for 'Oxford University Army Volunteers'.

Merton College, Oxford

Provenance: From an album compiled and given by Sir Basil Blackwell.

47

THE FIVE LAWRENCE BROTHERS
By an unknown photographer, 1910
Vintage print

This is the last known photograph of all five brothers together. It shows, from left to right, Ned, Frank, Arnold, Bob and Will.

Frank Lawrence was still at the City of Oxford High School. He would follow Ned to Jesus College, Oxford.

Arnold Lawrence, also at the City of Oxford High School, would develop an interest in archaeology. He later went to New College, Oxford and became Professor of Classical Archaeology at Cambridge. As T. E. Lawrence's heir and literary executor he has contributed introductions to *Seven Pillars of Wisdom* (1935), *Crusader Castles* (1936), *Secret Despatches from Arabia* (1939) and *The Mint* (1955). He also edited two collections of Lawrence's minor writings : *Oriental Assembly* (1939) and *Men in Print* (1940) as well as *T. E. Lawrence by his Friends* (1937) and *Letters to T. E. Lawrence* (1962).

Bob Lawrence had studied medicine at St John's College, Oxford. He was to serve as a doctor with British forces on the Western Front during the First World War and later became a medical missionary in China, where he was accompanied by his mother. He later edited *The Home Letters of T. E. Lawrence and his brothers* (1954) which contains letters home from Ned, Will and Frank Lawrence. He died in 1971.

Will Lawrence was at St. John's College, Oxford, and later worked as a teacher in India. He was only a year younger than Ned, and the two had many interests in common. In particular he shared his brother's enthusiasm for literature and writers. While Ned came to know James Elroy Flecker in Syria, Will became friends with Ezra Pound.

Private Collection

Not measured
Provenance : By descent from the Laurie family.
Literature : *Crusader Castles*, II, ill. frontis. ; *Home Letters*, ill. frontis.

48

THE HOLLOW LAND AND OTHER CONTRIBUTIONS TO THE OXFORD AND CAMBRIDGE MAGAZINE
By William Morris, London, 1903

Lawrence once wrote : 'Morris was a great poet : and I'd rather have written *The Well at the World's End* or *The Roots of the Mountains* or *John Bull* or *The Hollow Land* than anything of the 19th Cent. except *War and Peace* or *Moby Dick* . . . I suppose everybody loves one writer, unreasonably. I'd rather Morris than the world.'[1] He acquired this lasting affection during his undergraduate years, and his admiration is clear from the choice of this collected edition, bought to celebrate his Oxford First. For all that, he was not an uncritical admirer. In 1929 he told Charlotte Shaw that 'the charm and comfort of imperfection makes up for most of the failures of the world. We admire the very great, but love the less : perhaps that is why I would choose to live with the works of William Morris, if I had to make a single choice. My reason tells me that he isn't a very great writer : but then, he wrote just the stuff I like.'[2]

Private Collection

1. T. E. Lawrence to C. F. Shaw, 23.3.1927.
2. T. E. Lawrence to C. F. Shaw, [4.10.]1929.

Printed book, bound in limp vellum, 352 pp., 20.8
Inscribed in pencil : *T. E. L./Finals 1910*.
Provenance : Acquired from Lawrence's descendants.
(not illustrated)

49

THE LIFE AND DEATH OF RICHARD YEA-AND-NAY
By Maurice Hewlett, London, 1900

During his undergraduate years Lawrence formed a taste for romantic literature about the medieval world. One book he particularly enjoyed was this historical novel by Maurice Hewlett about Richard Coeur de Lion. In the spring of 1912 Lawrence took a copy with him to Kafr Ammar in Egypt where he worked for several weeks under Flinders Petrie. Afterwards he wrote home : 'Read *Yea and Nay* in Egypt for the ninth time. It is a masterpiece.'[1]

J. M. Wilson

1. T. E. Lawrence to his family, 20.2.1912, *Home Letters*, p. 193.

Printed book, 42 pp., 19.7
(not illustrated)

CARCHEMISH
1911-14

During the autumn of 1910 Lawrence asked Leeds whether there was a chance of getting a place on an overseas excavation. The request was totally unexpected: Lawrence was already committed to his B.Litt. research, and had started to visit collections of medieval pottery in England and France. Leeds was sorry that the idea had not come up sooner, knowing that Hogarth was about to begin an exploratory season at Carchemish in northern Syria for the British Museum, and that the expedition team had already been chosen. Nevertheless, Leeds sent Lawrence to see Hogarth, and eventually the British Museum agreed to let Lawrence go as an unsalaried assistant.

Early in December 1910 Lawrence left for Syria on board the SS *Saghalien*. The ship called at Athens and Constantinople where there was a delay for engine repairs. He was delighted to explore these historic cities about which he had read so much, and sent rapturous letters home.

His first destination was Jebail, the ancient Byblos, a small town on the Lebanese coast. The previous summer he had visited the American Mission School there and he now returned to take lessons in Arabic. He was very impressed with the school and its staff, and made lasting friendships with his Arabic teacher Fareedeh el Akle and with Mrs Rieder who taught European languages there.

Hogarth went out to Syria in February 1911, and Lawrence joined him for the journey to Aleppo where they met the third British member of the expedition, Reginald Campbell Thompson. The three archaeologists reached Carchemish, on the Euphrates seventy miles north-east of Aleppo, in the second week of March.

The initial four-month season in 1911 was purely exploratory: there were no plans for further work unless the site proved worthwhile. The expedition rented a house in the village of Jerablus, about fifteen minutes' walk from the Carchemish mound. Jerablus was a well established agricultural community like many others in northern Syria; but life here was quite unlike that in Europe and many of the adjuncts of western civilisation were lacking. Lawrence, who had not worked on an important archaeological site before, was one of just three Englishmen in charge of an enterprise which soon became a major source of local employment. The dig got off to an encouraging start when the first excavations exposed a large relief of a fertility goddess, which was soon dubbed 'the lady'.

Lawrence was well qualified to work at Carchemish for several reasons. At Oxford he had acquired an archaeologist's understanding of ceramics, and he was soon put in charge of recording the pottery found at the site. He was also an experienced photographer, and took over the expedition's five cameras, which included a very good half-plate camera of his own. Further, he had a working knowledge of Arabic which enabled him to help manage the labour force drawn from local villages.

His role with the workforce called for a thorough knowledge of the local economy and customs, and even of the personal relationships between the various families whose members were employed on the site: 'We are continually bothered by blood feuds, by getting into the same trench men who have killed each other's kin or run off with their wives.'[1] At first, much of this responsibility was carried by Gregori, a seasoned foreman who had worked under Hogarth at several previous excavations. Gregori, however, was a Greek Cypriot who spoke little Arabic. He soon took on a local man, Sheikh Hamoudi, as second foreman. Another employee on the excavations was a boy known as Dahoum (the dark one), then about fourteen. Dahoum proved to be intelligent and under Lawrence's instruction was to become a skilled photographic assistant.

T. E. Lawrence:
Photograph by Heinrich Franke, 1913
(detail, no. 63)

1. T. E. Lawrence to his family, 18.6.1911, *Home Letters*, p. 170.

Dahoum
By Francis Dodd, 1913
(no. 67)

During his stay in Oxford in 1913, Dahoum
helped to unpack some of the antiquities
shipped back from Syria to the Ashmolean.
C. F. Bell arranged for Dodd to record the
Museum's picturesque temporary assistant.

Hittite Carchemish was buried deep under the remains of a much later Roman town. When the digs were closed at the end of June 1911, Lawrence was still unsure whether the excavations had revealed enough of the Hittite city to convince the British Museum that further work was justified. He was a little despondent, but set off on a two-week walking tour, partly to look for Hittite seals, but principally to continue his study of crusader castles. During this journey he kept a diary, later published as the *Diary 1911*. At the time he was also planning to revise and enlarge his Oxford thesis for publication.

He returned to Jerablus at the end of July, very ill with dysentery, and was taken in and looked after in Hamoudi's house. The local Turkish authorities, however, wanted Lawrence out of their jurisdiction to avoid complications in case he died: Hamoudi was threatened with severe punishment should this happen, and was advised to turn Lawrence out. But Lawrence had already begun to attract the kind of personal loyalty that would be so important to him in the future, and Hamoudi with help from Dahoum continued to care for him, nursing him back to comparative health.

Still weak, Lawrence went back to England in August and spent some months convalescing. He took up his research on medieval pottery, and was again seriously planning to set up a printing press with Vyvyan Richards. When Jesus College demolished a medieval hall in Ship Street, Lawrence's father was persuaded to acquire and store the roof beams so that they could be used in a projected building to house the press.

In London, however, the British Museum had decided to continue digging at Carchemish. Walter Morrison, a philanthropist with a special interest in archaeological field-work, made an anonymous donation to the Museum which would pay for several more seasons. Lawrence had proved his worth to the expedition and was again offered a place on the dig. Hogarth, who was increasingly busy at the Ashmolean, could not be spared to work at Carchemish. He was replaced at the site by Leonard Woolley, whom Lawrence had met in Oxford some years before. Woolley and Lawrence were to be responsible for the British Museum's work at Carchemish during the five seasons of excavation which followed.

Lawrence returned to Carchemish briefly in December 1911, but left soon afterwards for Egypt. Hogarth had arranged for him to spend a short time working under the Egyptologist Flinders Petrie who was excavating a cemetery at Kafr Ammar. Lawrence helped at the dig for three weeks in January 1912, but did not enjoy the work. He was horrified by the sight of the mummified bodies that were dug up, and he disliked the rivalries and tensions which he found at the camp.

He was, therefore, delighted to go back to Carchemish for the opening of a new season in March 1912. However, the start was delayed when a local Turkish governor seized a chance to try and extract *backsheesh* from Woolley. On two occasions legal technicalities were raised to stop the expedition's work, in the hope that a bribe would be offered. Each time, however, Woolley overcame the problem with great success. He simply threatened to shoot the officials who stood in his way. The local population was delighted at this high-handed victory over their Turkish masters.

In late March Woolley and Lawrence were free to embark on a systematic excavation of the site. This involved clearing away the remains of Roman masonry which overlay Hittite Carchemish. There were few exciting Hittite finds during the season, which ended in June 1912.

Soon afterwards there was a serious epidemic of cholera in Aleppo and Lawrence, who had stayed on at Jerablus, was worried that the new German railway from Aleppo would bring the disease there. He remained for a while, preparing for the worst, but although he helped deal with outbreaks of less serious illness there were few cases of cholera in the village. In August he was in poor health himself and went to Jebail to recuperate, taking Dahoum with him. He also visited the poet James Elroy Flecker, then vice-consul at Beirut. Flecker, with whom he corresponded occasionally, became the first of his literary friends.

It now seemed likely that Lawrence would spend a large part of his time during the next few years at Carchemish. His future as a field archaeologist was secure for the time being at least, and the projected thesis on medieval pottery was shelved.

He continued to hold his scholarship at Magdalen, however, and was planning to follow the same kind of career as Hogarth. Several writing projects are mentioned in his letters. One was a 'monumental history of the Crusades', a natural extension of his special subject at Oxford; another was a historical background to the Bible; a third was to be a travel book about seven great cities of the East.

There was trouble again at the start of the third season in autumn 1912. A German construction company was building a railway bridge over the Euphrates adjacent to the Carchemish site. The engineers needed a regular supply of stone, and in the summer, while Woolley and Lawrence were away, they had started taking it from the Carchemish city wall. Haj Wahid, the archaeologists' cook, took it upon himself to hold the Germans off at gunpoint for several days until help arrived from Aleppo. Woolley was in England, but Lawrence telegraphed the Turkish authorities who contacted the government in Constantinople. As a result the German engineers suffered a humiliating public rebuke. This made a lasting impression on the local community. The railway employed many more people than did the excavations, but the archaeologists now had the pick of the labour. When the Turks introduced conscription during the Balkan Wars, Woolley and Lawrence took steps to protect their workers, and this boosted their popularity still further.

These victories over Turkish officialdom gave both of them a certain notoriety, but the local people looked to Lawrence rather than to Woolley. By this time Lawrence had involved himself in the affairs of the community. As his brother Will remarked during a visit to Carchemish a few months later, he had become 'a great lord in this place'.[2] It is not surprising that Oxford had lost its appeal. In September 1912 he wrote: 'I don't think anyone who had tasted the East as I have would give it up half-way, for a seat at high table and a chair in the Bodleian'.[3]

The archaeologists returned to England briefly that Christmas, and Lawrence took the opportunity to arrange for a motorised Canadian canoe to be shipped out to Carchemish. He was back in Syria by the end of January 1913, for the start of the fourth season.

The British Museum was increasingly concerned at the threat of a Kurdish revolt if the Turks suffered a defeat in the Balkans. Woolley and Lawrence had made friends with the local Kurdish chiefs but Carchemish appeared very vulnerable. The collapse of the Turkish Empire seemed quite possible and there was much speculation about the consequences. Although Lawrence had been brought up to accept imperial values, he had now witnessed wholesale abuse of power by the Turks, and was privy to unguarded discussions in the local community where the talk was of freedom and independence. If Turkey collapsed, the main obstacle to this freedom might well prove to be the French, who had long-standing colonial ambitions in the Levant. For Lawrence, who revered the untouched Arab life, the thought of French rule in Syria was anathema.

It is nevertheless wrong to present Lawrence as an unthinking Francophobe. He resented these French ambitions because of the profound difference between British and French colonial practice. The British, believing arrogantly that no foreign race could match their achievements, governed colonies through existing local institutions and thus preserved the essential character of each subject people. The French, no less arrogantly, considered that the most noble aim of every colonial citizen should be to become French in language, habit and custom. Their imperial policy tended, therefore, to destroy the indigenous culture which Lawrence thought so important.

In spite of these political worries the 1913 Carchemish seasons were highly rewarding. Systematic excavation produced many finds, including important carved reliefs and a hideous statue of a god: 'Woolley slept near it one night by accident in the court yard, and started up three times with evil dreams'.[4]

Although he was working for the British Museum Lawrence had by no means forgotten his loyalty to the Ashmolean. Hogarth had arranged that he should be free to buy antiquities for the Oxford collections provided that they were found more than ten miles from Carchemish; Lawrence, therefore, spent much time travelling in the surrounding districts.

The Ashmolean's special interest was in Hittite seal-stones, and Lawrence con-

2. W. G. Lawrence to his family, 16.9.1913,
Home Letters, p. 442.
3. T. E. Lawrence to his family, 13.9.1912,
Home Letters, p. 232.
4. T. E. Lawrence to E. T. Leeds, 13.5.1913,
T. E. Lawrence, *Letters to E. T. Leeds*, ed J. M.
Wilson, Whittington Press, 1988, p. 69.

Hittite carved relief showing two bulls charging each other with a sacred palm tree between them. Part of the Herald's Wall found at Carchemish, spring 1913, now in the Museum of Anatolian Civilizations, Ankara.
Limestone, 125 × 185

Photograph by courtesy of the
Trustees of the British Museum

Hittite carved relief thought to show two figures castrating a lion. Part of the Herald's Wall found at Carchemish, spring 1913. The right hand section is now in the Museum of Anatolian Civilizations, Ankara, the upper left section is in the British Museum.
Basalt, 125 × 150

Photograph by courtesy of the
Trustees of the British Museum

tributed a good deal to its collection which became the most important in existence. Of the 336 seals in the collection when Hogarth published a catalogue in 1920 well over a third had been bought by Lawrence between 1909 and 1914. Both he and Hogarth were pioneering collectors, since little was known about Hittite seal-stones at the time.

Lawrence returned to England in the summer of 1913 taking with him Hamoudi, the Carchemish foreman, and Dahoum. His family and Oxford friends were entertained by these unusual visitors. Lawrence amused himself by asking Hamoudi to assess the value, in Jerablus terms, of Janet Laurie, whom Hamoudi judged too scrawny to be worth anything, and his mother, who rated a cow.

The fifth season opened in October 1913, and confirmed once again the importance and success of the excavations. Lawrence now felt that his future lay in archaeology, and at last wrote to Vyvyan Richards withdrawing from their proposed printing venture.

After Christmas Hogarth published an article on Carchemish in *The Illustrated London News*, writing that it had 'proved the largest, and in many respects the most important and fruitful excavation which [the Trustees of the British Museum] have ever promoted.'[5] Lawrence had been extraordinarily fortunate. In 1910 he was fresh out of college; just three years later he had an established place in the world of archaeology.

Such was their position that Woolley and Lawrence were now called upon in a rather unusual way. Kitchener, the British Agent in Egypt, wanted a military survey party to travel through Turkish-held Sinai in order to complete the mapping of the peninsula. The Turks would not have permitted such an expedition, so it was to be disguised as an archaeological venture. Woolley and Lawrence were asked by Sir Charles Watson, Chairman of the Executive Committee of the Palestine Exploration Fund, under whose cover they would be working, to join the party, which was led by Captain Stewart Newcombe of the Royal Engineers. Their nominal objective was to look for archaeological remains in the desert of the Exodus. The six-week journey in January and February 1914 proved an amusing change from work at Carchemish; the whole area was new to Lawrence, and he now visited Akaba and Petra for the first time.

Afterwards they returned for their sixth season at Carchemish, which started in March 1914 and proved exceptionally busy. They reached Jerablus in time to defuse a serious incident between the German engineers and the Kurds. A minor disagreement over pay had blown up into a full-scale riot in which a Kurd was killed. The Germans were greatly outnumbered and would certainly have been massacred had not Woolley and Lawrence seen what was happening and, at considerable personal risk, used all their influence to calm the situation. They succeeded, and later helped to resolve the crisis by arranging for the payment of blood-money. The incident was widely reported in the international press.

In June 1914 Woolley and Lawrence left their belongings and notes in the house, fully expecting to return for another season in the autumn; funds had been arranged that spring for five more years' digging. Once in England they set to work to complete the report on their archaeological findings in Sinai. Within a week, however, the Archduke Franz Ferdinand had been assassinated at Sarajevo, and on 4 August 1914, twelve days before Lawrence's twenty-sixth birthday, Britain entered the Great War.

5. D. G. Hogarth, in *The Illustrated London News*,
24.1.1914.

50
DAVID GEORGE HOGARTH
By Augustus John, c.1920

D. G. Hogarth (1882-1927) came to the Ashmolean Museum as Keeper in January 1909, and Lawrence consulted him soon afterwards about the proposed walking tour in Syria. Thereafter Lawrence had little contact with Hogarth until the autumn of 1910 when he asked if it might be possible to go on an archaeological excavation overseas. Hogarth was about to reopen the British Museum's excavations at Carchemish in northern Syria for a trial season and helped Lawrence to obtain a research award from Magdalen College, Oxford, so that he could join the expedition.

In the event Hogarth spent only a few weeks at Carchemish during the 1911 season, and when it was decided to resume the dig in 1912 his place was taken by Leonard Woolley. A friendship nevertheless developed between Hogarth and Lawrence during these Carchemish years, largely because Lawrence volunteered to buy antiquities in Syria for the Ashmolean.

When war broke out in 1914 Hogarth helped Lawrence to obtain a post in the Geographical Section of the War Office in London. After this, however, their paths rarely crossed until 1919. Hogarth joined the Geographical Section of Naval Intelligence in 1915, and helped to prepare a series of reference works on the Middle East. In this connection he visited Cairo several times during 1915 and 1916 (acting as first Head of

the Arab Bureau for a few weeks). During the later stages of the war he took charge of a branch of the Arab Bureau at Allenby's headquarters in Palestine.

After the war Hogarth and Lawrence were both involved in official deliberations about the political settlement of the Middle East. Then, at the end of 1919, it was Hogarth who persuaded Lawrence to rewrite *Seven Pillars of Wisdom* after the manuscript had been lost. Their friendship became much closer during these immediate post-war years, and Hogarth viewed Lawrence's enlistment with deep concern. He was one of the small group of friends who helped launch the subscription edition of *Seven Pillars* in 1923; by this time Lawrence looked on Hogarth almost as a father. After Hogarth's death in 1927 Lawrence wrote that, since the war, 'whenever I was in a dangerous position I used to make up my mind after coming away from his advice. He was very wise for others, and very understanding, and comfortable, for he knew all the world's vices and tricks and shifts and evasions and pretexts, and was kindly towards them all. If I might so put it, he had no knowledge of evil: because everything to him was fit to be looked at, or to touch.'[1]

Neither Hogarth nor his wife liked this portrait, drawn by Augustus John for *Seven Pillars of Wisdom*, and Lawrence had some difficulty presenting it to the Ashmolean. It was finally accepted in 1935.

The Visitors of the Ashmolean Museum, Oxford

1. T. E. Lawrence to C. F. Shaw, 10.11.1927.

Charcoal, 50.2 × 35.5
Signed lower right : *John*
Provenance : Given by T. E. Lawrence, 1935.
Literature : *SPW 1926*, ill. ; *SPW 1935*, ill. fp. 504 ; Ashmolean Museum *Report of the Visitors*, 1935, p. 24.
Exhibitions : London, Chenil Galleries, *Paintings and Drawings by Augustus John*, 1923 (41) ; Leicester Galleries, 1927 (42).

51
ARCHAEOLOGICAL CAMERA, 1910

Lawrence had this camera built for him in late 1910, initially to take high-quality photographs of crusader castles. He used it throughout the Carchemish excavations.

In recent biographies there has been much ill-informed speculation about his possession of a telephoto lens. It has been suggested that there was no need for this in his work, and that he used it for secret Intelligence operations. In reality a lens of this kind is essential for architectural photography, as without one many inaccessible details of construction and decoration could not be recorded. Such lenses are also commonly used in archaeology to take undistorted photographs of small objects.

The camera has a rising and vertical swing lens-panel, used to correct converging parallels in architectural photography and in many other applications. There is a reflex viewfinder on the base board, and a ball-bearing levelling device with a metal plumb line. The shutter is timed for speeds from 1 to 1/250 of a second. The five lenses (four by Dallmeyer and one by Ross) include a wide angle and a telephoto.

Museum of the History of Science, Oxford (69-183 (34))

Main camera body : 15×16×10
Case inscribed : *Property of T. E. Lawrence, Pole Hill, Chingford, Essex*
Provenance : Given by A. W. Lawrence, 1969.

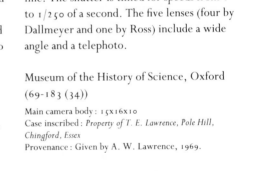

52
PHOTOGRAPHS AT CARCHEMISH
By T. E. Lawrence (1911-14)

(i) The Lower Palace staircase (1911)

The first British Museum excavations at
Carchemish in 1878 uncovered a great
staircase bordered with carved slabs and
inscriptions at the foot of the mound.
Hogarth naturally chose this as his starting
point in the 1911 trial season, and began by
clearing the area at the bottom of the
staircase. This part of the site was soon
christened the 'Lower Palace'.

(ii) Workmen hauling a fragment of masonry

In order to minimise the cost of the trial
season Hogarth took neither lifting
equipment nor a light railway to Carchemish
in 1911. Spoil from the digging had therefore
to be carried away in baskets by hand, and
heavy objects hauled out of the way by teams
of workmen. This proved to be a major
handicap because the site was strewn with
large blocks of Roman masonry. Lawrence
wrote home on 31 March 1911: 'Whenever
we break fresh ground dozens of these huge
blocks have to be moved. Some of them
weigh tons, and we have no blasting powder
or stone-hammers with us. As a result they
have to be hauled, prehistoric fashion, by
brute force of men on ropes, helped to a
small extent by crowbars. At this moment

something over sixty men are tugging away
above, each man yelling *Yallah* as he pulls:
the row is tremendous, but the stones usually
come away.'[1]

1. T. E. Lawrence to his family, 31.3.1911, *Home Letters*,
p. 143.

(iii) Carchemish mound seen from the other
side of the Euphrates

This view shows the extensive excavations
carried out on top of the mound in successive
seasons. The Lower Palace area and the city
of Carchemish lie on the far side. Digging
revealed that the mound was entirely man-
made. Excavations were severely hampered
by concrete foundations, the remains of a
Roman temple, which had to be broken up
and removed before the lower levels could
be examined.

(iv) General view of the dig from the
Carchemish mound (1914)

The reconstructed Lower Palace wall can be
seen in the centre, with light railways
running through a large area of deep
excavation beyond. The removal of spoil
would have been a much greater problem but
for successful co-operation between the
British archaeologists and the German
construction company working on the
Baghdad Railway line nearby. Accounts
written after the First World War gave the
impression that the two groups were
constantly at loggerheads. In reality, while
there was a certain rivalry (both were major
employers of local labour), their relationship
was generally harmonious.

British Museum (Dept. of Western Asiatic
Antiquities)

(i) 033816 (ii) 033828 (iii) 039213 (iv) 033819.

(ii)

(iii)

(iv)

(i)

53
CARCHEMISH, THE WORKFORCE
Photographs by T. E. Lawrence (1911-13)

(i)

(ii)

In 1911 Lawrence took a series of portrait photographs of men at Carchemish. Two of his subjects, shown here, were later to become headmen at the dig.

(i) Sheikh Hamoudi (1911)

Hamoudi (c.1880-c.1950) joined the excavations as a labourer, but his qualities as a leader were quickly recognised. He was trained to take charge of the labour gangs by Gregori, an experienced foreman who had worked with Hogarth on previous excavations. When Leonard Woolley took over from Hogarth in 1912 he retained Hamoudi, and the two later became close friends. Their partnership continued after the First World War at Ur, Woolley's most famous excavation.

(ii) Dahoum (1911)

Dahoum (c. 1896-1918) joined the excavations as a water boy and came to Lawrence's notice because he showed a higher level of intelligence than most of the workmen. At the end of the 1911 season Lawrence sent his parents the ten or twelve portrait photographs he had taken, commenting: 'the young boy who is turning up his eyes horribly is Dahoum, the boy with whose father I may stay this winter: the boy can read and write, and so would be the best teacher of Arabic in the district.'[1]
    Shortly afterwards Lawrence set off on a

tramp to visit crusader castles, and when he returned to Carchemish in late July he was extremely ill. Hamoudi took him in and nursed him, with Dahoum's help. Lawrence was soon well enough to return to England, but it was several months before he recovered fully. When the dig resumed in 1912 Dahoum again worked as water boy, and at the end of that season Lawrence took him as an assistant to help with the growing photographic workload.

1. T. E. Lawrence to his family, [12.6].1911, *Home Letters*, p. 176.

(iii) Group photograph of the Carchemish labour force (1913)

Front row, left to right: Abd-es-Salaam, Gregori, Lawrence, Woolley, Fuad Bey (site observer for the Imperial Ottoman Museum), Hamoudi, Dahoum.

British Museum (Dept. of Western Asiatic Antiquities)

(i) 195617 (ii) 195168 (iii) 033827

(iii)

54

OEUVRES
By François Rabelais, Paris (no date)

During the evenings of the 1911 season at
Carchemish Lawrence had time to read.
A letter in March mentions that he might
shortly ask for an edition of Rabelais to be
sent out to him, and at the end of the month
he wrote : 'It would be appreciated if Will
asked Blackwell's to write to Jean Gillequin,
publisher Bould. St. Michel Paris, ordering
the 3 volumes of the Rabelais in his 1 f. 25
collection (*La Renaissance du Livre*)'.[1] The
books arrived in May, and Lawrence wrote
again : 'The Rabelais has come : a beautiful
little edition and a great joy : very many
thanks for the quickness of it.'[2] In June he

reported that he was reading Rabelais every
night, 'a most profound comfort'.[3]

Many years later he wrote : 'My notion of
the world's big books are *War and Peace*, *The
Brothers Karamazoff*, *Moby Dick*, Rabelais, *Don
Quixote* . . . There's a fine set of cores of
darkness !'[4]

At this period Lawrence was interested in
all aspects of book production because he was
planning to set up his own private press. The
amateur binding on this set was probably
executed by him, perhaps as a bookbinding
exercise, during the months he spent in
England in the autumn of 1911. There is a
later reference in his letters to binding up
French novels in buckram. While the outside
of the binding is very presentable, the green

endpapers fail to conceal that the cloth has
been carelessly trimmed where it is turned
over onto the inner side of the covers.

Private Collection

1. T. E. Lawrence to his family, 31.3.1911,
Home Letters, pp. 146-7.
2. T. E. Lawrence to his family, 29.5.1911,
Home Letters, p. 164.
3. T. E. Lawrence to his family, 19.6.1911,
Home Letters, p. 172.
4. T. E. Lawrence to E. Garnett, 1.12.1927, *Letters*,
p. 548.

Printed book, cloth bound, three volumes, I : 252 pp.,
II : 247 pp., III : 211 pp., each 18.3
Each volume inscribed on flyleaf : *T. E. L./Carchemish/
1911*
Provenance : Acquired from T. E. Lawrence's family.
Literature : *Home Letters, passim*.
(not illustrated)

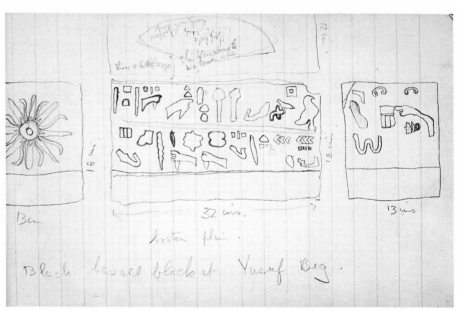

55

STELE-BASE FROM YUSUF BEG
Northern Syria (Hittite), 9th century BC

Under Turkish regulations all finds at the
Carchemish excavations were the property of
the Imperial Ottoman Museum. The British
Museum was, nevertheless, keen to use this
opportunity to acquire antiquities for its own
collection. Woolley and Lawrence were
therefore encouraged to make contacts with
local dealers and to scour the villages round
about for suitable acquisitions. In the
interests of the Ashmolean, Hogarth had
arranged that while the British Museum
should have exclusive rights to any
antiquities purchased within ten miles of
Carchemish, the Ashmolean would have first
choice of anything bought outside this limit.

E. Wallis Budge, Keeper of the
Department of Egyptian and Syrian
Antiquities at the British Museum, was
particularly keen to acquire a large Hittite
monument of some kind. Lawrence was
therefore pleased to discover a rectangular
base for a statue or stele in the village of
Yusuf Beg, seven miles south-west of
Carchemish. The stone is inscribed on the
front and right side in archaic characters,
with a rayed sun or star on the left.

Trustees of the British Museum
(W.A.125008)

Black basalt carved in bas relief, 48 × 81 × 35
Provenance : Purchased by T. E. Lawrence at Yusuf Beg
for the British Museum, 1911.
Literature : *Carchemish* III, p. 278, ill. pl A.30 h, h★.

56

EXPEDITION NOTEBOOK FROM
CARCHEMISH
1911

One of the archaeological notebooks from
Carchemish, opened at Lawrence's drawing
of the inscriptions on the Yusuf Beg stone.

Trustees of the British Museum

Notebook, unbound, 18.5 × 11.5
Inscribed on first page : *No. 4*
Provenance : Working papers of the British Museum's
Carchemish excavations, Department of Western Asiatic
Antiquities.

57
JAMES ELROY FLECKER
Three photographs by T. E. Lawrence, 1912
Vintage prints

The British Museum's excavations at
Carchemish involved frequent dealings with
the Ottoman authorities. Woolley and
Lawrence were therefore heavily dependent
on advice from the local British Consular
staff. Ralph Fontana, the British Consul in
Aleppo, and his wife Winifred were very
pleasant company; they possessed an excellent
library of contemporary literature and
Lawrence often visited them to borrow books.
It was probably through them that he heard
that James Elroy Flecker (1884-1915) had
been appointed British Vice-Consul at Beirut.

Lawrence was in Beirut on his way to
England when Flecker and his wife arrived
there in August 1911, and they spent a whole
day together. Thereafter Lawrence was
welcomed by the Fleckers whenever he
passed through Beirut. They regarded him
and Fontana as the most civilised company
they had found in the East. In the summer of
1912, after Lawrence had been forced to
abandon his plans to go on a trek in Syria,
he and Dahoum spent the month of August
in Jebail. While there, they visited the
Fleckers at Areya where these photographs
were taken. By the spring of 1913 Flecker
was already sick with tuberculosis and he was
forced to leave Beirut. Lawrence continued
to correspond with him, and after the war

kept in contact with his widow.

In 1925 Lawrence attempted to write a
short essay giving his impressions of Flecker,
but he abandoned it unfinished.[1]

James William Flecker, Nephew and Trustee
of James Elroy Flecker

1. See T. E. Lawrence, *Men in Print*, ed. A. W.
Lawrence, London, 1940, for an edited version of
the text.

10.8 × 8.2 each
Seated photograph inscribed in pencil: *Roy in Arab dress*
Provenance: By descent.
Literature: H. Flecker in *Some Letters from Abroad of James
Elroy Flecker*, 1930, p. 59, ill. frontis.

58
*SOME LETTERS FROM ABROAD OF JAMES
ELROY FLECKER*
London, 1930

Plate facing page 64, showing T. E. Lawrence
photographed by James Elroy Flecker in
August 1912.

J. M. Wilson
Printed book, 208 pp., 22.6

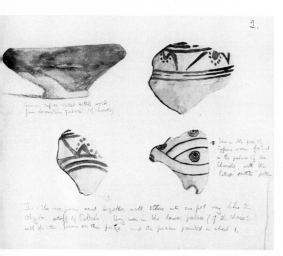

59
TWO SHEETS OF WATERCOLOUR ILLUSTRATIONS OF POTTERY FOUND AT CARCHEMISH
By Reginald Campbell Thompson with autograph notes by T. E. Lawrence, 1911

Lawrence had learned how to identify and catalogue medieval pottery at Oxford, and Hogarth therefore put him in charge of pottery finds at Carchemish. At first very little was found; the city had been sacked at some stage in its history and few small objects survived in the area where the excavations began. It was only much later in the trial season, after Hogarth had returned to England, that pottery began to be discovered in quantity. In particular, numerous Bronze Age cups shaped like champagne glasses were found in cist graves on the mound.

But for these pottery finds it is doubtful that the excavations would have been continued after the trial season. Lawrence wrote to Vyvyan Richards in late August: 'Hogarth is pressing the British Museum for a second season at Carchemish as a result of the wonderful pottery finds of the last two months . . . my star is in the ascendant as you can imagine.'[1] These coloured drawings are referred to in a letter from Lawrence to Hogarth of 6 August. They were necessary for the purposes of identification since there was no colour film at that date.

Trustees of the British Museum

1. T. E. Lawrence to V. W. Richards, 26.8.1911, *Letters*, p. 120.

Pencil, ink and watercolour, both 29 × 23
Provenance: Working papers of the British Museum's Carchemish excavations, Department of Western Asiatic Antiquities.
Literature: *Carchemish* III, pp. 227-37.

60
HITTITE HORSE AND RIDER
Northern Syria, 9th century BC

Terracotta animal figures were found at Carchemish in large numbers, and the evidence showed that they had been popular with the inhabitants over a very long period. One late-Hittite house excavated in 1911 contained nine model horses.

The archaeologists concluded that these animals were much too numerous to be religious objects. They may have been used as toys or simply for decoration. Examples were found at other nearby sites, and Lawrence sent several to the Ashmolean. He kept this one in his rooms at All Souls after the War, and later gave it to Lionel Curtis.

The Warden and Fellows of All Souls College, Oxford

Terracotta, 7 h.
Provenance: Given by Lionel Curtis, 1924.
Literature: *Friends*, p. 329.

61
REPORT ON THE EXCAVATIONS AT CARCHEMISH
By R. Campbell Thompson and T. E. Lawrence, 1911

At the end of the 1911 season the British Museum had to decide whether to undertake further excavations at Carchemish. As D. G. Hogarth had spent only a few weeks at the dig the task of writing a full report fell to his two assistants, R. Campbell Thompson and Lawrence.

Campbell Thompson was a cuneiformist, and had been very disappointed when the dig produced no cuneiform inscriptions. He told Lawrence privately that he would recommend against any further seasons. Lawrence, on the other hand, very much wanted to continue work in Syria, and the pottery found had proved very interesting.

The decision to work a second season was taken because no worthwhile scholarly conclusion had been achieved in 1911. Moreover, the Turkish authorities had made it clear that they expected the dig to be carried through to a satisfactory result. The British Museum therefore knew that no

excavation licence would be granted to it
elsewhere in the Turkish Empire until the
Ottoman authorities were convinced that
everything reasonable had been done at
Carchemish.

Trustees of the British Museum

Bound typescript with MS annotations and photographs,
44 × 30
Provenance : Report submitted to the Director of the
British Museum.
(not illustrated)

62
SIR WILLIAM FLINDERS PETRIE
By Philip de Laszlo, 1934

When Lawrence decided that he wished to
continue excavating in the Middle East after
the first Carchemish season, Hogarth
arranged for him to spend some weeks
gaining experience in Egypt at Kafr Ammar,
a dig supervised by the distinguished
Egyptologist Flinders Petrie (1853-1942).

Lawrence joined this excavation in
January 1912. He was impressed by Petrie,
but disliked digging up Egyptian graveyards :
'It is a strange sight to see the men forcing
open a square coffin, and taking out the
painted anthropoid envelope within, and
splitting this up also to drag out a mummy,
not glorious in bright wrappings, but dark
brown, fibrous, visibly rotting – and then the
thing begins to come to pieces, and the men
tear off its head, and bare the skull, and the
vertebrae drop out, and the ribs, and legs and
perhaps only one poor amulet is the result :
the smell and sights are horrible . . . Mr.
Hogarth was quite right in arranging for no
longer : I'm no body snatcher, and we have
a pile of skulls that would do credit to a
follower of Jenghis Khan.'[1]

Petrie was evidently impressed by
Lawrence, because he offered him £700 to
run an excavation of his own in Bahrein if
there were no further seasons at Carchemish
in 1913.

The Badarian vase (*c*.5000 BC) shown in
the portrait is one of a series found by Petrie
at Naqada in 1895.

National Portrait Gallery (NPG 4007)

1. T. E. Lawrence to his family, 11.1.1912, *Home Letters*,
p. 185.

Oil on canvas, 90.2 × 59.4
Signed and dated br. : *de Laszlo/1934*
Provenance : Given in 1949 by the artist's son John de
Laszlo to Professor S. R. K. Glanville of University
College, London, for his lifetime and subsequently
(1956) to the National Portrait Gallery.
Literature : O. Rutter, *Portrait of a Painter : the authorised
life of Philip de Laszlo*, 1939, p. 373 ; D.Clifford, *The
Paintings of P. A. de Laszlo*, 1969, p. 124, ill. pl. 44.
Exhibitions : London, Wildenstein, *Paintings by Philip A.
de Laszlo*, 1937 (8).

63

T. E. LAWRENCE AND LEONARD WOOLLEY, CARCHEMISH
Photograph by Heinrich Franke, 1913
(printed c.1940s)

During 1913 passenger services as far as Jerablus on the newly built Baghdad railway line began to bring large numbers of visitors to the Carchemish excavations. This photograph of Lawrence with Leonard Woolley (1880-1960) was taken by a visiting German in 1913.

Woolley had been put in charge of the excavations in 1912 replacing D. G. Hogarth, whose responsibilities at the Ashmolean prevented him from taking any active part in the dig after the 1911 trial season. It was therefore with Woolley rather than Hogarth that Lawrence worked at Carchemish during five seasons between 1912 and 1914.

Judging by contemporary correspondence their relationship was very successful. The workforce was divided into two groups, one under Woolley and the other under Lawrence. Woolley took overall decisions and wrote most of the field notes. Lawrence was responsible for pottery, photography, and for cataloguing the finds when they were moved into the expedition store. One of his more valuable talents was an ability to recognise fragments from broken carvings and inscriptions, and this enabled him to reassemble many important monuments.

Liddell Hart Centre for Military Archives, King's College London

10.2 × 16.5
Provenance: Sent by the photographer to Basil Liddell Hart; acquired, 1973.

64

T. E. LAWRENCE AND DAHOUM AT CARCHEMISH
Photographs taken by the sitters (c.1912)

After the second season's excavations in the summer of 1912 Lawrence planned to go tramping again in Syria. The illness he had contracted while travelling alone the previous summer made him more cautious than before, and he now intended to take Dahoum with him as a servant. Dahoum would also be a useful companion as Lawrence's command of Arabic was still fairly limited.

The official letters of introduction he had asked for from the Turkish authorities turned out to be phrased in such resounding terms that he feared to use them. He wrote home: 'It is rather quaint that a person of my superlative attainments should travel with a donkey and a boy to push it.'[1]

In the event there was an epidemic of cholera in the region, and they were unable to make any long journeys. They went on some shorter expeditions, however, and on one or two of these Lawrence wore Arab dress. His object was to avoid attracting attention when looking discreetly at antiquities he might want to purchase.

The photograph in which Lawrence appears probably records one of the first occasions on which he tried wearing Arab clothes. The outer garments and head-dress were borrowed from Dahoum.

British Library (Add.MS 50584 ff. 115, 116)

1. T.E. Lawrence to his family, 24.6.1912, *Home Letters*, p. 219.

Provenance: From prints given by T. E. Lawrence to Charlotte Shaw; given to the British Museum by G. B. Shaw, 1944.

65
'THE KAER OF IBU WARDANI'[1]
By T. E. Lawrence
Facsimile of an article in the *Jesus College Magazine*, January 1913

During the winter of 1912-13 Lawrence received an appeal for contributions to a new *Jesus College Magazine*, and in February he sent in an account of a visit he had made with Dahoum during the previous summer to the fabled palace of Ibn Wardani. According to popular legend every room in the ruined building had been scented with a different perfume; Lawrence wrote home that his description of it was 'more like the rumour than the reality.'[2]

This essay was the first piece of his descriptive writing about the Middle East to be published. Its closing page invokes the barren nomad philosophy that was to have such a deep influence on his own life: 'At last we came into a great hall, whose walls, pierced with many narrow windows, stood to more than half their height. "This,", said he, "is the *liwan* of silence: it has no taste," and by some crowning art it was as he had said. The mingled scents of all the palace here combined to slay each other, and all that

one felt was the desert sharpness of the air as it swept off the huge uncontaminated plains. "Among us," said Dahoum, "we call this room the sweetest of them all," therein half-consciously sounding the ideal of the Arab creed, for generations stripping itself of all furniture in the working out of a gospel of simplicity.'

The visit is also described in Chapter 3 of *Seven Pillars of Wisdom*.

Jesus College, Oxford

1. In the title of this *Jesus College Magazine* version the word 'Ibn' in the title is misprinted 'Ibu'.
2. T. E. Lawrence to his family, 22.2.1913, *Home Letters*, p. 248.
(not illustrated)

66
THREE BRONZE BOWLS
Northern Syria (Hittite), 9th century BC

In February 1913 Lawrence heard that villagers in Deve Huyuk, a village between Carchemish and Aleppo, had discovered an early grave site. They were excavating it in order to sell any antiquities found. Lawrence sent Dahoum to report on the position, and then went there himself. He quickly realised that the site was extremely important. When Woolley saw specimens of the finds he sent Hamoudi to supervise the digging and keep dealers away.

Deve Huyuk proved to be very rich in finds, and since it was more than ten miles from Carchemish the distribution was carried out by Hogarth. Much went to the Ashmolean, but there were many duplicates, and specimens were purchased by several other museums. A large number of bronze bowls was found, and it is very probable that the three exhibited here came from Deve Huyuk.

Nicolas Barker Esq.

Bronze, diameters: 12.9, 13.1, 17.5
Provenance: Given by T. E. Lawrence to Sir Ernest Barker, 1913; by descent.

67
DAHOUM
By Francis Dodd, 1913

In the summer of 1913 Lawrence took Sheikh Hamoudi and Dahoum with him on a brief visit to England; both now ranked as headmen at Carchemish.

Lawrence was present at the sitting for this portrait: 'Dodd came up smiling in the morning and got to work like a steam engine:— black and white, with little faint lines of colour running up and down in it. Number 1 was finished by midday, and was splendid: Dahoum sitting down, with his most-interested-possible expression. . . he thought it great sport — said he never knew he was so good-looking — and I think he was about right. He had dropped his sulkiness for a patch.'[1] Dodd made two further sketches. The first was discarded as a failure; the other no longer survives. This portrait was later

hung in the living room of the expedition's house at Carchemish (see no. 68 iii).

It may have been through watching Dodd at work that Lawrence first became interested in portraiture, which was to become a lifelong fascination.

B. D. Thompson Esq.

1. T. E. Lawrence to C. F. Bell, 12.8.1913.

Pencil and crayon, 36.8 × 26.7
Signed bl.: *F Dodd/1913*/[illegible Arabic inscription]
Provenance: Commissioned for T. E. Lawrence by C. F. Bell; given by A. W. Lawrence to Sidney Collard; given by him to present owner.
Literature: T. E. Lawrence, *Letters to E. T. Leeds*, ed. J. M. Wilson, Whittington Press, 1988, pp. 75-6.
(illustrated in colour p. 28)

68

CARCHEMISH, THE ARCHAEOLOGISTS' HOUSE
Photographs by T. E. Lawrence (1913-14)

(i) General view of the exterior (1913)

The C-shaped house was begun in 1912 and gradually expanded as the archaeologists' needs increased. By the time this photograph was taken in the summer of 1913 there were eleven rooms : bedrooms for Hogarth, Woolley, Lawrence and Gregori ; a living room ; kitchen ; bathroom ; photographic dark room ; store room, and two 'Museums' where the smaller antiquities were catalogued and preserved. In October 1913 four new rooms were built creating a second courtyard in front of the one seen here. The expedition cook, Haj Wahid, lived with his family in another building a few yards away from the main house.

To the right of the photograph are two camel bells suspended from a frame. In March 1912, before the expedition house had been completed, Lawrence wrote about them to his friend E. T. Leeds : '. . . did I tell you of the bells? How in the spice-bazaar of Aleppo there came down, stepping solemnly, a long line of camels from Baghdad, marching to the booming of two huge iron bells slung under the belly of the foremost : such mighty bells, nearly two feet high, each with a little bell inside it. And I stopped the caravan, and bought the bells, and walked back to the hotel, making a noise like a caravan from Baghdad, ''Oah Oah'', and the crowds in the narrow places divided to give me room.'[1]

1. T. E. Lawrence to E. T. Leeds, 18.3.1912, T. E. Lawrence, *Letters to E. T. Leeds*, ed. J. M. Wilson, Whittington Press, 1988, p. 40.

(ii) Haj Wahid standing in the entrance to the living room

The most remarkable feature of this entrance is the lintel, which Lawrence decorated in the summer of 1912 when staying at the house between digging seasons : 'As I had no chisels I carved it with a screw-driver and a knife. It is a Hittite design and use, and looks very fitting.'[1] It proved to be a source of mischievous amusement, since visitors to the site admired it as a genuine Hittite carving.

1. T. E. Lawrence to his family, 18.9.1912, *Home Letters*, p. 233.

(iii) The living room (1913)

Woolley and Hogarth were both interested in near-eastern antiques, and the Carchemish house was richly furnished with carpets and other objects acquired from dealers in Aleppo and elsewhere. This photograph was probably taken in the autumn of 1913. Dodd's portrait of Dahoum (see no. 67) hangs on the left.

(iv) The living room (1914)

The house was extended during the winter of 1913-14, and some furniture was moved out of the old living room. Lawrence sent a print of this photograph to his parents, writing : 'the ink-pot please note as an incense-burner from a mosque in Aleppo. . . the flower vase next it on the table is Hittite and Bronze Age : on a little side table of a Greek column and a Byzantine hearth-stone are a late Hittite stone bowl (usually full of roses, but now with oranges inside) and a three-legged cooking pot, early Hittite, with daisies inside. There is a large chest at the end of the room near the window, Aleppo work, carved with human figures, and birds and vines, with lion-feet : and the tiles of the fireplace are Damascus and Aleppo.'[1]

British Museum (Dept. of Western Asiatic Antiquities)

1. T. E. Lawrence to his family, 8.5.1914, *Home Letters*, p. 297.

(i) 033795 (ii) 033799 (iii) 033802 (iv) 039254

69

'REVEALING THE CIVILISATION OF THE HITTITES OF SYRIA : EXCAVATIONS AT CARCHEMISH'

By D. G. Hogarth

Facsimile of an article in *The Illustrated London News*, 24 January 1914

It was no easier to raise funds for major archaeological expeditions in the early 1900s than it is today. The trial season at Carchemish in 1911 had been financed by the British Museum, and there was enough of the original budget left over to make a substantial contribution to the second season in 1912. At that point, however, a lecture by Hogarth about Carchemish attracted an anonymous donation of £5,000.

In the autumn of 1913 Woolley reported that several more years' work would be necessary to bring the excavations to a satisfactory conclusion ; yet the funds were nearly exhausted. Hogarth therefore decided to publicise Carchemish in order to attract more support. On 24 January 1914 articles were published simultaneously in *The Times* (by Woolley) and *The Illustrated London News*, where Hogarth began : 'Three years ago the Trustees of the British Museum undertook what has proved the largest, and in many respects the most fruitful excavation which they have ever promoted.' After listing some of the principal discoveries he ended : 'when so much can be said for three years' work on a part only of this great site, it will be agreed that it is well worth digging completely.'

By good fortune the original anonymous benefactor had already decided to finance further excavations, and as a result a £10,000 fund was set up. Within months, however, progress at Carchemish was halted by the First World War.

The anonymous benefactor was Walter Morrison (see no. 70).

THE ILLUSTRATED LONDON NEWS, Jan. 24, 1914.—132

REVEALING THE CIVILISATION OF THE HITTITES OF SYRIA : EXCAVATIONS AT CARCHEMISH

OF THE LATER PERIOD (EIGHTH-SEVENTH CENTURY) : A BACK VIEW OF A HEAD WEARING A TURBAN, FOUND AT THE SOUTH-WEST GATE.

CARCHEMISH.

THE FINEST HITTITE WORK YET DISCOVERED AT JERABLUS, WHERE ONCE STOOD CARCHEMISH : THREE MALE HEADS FROM A BROKEN DOLERITE RELIEF

A FRAGMENT OF A STATUE IN DOLERITE : A HITTITE OF THE PEOPLES WHOSE HISTORY IS BEING OPENED UP FOR US.

THREE years ago the Trustees of the British Museum undertook what has proved the largest, and in many respects the most important and fruitful excavation which they have ever promoted. When the enterprise was in the initial stage, in which I myself and Mr. Campbell Thompson conducted it, I wrote in these columns a preliminary notice, giving the history and a description of the site at Jerablus, where the work had been begun, and indulging in a little prophecy of our hopes. Now three years have seen six campaigns in the soil on which there is no reasonable doubt once stood Carchemish, the leading city among the Hittite peoples of Syria. Mr. C. L. Woolley, well known for his Nubian researches, and Mr. T. E. Lawrence, who worked under Mr. Thompson and myself, have been in charge for the most part of this time, carrying on the excavation for a spring season and an autumn season in each year with between two and three hundred men. They have had their difficulties, and even their dangers, for Jerablus lies in a lawless region, among Kurdish tribes excited by recent events in Turkey ; but they have faced and surmounted them with courage, persistence, and signal use of the faculty which so many Britons possess for gaining the confidence of wild fighting folk. By the end of next spring season the Trustees, who have been splendidly supported by private munificence, will have expended some £10,000 on the site ; but the work, which is opening up Hittite history for us, and the nature of the civilisation occupying the geographical space between the Semites and the Hellenes, will not be much more than half done. In the hope that the completion of this British enterprise will not have to be resigned to alien hands (if we do not finish it, the German scholars who follow up the Baghdad Railway, now running to Jerablus, will surely do so : and, failing us, more power to

PROBABLY OF BETWEEN 2000 AND 1500 B.C. : VASES OF THE PECULIAR FORM CHARACTERISTIC OF THE EARLY CIST GRAVES.

their elbow !) the Trustees permit me to put some photographs and a brief statement of results before your readers.

The site consists of what is called a " royal city " ; that is, a strongly fortified enclosure containing palaces and their appurtenances, with a citadel, and an unfortified area inhabited by the commons. It is the first which is being explored. Its ring-wall, which enclosed about half a square mile on the bank of the Euphrates, has been stripped away to build a later town ; but the huge mound on which the wall stood still remains, rising from the moat to a height, in places, of nearly fifty feet. Also three gates remain, of which two have been explored. Here, under Hellenistic and Roman structures, the explorers have laid bare remains of Hittite buildings, consisting of flanking towers and successive lion-guarded portals, one within another, divided by open courts, in each of which an enemy, breaking in, would have had to encounter flanking fire. The line masonry of the south-west gate is well shown in one of our views, in which the spectator looks outwards over the plain on which Nebuchadnezzar settled accounts with Pharaoh Necho in 605 B.C. Now it is diversified by the line, sheds, and other constructions of the Baghdad Railway. In excavating this gate, the explorers found a fine head of a god or king of the latest Hittite Age, when, in the seventh century

LEADING UP TO THE CITADEL : THE LOWER PART OF THE GREAT STAIRWAY.
Some of the bordering sculptures of this were found in 1879 and sent to the British Museum.

FOUND ON THE CITADEL OF THE STRONGLY FORTIFIED "ROYAL CITY" : A COLUMN BASE SUPPORTED BY TWO LIONS.

FROM THE DADO OF MYTHOLOGIC SLABS : A HUMAN AND LION-HEADED SPHINX WITH TAIL ENDING IN A BIRD'S HEAD.

B.C., perhaps, the lords of Carchemish were Aramæan Semites. Our view gives the back of the head to show the turban-like covering worn by the figure. The North Gate, of still more elaborate construction and plan, is still under excavation.

Within the walls a large complex of Hittite palatial buildings has been partially cleared, together with a water-gate on the river bank which was flanked by great lions in dolerite, inscribed with Hittite hieroglyphic texts. The westernmost member of this complex is a large building entered by a portal from both jambs of which run, as far as the clearance has yet been made, dadoes of sculptured slabs, alternately of black dolerite and white limestone. The finest reliefs, those on the façade of the portal itself, show two men, probably two Kings, one being an ally, followed by eight children, of whom the last still totters, holding to a

staff, and a baby in the arms of a woman, who leads a pet animal. She should be the Queen, who appears nowhere else in the group. The children throw knuckle-bones or carry whipping-tops according to sex and age. In front of the whole group is a hieroglyphic inscription, the longest known, which, with the legends graven near the head of each member of the group, would tell us who they all were, could we read the script. We can, however, guess safely that it is a royal group of about the ninth century B.C.

The style and execution of these reliefs upset all our previous ideas about the quality of Hittite art ; as do also the sculptures which line the opposite side of the portal—royal ministers and servants in whose delineation has been used a grace which is almost Greek. Of the soldiers who follow them—note their " Carian " helmets, as the Greeks would have thought—of the long file of priestesses and acolytes bearing animals for sacrifice, of the slabs of mythologic scenes beyond the soldiers, and of the other inscribed inner doorways, we can give only two or three specimen views. As excavation proceeds, this great series of sculptures will no doubt be found to be prolonged at either end.

From this building a wall, also bearing reliefs along all its length, runs up to a great staircase, which climbs up the face of the Acropolis, and is (or was) lined with sculptures of which some are still in position. To the left is another building of the palatial complex built on the terraced slope. Here was found a small, shrine-like chamber with elaborately inscribed portal, before which stood a great laver, supported, like Solomon's, by two bulls, which are shown in one of our views.

On the Acropolis the remains are less well-preserved because in Roman days a great temple was built there, whose foundations almost destroyed the large brick buildings of the Hittites. At the north end, too, Sargon the Assyrian, who captured Carchemish in 717 B.C., built a residence for his officer. This has been cleared and its remains appear in one of our photographs, which looks northwards up the Euphrates. But the Acropolis has yielded a most important set of early tombs, with which we can now compare the contents of another cemetery outside the walls.

From Jerablus and its neighbourhood we have a long series of graves which show us the pottery and implements and seals of the Syrian Hittites from about 2000 to about 400 B.C. ; and when it is said, in conclusion, that the stratification of the city site gives us orderly evidence from the Neolithic Age to the close of the Bronze Age ; that the development of Hittite plastic art can now be studied from its cradle to its grave ; that the same is true of the hieroglyphic script, of which over a hundred new texts have come to light ; that we have cuneiform inscriptions already, and may at any moment get a bilingual key to the hieroglyphic puzzles—when so much can be said for three years' work on a part only of this great site, it will be agreed that it is well worth digging completely. D. G. HOGARTH.

70
WALTER MORRISON
Photograph by H. W. Salmon and Sons,
c.1900
Vintage print

Walter Morrison (1836-1921) was a
successful businessman, noted philanthropist,
and MP. After gaining First Class Honours at
Oxford he travelled in the Middle East and
America. He inherited a very considerable
fortune which he increased substantially
through his own business activities, yet his
personal tastes were extremely simple. He
spent much of his time on a moorland estate
at Malham Tarn in Yorkshire, where he took
an active part in local affairs. It was during
a visit to Malham by Charles Kingsley that
the idea of *The Water Babies* was conceived,
in which the Squire was based on Morrison.

The full extent of Morrison's
philanthropy cannot be assessed because his
gifts were generally anonymous. It is known
that he contributed large sums to northern
universities, and that he built and furnished
the remarkable chapel at Giggleswick
School. His immense gifts to the University
of Oxford included £30,000 for a readership
in Egyptology and other projects, and
£50,000 to the Bodleian Library (in real
terms one of the largest gifts the Library has
ever received). A few of his benefactions
were eccentric: he disliked the Victorian
chapel at Balliol College, Oxford (where he
had been an undergraduate), and once offered
money to rebuild it in the style of the
original. The offer was declined.

One of his passions was archaeology. He
financed the Society of Biblical Archaeology

and was the founding benefactor of the
Palestine Exploration Fund. It was he who
contributed the anonymous donations which
financed the British Museum's Carchemish
excavations, £5,000 in 1911 and a further
£10,000 in 1914.

Palestine Exploration Fund

64 × 50
Literature: *PEF. Quarterly Statement*, 1921, ill.

71
SIR FREDERIC KENYON
Photograph by Bassano (1921)

Sir Frederic Kenyon (1863-1952) was
appointed Director of the British Museum in
1909. He had worked for the previous
twenty years in the Museum's Department of
Manuscripts, during which time he had
achieved great distinction as a scholar in the
fields of classical papyri and early biblical
texts; he had also prepared editions of the
letters and poetry of Elizabeth Barrett
Browning. He was an excellent chairman and
administrator, and is considered to have been
one of the greatest Directors of the British
Museum. Although his previous career had
been in librarianship and textual scholarship,
his files relating to Carchemish show a
thorough grasp of the problems involved in
running a major excavation, a readiness to
listen to expert advice, and an acute
judgment of situations and personalities.

He met Lawrence on several occasions,
the first being in 1911 after the initial trial
season at Carchemish, when he was trying to
assess the case for further excavations there.
His judgment in all such matters was rigidly
impartial. Lawrence had no success when he
tried on one occasion to persuade him that
a grave group acquired just outside
Carchemish (i.e. within the ten-mile radius
where the British Museum had a right to all
purchases) should go to the Ashmolean.[1]

Kenyon evidently had some regard for
Lawrence, and when the Carchemish
excavations were suspended at the beginning
of the First World War he offered Lawrence
work in the Museum. In 1927 Lawrence
came into contact with Kenyon again when
he presented a copy of the subscribers' *Seven
Pillars* to the British Museum Library.

National Portrait Gallery (NPG X31199)

1. See J. M. Wilson, *Lawrence of Arabia*, London, 1988,
pp. 115-17.

72
LETTER FROM SIR FREDERIC KENYON
TO SIR CHARLES WATSON
British Museum, 21 November 1913
Facsimile

In 1913 the British Agent in Cairo, Lord
Kitchener, decided that military consider-
ations made it very desirable to survey a
narrow triangle of land stretching north from
Akaba to Beersheba and the Dead Sea.

There were already good maps of the
adjoining regions, but this area to the west
of the Egyptian frontier in Sinai was under
Turkish control, and it was not possible to
send a survey party of Royal Engineers there
without some good excuse.

In the autumn of 1913 the War Office
approached the Palestine Exploration Fund,
under whose auspices the Survey of Palestine
had been carried out (by Kitchener himself)
many years previously. It was agreed that the
new survey should be presented as an
extension of this earlier work in Palestine,
and the PEF therefore decided that it would
be proper to send an archaeologist to
examine any biblical remains in the region.

Their first choice was the Egyptologist
T. E. Peet, but he was not available at the
required time. D. G. Hogarth, who was a
member of the PEF committee, then
suggested that Leonard Woolley might go.
The idea was taken up by Frederic Kenyon
at the British Museum, who suggested that
both Woolley and Lawrence might be sent,
and wrote accordingly to Sir Charles
Watson, Chairman of the PEF Committee.
Kenyon's enthusiasm was not entirely
academic: the British Museum had agreed to

keep Woolley and Lawrence at Carchemish during the break between digging seasons on half pay, as this was cheaper than their return expenses to England. If they were paid by the PEF to take part in the Sinai survey, the Museum would be relieved of considerable expense.

The letter reads:

British Museum
London: W. C.
Nov. 21st 1913

Dear Sir Charles,

Hogarth concurs in the idea of lending our men from Jerablus to the P.E.F. survey for about two months from the latter part of December, and supports that, as the time is short, *both* should go. Their names are C. L. Woolley and T. E. Lawrence. The former is the senior man, with rather wider experience; the latter is the better at colloquial Arabic, and gets on very well with natives. He has, I think, more of the instincts of an explorer, but is very shy.

Time being short, I have written already to Jerablus, to ask if either or both care to entertain the idea, and to cable their answer. I have warned them that you may have engaged some one else in the interval, or that you may not be able to take both of them. You are therefore quite uncommitted, and can take either, neither, or both when their answer comes. Both are good men: Hogarth can tell you more about them, if you wish.

Yours sincerely
F. G. Kenyon

Palestine Exploration Fund

(not illustrated)

73
MAP OF NORTH EASTERN SINAI
By B. V. Darbishire, 1914

Lawrence took a considerable interest in the work carried out in Sinai by the military survey party under Captain Stewart Newcombe. His studies of medieval campaigns had taught him the importance of geography in warfare. From Newcombe, a military surveyor, he learned to observe the landscape in a much more disciplined manner. This experience was to qualify Lawrence for work in the Geographical Section of the War Office some months later, and would also prove invaluable during the desert campaigns.

During the latter part of the expedition the surveyors worked in different areas, and Lawrence accompanied Newcombe's party down to Akaba. In this way he was able to travel over a region which would become very important during the Arab Revolt. In particular, he saw for himself the approaches to Akaba from the east, and realised that it would be very difficult indeed for a force landing there to advance up the Wadi Itm towards Maan. This conclusion was by no means evident from the maps then available, and Lawrence's memoranda on the subject written from the Cairo Intelligence Department in 1915 and 1916 were to save the British the costly mistake of landing there in force.

This map shows the area covered by the Sinai Survey. It was drawn for publication in the archaeological report on the survey (see no. 79) and is based on the larger-scale map drawn by the War Office from data provided by Newcombe's survey (see no. 77).

Palestine Exploration Fund

Pen and ink, 57.3 × 42.5
Literature: C. L. Woolley and T. E. Lawrence, *The Wilderness of Zin*, Palestine Exploration Fund, London, 1914, ill. p. 2.

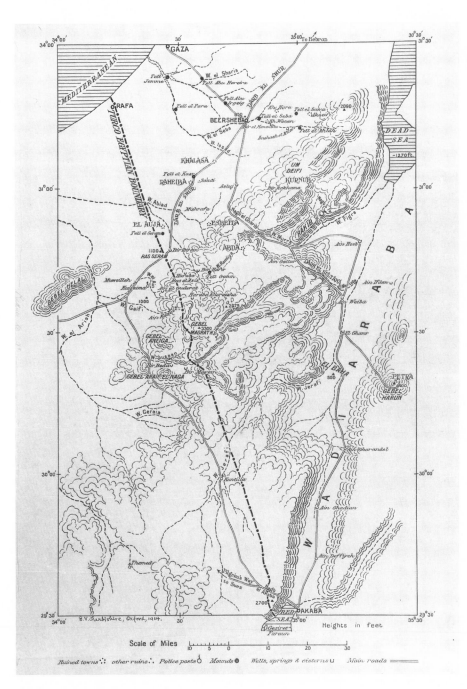

(i)

(ii)

(iii)

(iv)

74
THE SINAI SURVEY
Photographs by T. E. Lawrence (January –
February 1914)

Lawrence, Woolley and Dahoum left
Carchemish to join the Sinai Survey at the
end of December 1913. When they reached
Beersheba they discovered to their surprise
that no equipment or stores had been
provided for them, and they were therefore
obliged to buy almost everything they would
need for the six-week expedition.
Fortunately, Lawrence had taken his own
camera and a supply of film.

These photographs were taken during the
survey and show the arid nature of the flinty
desert through which they travelled. They
found little to interest biblical archaeologists,
since the only substantial ruins were from the
Byzantine period.

(i) Wadi Deira, rock-cut cistern

(ii) Raheiba, reservoir
Note Dahoum, standing in the reservoir to
indicate its scale.

(iii) Kurnub, capital and voussoirs of the west
church

(iv) Esbeita, south church

Palestine Exploration Fund

Literature : C. L. Woolley and T. E. Lawrence, *The
Wilderness of Zin*, Palestine Exploration Fund, London,
1914, ill. pls. xxxiii, xxviii, xxxi, xix.

75
BAB-ES-SIQ, PETRA
By David Bomberg, 1924

During his work with the Sinai Survey Lawrence visited Petra for the first time. Afterwards he described it in a letter to E.T. Leeds as 'the most wonderful place in the world, not for the sake of its ruins, which are quite a secondary affair, but for the colour of its rocks, all red and black and grey with streaks of green and blue, in little wriggly lines. . . and for the shape of its cliffs and crags and pinnacles, and for the wonderful gorge it has, always running deep in spring-water, full of oleanders, and ivy and ferns, and only just wide enough for a camel at a time, and a couple of miles long. But I have read hosts of most beautifully written accounts of it, and they give one no idea of it at all. . . and I am sure I cannot write nearly as nicely as they have. . . so you will never know what Petra is like, unless you come out here. . . Only be assured that till you have seen it you have not had the glimmering of an idea how beautiful a place can be.'[1]

David Bomberg, who had originally come out to Palestine under the auspices of the Zionist Organisation, painted many scenes at Petra in 1924. This tour was arranged by Ronald Storrs, at that time Governor of Jerusalem and Judea.

Birmingham Museums and Art Gallery (555'28)

1. T. E. Lawrence to E. T. Leeds, 28.2.1914, *Letters*, p. 167.

Oil on canvas, 51.2 × 61
Signed br. : *Bomberg 24*
Provenance : Purchased from the Leicester Galleries, 1928.
Literature : M. Chamot, *Modern Painting in England*, 1937, ill. pl. 22; R. Storrs, *Orientations*, 1937, p. 495; City Museum and Art Gallery Birmingham, *Catalogue of Paintings*, 1960, p.12.
Exhibitions : Leicester Galleries, *David Bomberg: Paintings of Palestine and Petra*, 1928 (9); Arts Council, *David Bomberg*, 1958 (14); Jerusalem, The Israel Museum, *David Bomberg in Palestine 1923-1927*, 1983 (31).

RIOT ON THE BAGDAD RAILWAY

MANY REPORTED KILLED AND WOUNDED.

1914

CONSTANTINOPLE, March 24.

A serious riot is reported to have taken place on the 20th inst. on the Bagdad Railway, near Jerabluss. Several hundred Kurdish labourers rebelled against their chiefs on the question of pay. According to a telegram received at the offices of the Anatolian Railway Company, in the course of the disturbance the Kurds destroyed some sheds belonging to the works and attacked the German engineers, eight of whom were wounded. One Austrian and one British subject were also wounded. The nature of their wounds is not stated.

A telegram from the British Consul at Aleppo does not mention any British wounded, but adds that two British subjects, Messrs. Wooley and Lawrence, engaged in excavations on behalf of the British Museum, exerted themselves to restrain their own Kurds from joining the other Kurdish labourers in an attack upon the Germans, and that one of them was fired upon by the Circassian guard belonging to the Germans, but was not hurt.

An earlier telegram states that three Kurds were killed and five are believed to have fallen into the river and been drowned, while many were wounded. The Vali of Aleppo, with the British and German Consuls, the chief engineer of the company, the Public Prosecutor, and a detachment of troops left for the scene of the disturbance, and it is presumed that order has been restored.—*Reuter.*

Times

76

'RIOT ON THE BAGDAD RAILWAY'
Facsimile of an article in *The Times*,
25 March, 1914

The German construction engineers responsible for the Baghdad Railway works at Jerablus were unable to establish a good relationship with their workforce. By the spring of 1914 a number of minor incidents had already taken place, and it seemed inevitable that there would one day be more serious trouble. This finally occurred at the end of March, when a minor dispute over pay turned into a shooting incident and then into a riot. But for courageous intervention by Lawrence and Woolley, the German staff would certainly have been massacred. The affair was thoroughly investigated by Turkish, British and German officials, all of whom praised Woolley and Lawrence for their bravery in the face of an armed mob.

Unfortunately the incident was reported by Reuter, and this news story in *The Times* caused great consternation in the Lawrence household.

77

THE NEGEB OR DESERT SOUTH OF BEERSHEBA
Ordnance Survey map, printed for the Palestine Exploration Fund by the General Staff, Geographical Section, War Office, 1921.

The first printing for general circulation of the War Office map made from Newcombe's survey notes.

99.2 × 70.2
(not illustrated)

78

LETTER FROM LEONARD WOOLLEY TO D. G. HOGARTH
Danbury, Essex, ?October 1914

Woolley and Lawrence began work on the Sinai report during the final season at Carchemish in the spring of 1914. When war broke out in August, the Turkish government did not immediately commit itself. Kitchener hoped that Turkey might remain neutral and urged that the PEF archaeological report should be published as quickly as possible in order to allay any suspicions about the purpose of the expedition. Lawrence worked on the report in Oxford throughout the summer, consulting earlier sources in the Bodleian Library. In October, when he went to London to join the Geographical Section of the War Office, he returned the text to Woolley.

This letter from Woolley to Hogarth probably dates from late October; Lawrence saw it shortly afterwards, and added a note protesting at the insertion of his name on the title page. His objections were over-ruled, since he had in reality contributed substantial sections of the text.

Palestine Exploration Fund

Autograph letter with annotations in red ink by T. E. Lawrence, single folded sheet, bound into volume, 17.6 × 11.3
(not illustrated)

PALESTINE EXPLORATION FUND,
1914.

THE WILDERNESS OF ZIN
(ARCHÆOLOGICAL REPORT.)

By
C. LEONARD WOOLLEY
and
T. E. LAWRENCE.

With a Chapter on the Greek Inscriptions by M. N. TOD.

PUBLISHED BY ORDER OF THE COMMITTEE
AND SOLD AT
THE OFFICES OF THE FUND, 2, HINDE STREET, MANCHESTER SQUARE, W.

79

*THE WILDERNESS OF ZIN
(ARCHÆOLOGICAL REPORT)*
By C. Leonard Woolley and T. E. Lawrence, London, Palestine Exploration Fund, 1914
(PEF Annual 1914-15)

The archaeological report on Sinai, finally published in the late autumn of 1914. Although it was printed in a very small edition, copies were still available when Lawrence died. As a result of the surge of interest which followed general publication of *Seven Pillars of Wisdom* in 1935, a second edition of *The Wilderness of Zin* was issued in 1936.

J. M. Wilson

Printed book, 174 pp., 28.5

THE WAR
1914-18

When the great European war began in August 1914 there was a surge of patriotism in Britain; recruiting offices were overwhelmed with volunteers. Bob, the eldest of the Lawrence brothers, was studying medicine, but Frank left college to join up and Will, who was teaching in India, soon decided to come back and fight.

There was no immediate prospect of a role for Lawrence in the Middle East, but if Turkey entered the war on the German side, as was generally expected, there would be work for people with specialist knowledge of the region.

During the summer and early autumn he divided his time between the PEF's archaeological report on Sinai and work at the Ashmolean. In October, however, it became clear that the Turks would soon take up arms, and they did so at the end of the month. Ten days previously Lawrence had joined the Geographical Section of the War Office. He stayed there for several hectic weeks helping to complete the new Sinai maps now urgently required by British headquarters in Cairo, and he also compiled a book of routes through the Sinai peninsula.

On 8 December 1914 he left for Egypt to join the new Military Intelligence Department in Cairo which was to be headed by Stewart Newcombe, under the overall direction of Colonel Gilbert Clayton. Woolley was there as well, and the department was soon to boast a remarkably talented staff.

The workload proved to be immense; they were expected to assimilate vast amounts of information of varying reliability, and to produce frequent and accurate summaries. Secret reference works such as the *Turkish Army Handbook* had to be continuously updated. Lawrence, for his part, was also responsible for collecting the geographical data needed by the Survey of Egypt to improve its maps. His interest in printing was revived when he found himself working closely with the Egyptian Government Press.

The atmosphere in the Intelligence office was informal, more like that of a university department than that of a military establishment; its staff was casual about procedure, rank and uniform. This attitude was something of an irritant to regular officers at Headquarters, but the British army was well able to absorb such unconventional talent in an emergency. While Lawrence occasionally gave offence his services were valued by the small group of people who came into close contact with him and knew what he was doing. As the Director General of the Survey of Egypt, Sir Ernest Dowson, wrote later, 'the weight of his real personality and wide knowledge rapidly effaced the initial impression of boyish irresponsibility and unseasonable trifling that he delighted to present.'[1]

Lawrence found much of his routine work tedious. He recognised its importance, yet rarely enjoyed any sense of achievement. His greatest enthusiasm was for the stirrings of Arab nationalism, and he hoped passionately that the Arabs would take advantage of the war to throw off the yoke of Turkish rule. Papers dating from 1915 and 1916 show that he was deeply involved in the Intelligence work that lay behind the Arab Revolt, and well aware of the complex and secret diplomacy which preceded it.

During 1915 his brothers Frank and Will were killed on active service in Europe. He felt guilty living peacefully in Cairo while so many were risking their lives on the battlefront. Nevertheless his contribution had been noticed in higher quarters. In March 1916 he and Woolley were mentioned in dispatches, and with Newcombe he received the *Légion d'Honneur*.

That month he was also promoted Captain, and given an extraordinary task. An Anglo-Indian force commanded by General Townshend had been under siege at Kut al Amara in Mesopotamia for four months and could not hold out much longer.

T. E. Lawrence
By an unknown photographer, c.1917
(no. 130)

1. *Friends*, p. 138.

Facing page
T. E. Lawrence
By Augustus John, 1919
(no. 115)

Lawrence was sent from Cairo to join the relief force, with two briefs. The first was to try and bribe one of the senior Turkish army officers to take pressure off Townshend; but by the time Lawrence arrived the position at Kut was already beyond recall. He went officially with two other British officers to the Turkish headquarters, and tried to negotiate an honourable release for the trapped army. All they could achieve was an exchange of the British wounded for healthy Turkish prisoners of war.

In the past, very little has been said about another part of this mission, which might have become extremely important. Lawrence had acquired a deep knowledge of the political forces at work in the Arab areas behind enemy lines, and during this visit to Mesopotamia he met Arab leaders and discussed with them the possibility of raising a revolt there against the Turks. His conclusion was disappointing: there was insufficient feeling, at any rate in the southern regions, and the new Anglo-Indian administration was strongly opposed to anything which might encourage nationalist aspirations.

While the main results of his visit to Mesopotamia were negative, Lawrence conducted useful discussions at the Indian Expeditionary Force headquarters. The report he wrote afterwards was so impressive that his superiors in Cairo shortly entrusted him with another important mission.

When he arrived back in Egypt at the end of May 1916 he found that Hogarth, who had previously spent much of the war in London, had returned briefly to Cairo to help set up a new Intelligence unit called the Arab Bureau. Hogarth had long been recognised in academic circles as an expert on the Middle East, and he was now working in the Geographical Section of the Naval Intelligence Department at the Admiralty. This section had been formed in 1915 to produce a series of geographical guides to various theatres of the war, and Hogarth was working on a handbook to Arabia which was eventually published as a comprehensive 1,200 page reference work. One of the Arab Bureau's tasks would be to compile smaller geographical guides and political handbooks, based partly on local information and partly on Admiralty material. Hogarth was to provide a link between the two organisations. Throughout the summer of 1916 Lawrence worked part-time for the Bureau since its tasks duplicated some of his responsibilities in the Military Intelligence Department. He contributed a great deal of material to the first issues of its secret journal, the *Arab Bulletin*. As the Bureau grew in stature it began to recruit more staff of its own, and Lawrence was an obvious candidate.

The work of the new department became increasingly important when the long-hoped-for revolt against the Turks broke out in the Hejaz at the beginning of June 1916. After a protracted correspondence with the British, Hussein, the Sherif of Mecca, had committed himself to the Allied side in exchange for promises of military support and guarded assurances of Arab independence in the event of victory.

In the autumn it was arranged that Lawrence should be transferred to the staff of the Arab Bureau, but first he was sent to Jidda to report on the situation in the Hejaz. The Arab Revolt seemed to have come to a standstill, and there was little reliable information about the capacity of its forces or the ability of its commanders. During two weeks in Arabia, Lawrence met Hussein's sons, Ali, Abdullah, Feisal and Zeid, and formed his own conclusions about them. He later wrote that he felt at first glance that the Emir Feisal 'was the man I had come to Arabia to seek – the leader who would bring the Arab Revolt to full glory.'[2]

While travelling back to Cairo he wrote a remarkable series of reports about the situation, and shortly afterwards he was sent back to the Hejaz to act as British liaison officer with Feisal.

During the next two years he was almost continually in the field with the Arab forces, living, travelling, and fighting as they did. He was subsequently to write a magnificent account of his experiences during the desert campaign in *Seven Pillars of Wisdom*.

Two shorter accounts by Lawrence are included here to provide an outline of the Revolt. The first is part of an article on the origins of the Arab movement, and concerns the historical background to the campaign. The second is a previously unpublished narrative of the Revolt itself, written by Lawrence during the 1919 Peace

2. *SPW 1935*, ch. 12, p. 91.

Conference for a member of the American Delegation. It sets out clearly and concisely what the Arabs achieved, with hardly any reference to his own part.

Story of the Arab Movement[3]

A 'Sherif' (plural 'Ashraf') in the Moslem world is one who claims descent in the male line of the Khalif Ali (656-661 A.D.) by his marriage with Fatima, daughter of the Prophet Mohammed (died 632). There are many of these Ashraf in Arabia, Morocco and the Sudan, but among those generally accepted as such, only the Ashraf inscribed in the Register of Mecca, which has been strictly kept for many centuries past, if not from the days of the Prophet himself, are of absolutely unquestioned authenticity. They are divided into a number of clans living mostly in the Hejaz, and form an accepted aristocracy with peculiar privileges under a law of their own.

For the first four centuries after the death of the Prophet, the Ashraf were not very numerous and had not as yet established their position as a political power. Towards the end of the tenth century, however, one of the Ashraf of Mecca got possession of his native town and inaugurated in the Hejaz a tradition of Sherifian temporal power, the holder of which was regarded as the Emir and head of the Ashraf, or, as he has for centuries been known in Europe – 'The Grand Sherif of Mecca'.

In course of time a fighting Sherif of the Juheinah clan, by name Qatada, became Emir and a Prince of his dynasty during the sixteenth century, established the undoubted predominance of the Emirate of Mecca over the Hejaz, and secured for his own family an exclusive right to the throne. The reigning representative of the senior line of the dynasty founded by the Emir Qatada succeeded to the throne of Mecca as the Emir Husein in 1908, and so long as it was possible to reconcile his position as a vassal of the Sultan of Turkey with his dignity as an Arab Prince and head of the Ashraf, he remained a loyal subject of the Ottoman Empire, but at the beginning of the war the Turkish atrocities in Syria which came on top of the violent attempts of the Constantinople Government forcibly to Ottomanize all nationalities under its authority, made a revolt of the Arab nation against its oppressors inevitable.

In May 1916, the position of the Emir of Mecca was threatened by the arrival of a picked force of 3,000 Turkish troops in Medina. Their plan of campaign was to march through the Hejaz consolidating the waning Ottoman authority in that principality, and then to proceed to the Yemen in order to reinforce the Turkish army operating against Aden. The foresighted policy of the Emir in preventing the prolongation of the Hejaz railway from Medina to Mecca, caused a much needed delay in the progress of the Turks, and the Emir decided that the privileged position of the Hejaz and possibly his own authority would be menaced by the arrival of so large a Turkish force. He placed himself at the head of the national cause and drew his sword in the defence of the Arab as against the Turk.

The Arab Revolt[4]

The Arab revolt broke out in June 1916 at Mecca and Medina simultaneously. At Mecca the Sherif himself took command, and had under him nearly 6,000 townsmen and tribesmen. They had no artillery, and so failed to carry the main barrack and Fort Jiad. These held out for two weeks until Sir Reginald Wingate sent over to the Hejaz four mountain guns from the Egyptian Army in the Sudan. With these the fort and barracks were easily destroyed.

Meanwhile 4,000 Harb tribesmen had attacked Jidda. The Turkish garrison of 1,200 had prepared an entrenched position, but they were bombarded by warships which Great Britain had sent to help the Arab forces, and the place fell in four days.

Meanwhile Sherif Abdulla (second son of Sherif Hussein) with about 3,500 tribesmen and villagers from the neighbourhood was besieging Taif,

3. *The Advance of the Egyptian Expeditionary Force*, ed.
C. H. C. Pirie Gordon, 1919, text facing pls. 51-2.
4. T. E. Lawrence to Major S. Bonsal, 22.1.1919.

(80 miles SE. of Mecca) where the Turkish summer headquarters were. The Egyptian artillery from Mecca was sent on to him, but their guns were too light to cope with the Turkish artillery, and the siege dragged for three months, till Abdulla got the loan of a 5 inch howitzer. With this in action Taif fell in three days more.

By this the surrender of the [Turkish] Hejaz H.Q. was complete. The Arabs had taken 6,000 prisoners without much cost in men. The siege at Medina was less fortunate. Ali and Feisal, sons of the Sherif, had raised about 7,000 villagers and tribesmen, but the Turkish force there was nearly 11,000, and increasing daily, and had a powerful artillery. Ali and Feisal had men, but were short of rifles, and had no machine guns or guns. They had no explosives, and could not cut the Hejaz Railway permanently.

In consequence they were defeated with heavy losses, and had to fall back to cover the three roads to Mecca. They raised some 14,000 Harb tribesmen, 11,000 Beni Salem villagers, and 9,000 Juheina, and with the terrain in their favour were able to hold up the Turks (who were trying to rush down and relieve Taif) till the British could send them up rifles, and explosives and stores.

A long pause then took place, during which the Sherif's cause was announced to the world, and volunteers of Mesopotamian or Syrian origin flocked to him from the Turkish prisoner of war camps in Egypt and India. The British equipped these volunteers (who formed the nucleus of the Arab Regular Army) with uniforms, arms, and transport. They were mostly technical troops (gunners, machine gunners, and staff) and relied on the tribes for their infantry and demolition parties. No tribesman ever joined the Arab Regular Army, since military service is against their principles.

Before the Arab army was reorganised the Turkish forces in Medina had risen to some 23,000, and showed very great activity westward and southward. The situation of the Arabs was critical throughout November and December 1916.

In January 1917 Feisal was strengthened by the approach of his brother Abdulla, with his 4,000 men from Taif. Abdulla moved on to the eastern flank of the Medina position, and the Turks had to restrain their activities on the west. Feisal seized the opportunity to slip away unperceived, with 8,000 men northward, along the coast, where a Turkish independent force at Wejh threatened his seaboard communications.

With the help of the British Navy the difficulties of a march of nearly 300 miles over bad country were surmounted, and Wejh taken on January 23, 1917. Feisal then sent his 8,000 men back to near Medina, to join Abdulla, who had crossed to the West to take Feisal's place, and raised for himself a new force, of about 6,000 Billi, and 2,000 Aneyze, to attack the Hejaz Railway about El Ula. At Wejh he also began to form his own section of regular army, and sent recruiting missions to Egypt, where they persuaded about two thousand Syrian and Mesopotamian prisoners of war to volunteer for his forces.

Meanwhile Feisal was trying to get yet further North, with an eye to the deliverance of Syria from the Turks. To this end in May 1917 he sent a small expedition northward, and in July 1917 they were able to take Akaba from the east, without naval help.

Feisal then handed over the command in the Wejh area to Sherif Sharaf, one of his cousins, and transferred his own headquarters, and that of his regular troops (now 3,000 strong) to Akaba. The British added a battery of armoured cars, and a flight of aeroplanes to his forces. In Akaba Feisal enlisted about 5,000 Beni Atiyeh tribesmen, about 8,000 Howeitat, 8,000 Beni Sakhr, and 4,000 from other smaller tribes. With these he undertook serious and sustained operations against the Turkish forces holding the Maan area. Before the end of the year he took the village of Wadi Musa

The Emir Feisal
By Augustus John, 1919
(no. 98)

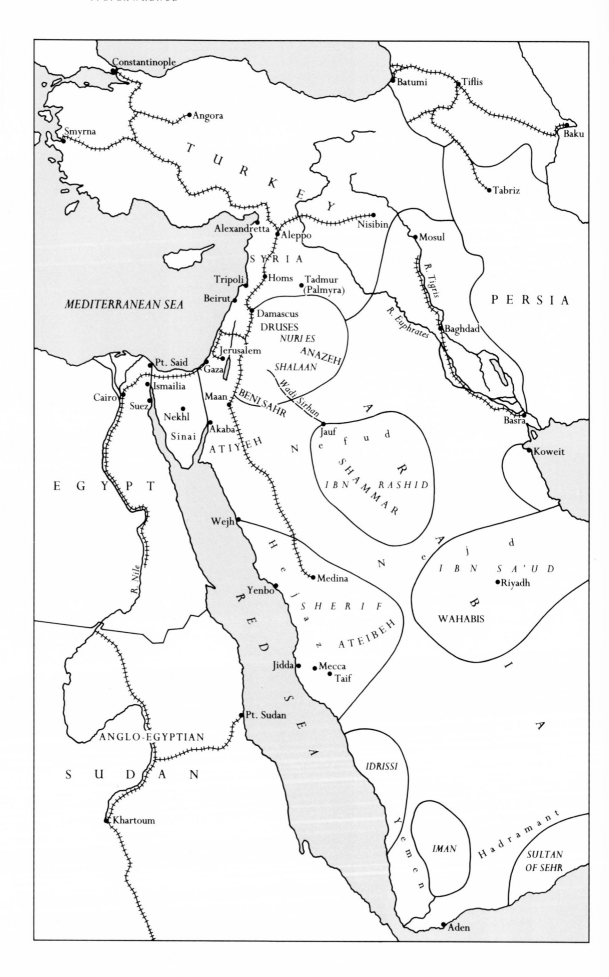

(Petra) and held it against attacks, and later wrested part of the Maan plateau (Ab el Lissan) from the enemy.

In January 1918 he sent a force of 3,000 men northward from Wadi Musa, and took the town of Tafileh, and six other villages, and joined up with the British at the south end of the Dead Sea. The Turks attacked him frequently in this area, with varying result, but Feisal was able always to retain his hold on the western part of the Maan plateau.

General Allenby recognised the value of the Arab army as his extreme right wing as soon as he reached Egypt in July 1917, and helped Feisal liberally with equipment. In consequence the Arab Regular Army took efficient shape, and increased to nearly 6,000 strong.

In April 1917 Feisal undertook direct operations against Maan, as part of Allenby's thrust against Amman; he materially improved his position but failed to take Maan itself. He did however succeed in cutting the Hejaz Railway from Maan southwards, finally, so that the ultimate surrender of Medina became only a matter of time. His brothers Ali and Abdulla were still camped about the city, keeping up a close blockade with very considerable forces: this they maintained till January 1919 when the town at last capitulated.

In July and August 1918 Feisal, while maintaining his constant pressure against Maan, spent most of his time preparing an important flying column, to co-operate in the attack which General Allenby intended to deliver against the Turkish army in Palestine in September. Allenby assigned to the Arab Army the duty of cutting the Turkish railway and telegraph communications between Damascus and Palestine two days before his attack and keeping them cut. The Arab army was also to demonstrate against Amman, so as to strengthen the Turkish delusion that the main British-Arab attack was to be delivered in the Jordan valley. The second intention was very successfully carried out, and the Turks had more than one third of their total force on this entirely useless flank when Allenby struck.

For his main objective Feisal prepared a flying column of 4 guns, 40 machine guns, four armoured cars, and two aeroplanes, of the Regular forces. He added to these about 8,000 tribesmen, for preliminary operations, and had assurances from the villagers and townsmen of the district about to be attacked, that they would join his forces when the moment came. He attacked Deraa on Sept the 16th and kept the three Turkish railways, and all their telegraphs cut until 27th September, when he took Deraa, after scattering the last columns of the disordered fourth Turkish army. Next day the British cavalry joined him, coming from Galilee, and the combined forces moved north swiftly upon Damascus, which was entered on Sept the 30th amid scenes of tremendous joy. Feisal had mobilised about 11,000 of the peasantry of the Hauran from Sept 20th onward, and had prevented nearly all the stragglers of the Turkish army from getting away to Damascus.

On October the first, the people of Beyrout, in emulation of the Damascenes, turned on their Turkish garrison of 700 men, and took them prisoner. They then hoisted the Arab flag, and proclaimed their independence. On October the third, the infection had reached Tripoli. On the fifth Ladikia [Latakia] in the north, and Baalbek on [sic] the south, also proclaimed the Arab rebellion. On the seventh the Arab flag was hoisted in Antioch, and the Turks were confined in Syria to Aleppo itself, and the strip of railway running from Aleppo to Homs. On the eighth of October the allied troops entered Beyrout. The Arab rising there had been suppressed in the newspapers, so that the French troops might claim the honour of its liberation from the Turks.

A few weeks later Allenby was able to organise a cavalry force to attack Aleppo, and a detachment of the Arab army marched north with them. They had a vigorous fight to win Aleppo, and the last scene was in the

Facing page
General map of Arabia and the Middle East during the campaigns 1916–18

Town Hall there, when two Turkish machine guns were rushed by an Arab bombing party, and destroyed.

From Aleppo the Arab army marched out to Muslimiyeh, the junction of the Anatolian, Syrian, and Bagdad railways, and took it, the day before the Turks asked for an armistice.

The Arab army had no separate share in the conquest of Syria, and do not wish any attempt to be made to estimate their individual importance. They placed themselves (by Feisal's personal action) under the orders of General Allenby, and regard the common triumph as one in which all the forces engaged (except the Turks) did their best.

Until they joined General Allenby they had taken some 20,000 prisoners.

The Arab Regular Army was never more than 9,000 strong. The numbers of the irregulars are difficult to estimate. They came up to fight when called, and went home after the action. The whole male population of the districts in which he happened to be operating were at the disposal of Feisal, and we used to summon few or many according to the object we had in view. The Arab front at the last was about 800 miles long, and forces were spread out nearly all along it, though fighting was by no means continuous. The irregulars were all volunteers (in service as well as in enlistment) and provided their own supplies and arms and transport. They fought under their own chosen leaders. I have never seen more than 11,000 of them together, and more often we had only a few hundreds. The total who bore arms for the Sherif at one time and another must have been very large, and probably ran into hundreds of thousands: but nothing like this was ever under arms at one time.

From the British point of view, therefore, the Arab Revolt achieved two things. First, sporadic raids on the 800-mile Hejaz railway which ran southwards from Damascus through the desert to Medina made it necessary for the Turks to garrison and patrol the line. The thousands of enemy troops tied down in this largely futile work would otherwise have been available to oppose Allenby's advance in Palestine. Thus the principal value of the Arab fighters lay in their hardiness and mobility, which were exploited to the full. Lawrence wrote in *Seven Pillars*: 'Most wars were wars of contact, both forces striving into touch to avoid tactical surprise. Ours should be a war of detachment. We were to contain the enemy by the silent threat of a vast unknown desert, not disclosing ourselves till we attacked . . . Many Turks on our front had no chance all the war to fire on us, and we were never on the defensive except by accident and in error.'[5]

T. E. Lawrence with his bodyguard of Arab tribesmen, Akaba
Photograph by R. G. Goslett, summer 1918
(detail, no. 143)

The railway raiding party
Left to right, standing: Lt.-Colonel Newcombe, Ahmed (Suida), Aziz, Lt. Hornby; seated: Nurel Din, Abdu
Photograph by ?T. E. Lawrence, 1917
(no. 117 vii)

5. *SPW* 1935, ch. 33, p. 194.

Nakhl Mubarak, scene in camp at dawn
Photograph by T. E. Lawrence, 1916/17
(no. 117 ii)

Secondly, when the Palestine campaign began in the autumn of 1917, the Arab forces served as a valuable protection to its inland flank. During the year-long drive northward the Arabs worked more and more closely with Allenby, until the two forces converged as they approached Damascus. If the Arabs had sided with Turkey rather than with Britain, Allenby's advance would have been dangerously exposed to attacks over an increasingly extended inland front. Instead of being a liability to the Turks, the Hejaz Railway would then have been an invaluable line of supply and reinforcement.

The extent of Lawrence's contribution to the Arab Revolt has been warmly debated. Discussion has been complicated by the nature of his own account in *Seven Pillars*, which was clearly intended to be a contribution to epic literature rather than a sober military chronicle. It has been suggested that Lawrence distorted history for the sake of drama. At the very least, personal names were changed, minor events run into one another and so on: might he not at the same time have exaggerated his own importance?

No one could begin to answer this question until the Arab Bureau papers and other official files became available in the late 1960s. Since then, however, it has been shown that *Seven Pillars* is remarkably accurate as a military history, even though parts of it were written from memory.[6] In retrospect, this accuracy is not wholly surprising: Lawrence sent a draft of *Seven Pillars* for factual correction to several of the officers who had either served on Allenby's staff or in the Revolt, among them Bartholomew, Dawnay, Hogarth, Newcombe, Stirling, and Wavell.

6. The accuracy of *Seven Pillars* as military history is examined in Konrad Morsey, *T. E. Lawrence und der arabische Aufstand*, Osnabrück, 1976 (a revised edition in English is currently in preparation).

In the 1930s the military historian Liddell Hart discussed Lawrence's role in the Revolt with many of the leading British participants. He later wrote: 'as my study went further and deeper . . . the events that had significance were seen to have their source in his action, and, still more, in his conception. The others faded into insignificance. I saw that there was a truth greater than its superficial suggestion in his deprecatory comment that his part – "was only synthetic. I combined their loose shower of sparks into a firm flame: transformed their series of unrelated incidents into a conscious operation" . . . But for him the Arab Revolt would have remained a collection of slight and passing incidents. Through him it had an important bearing on the course of outer events both during and since the war.'[7] The same conclusion must be reached by anyone who reads through the military and diplomatic archives now available.

In particular, Lawrence should be given credit for the initiative which led to the capture of Akaba in July 1917. Without this action, the Revolt would almost certainly have remained a local affair in the Hejaz, and the Arabs of Syria and Mesopotamia would have had no hope of political recognition after the war. Lawrence knew that Britain had secretly agreed with France that unless Hussein's forces occupied the four Syrian cities of Damascus, Homs, Hama and Aleppo, Arab claims to independence anywhere outside the Arabian Peninsula would be discounted. For Lawrence, therefore, the only victory worth winning was in the north.

The great bulk of the Arab forces saw Lawrence as a demolition expert and the channel through which Feisal asked for British funds and supplies. The documents show, however, that his principal role was that of adviser. His influence with Feisal doubtless owed much to the very real understanding that grew up between them; but Lawrence was also the representative of Britain, and Feisal knew that without British money, arms, and materials the Revolt would collapse.

Lawrence was the first British officer to serve in the field with the Arab forces, and he remained there longer than any other. In 1917 he wrote a fascinating document counselling other British officers involved in liaison work with the Arab forces. It was called 'Twenty-seven Articles', and its contents are still highly regarded by western military advisers working with armies in the third world. Lawrence concluded: 'The beginning and ending of the secret of handling Arabs is unremitting study of them. Keep always on your guard; never say an inconsidered thing, or do an unnecessary thing: watch yourself and your companions all the time: hear all that passes, search out what is going on beneath the surface, read their characters, discover their tastes and their weaknesses and keep everything you find out to yourself. Bury yourself in Arab circles, have no interests and no ideas except the work in hand, so that your brain shall be saturated with one thing only, and you realise your part deeply enough to avoid the little slips that would undo the work of weeks. Your success will be just proportional to the amount of mental effort you devote to it.'[8]

As Arab historians freely acknowledge, Lawrence's success lay in this ability to assimilate himself with the Bedouin. 'If you can surpass them,' he wrote, 'you have taken an immense stride towards complete success, but the strain of living and thinking in a foreign and half-understood language, the savage food, strange clothes, and stranger ways, with the complete loss of privacy and quiet, and the impossibility of ever relaxing your watchful imitation of the others for months on end, provide such an added stress to the ordinary difficulties of dealing with the Bedu, the climate, and the Turks, that this road should not be chosen without serious thought.'[9]

No easy form of courage could meet the difficulties of this special role. There would have been no official rebuke if Lawrence had shirked the hardships, dangers, and heavy responsibilities which he faced during the Revolt. As George Bernard Shaw later wrote: 'he was not like Haig or Allenby or Foch or Ludendorff, giving orders and seeing little or nothing of their sanguinary effect. He had to do the most diabolical things with his own hands, and see their atrocious results close up. He had to lay the mine, watch the approaching train, press the contact, and see truckfuls of Turks blown to screaming bloody fragments about his own ears.'[10]

Like other soldiers, Lawrence resigned himself to the horrors of war. But for him personally there was a deeper problem of morality, and he had to face it alone. From

7. B. H. Liddell Hart,
'T. E. Lawrence' in Arabia and After, 1934, p. 7.
8. T. E. Lawrence, Twenty-seven Articles',
Arab Bulletin, no. 60, 1917.
9. ibid.
10. Friends, p. 246.

the very beginning he knew that British policy towards the Middle East had been confused and opportunist. Different government departments had pursued their own objectives, and in the turmoil of the European war inconsistencies about future policy in the Middle East hardly seemed to matter. Even before the Revolt began, the undertakings given to Hussein about future Arab independence had been compromised by secret agreements between Britain, France and Russia. There seemed every chance that after an Allied victory the Powers would simply carve up the remnants of the Turkish Empire between them.

Lawrence knew the terms of these agreements, and he became deeply worried by the role he was playing as a British representative with the Arab forces. His predicament, as he saw it, is described in *Seven Pillars*:

'The Cabinet raised the Arabs to fight for us by definite promises of self-government afterwards. Arabs believe in persons, not in institutions. They saw in me a free agent of the British Government, and demanded from me an endorsement of its written promises. So I had to join the conspiracy, and, for what my word was worth, assured the men of their reward. In our two years' partnership under fire they grew accustomed to believing me and to think my Government, like myself, sincere. In this hope they performed some fine things, but, of course, instead of being proud of what we did together, I was continually and bitterly ashamed.

'It was evident from the beginning that if we won the war these promises would be dead paper, and had I been an honest adviser . . . I would have advised them to go home and not risk their lives fighting for such stuff: but I salved myself with the hope that, by leading these Arabs madly in the final victory, I would establish them, with arms in their hands, in a position so assured . . . that expediency would counsel to the Great Powers a fair settlement of their claims. In other words, I presumed (seeing no other leader with the will and power) that I would survive the campaigns, and be able to defeat not merely the Turks on the battlefield, but my own country

*Irish Troops in the Judean Hills surprised by
a Turkish bombardment
By Henry Lamb, 1919*
(no. 139)

and its allies in the council-chamber. It was an immodest presumption . . . it is clear that I had no shadow of leave to engage the Arabs, unknowing, in such hazard. I risked the fraud, on my conviction that Arab help was necessary to our cheap and speedy victory in the East, and that better we win and break our word than lose.'[11]

He was, however, unable to forgive himself for this duplicity. On the one hand stood the rigid moral values he had absorbed during his childhood and the real affection that he felt for the Arabs. On the other stood his patriotic duty, at a time when young men of his age, some of them his friends, were dying by the thousand on the Western Front. Once, in the spring of 1917, he had made an almost suicidal journey behind Turkish lines, half-hoping that he would not return. But he had survived, and his sickening role continued. Believing his promises, the Arabs risked injury, death and hideous Turkish reprisals. Every day he witnessed this sacrifice, in the full knowledge that their trust in him would be betrayed. His position became more unbearable as the Revolt spread into Syria. 'In the Hedjaz', he wrote, 'the Sherifs were everything, and ourselves accessory : but in this distant north the repute of Mecca was low, and that of England very great.'[12]

On its own, a sense of patriotic duty would not have carried Lawrence through the Arab campaigns. Like many soldiers, he looked for some simple untarnished image to cling to in the midst of war. Some men found it in religion, others in loved ones at home. But Lawrence had seen little of his family during the years of happiness at Carchemish, and it was there that he found the image he needed. At the end of *Seven Pillars* he wrote : 'The strongest motive throughout had been a personal one, not mentioned here, but present to me, I think, every hour of these two years.'[13] It was, as he explained elsewhere, that he liked a particular Arab very much, and . . . thought that freedom for the race would be an acceptable present.'[14] The 'particular Arab' can only have been Dahoum, his friend since 1911.

The experience of war brought another change in Lawrence's life, though the war itself could hardly be considered responsible. In November 1917, while reconnoitring the small town of Deraa on the Hejaz railway, Lawrence was captured and taken before the governor. To his astonishment and disgust, the Turk made homosexual advances. When Lawrence resisted he was taken away, savagely beaten, and sexually abused.

It is impossible to judge the physical severity of his treatment, but he had enough strength to escape a few hours later and return on foot to the Arab camp. There is no doubt, however, that the experience left deep psychological scars. From that time on he hated being touched and developed almost an obsession for cleanliness. The idea of a sexual relationship became abhorrent. His reaction to this homosexual rape took months, if not years, to develop : until the fall of Damascus his mind was occupied completely by the Arab campaign. It was probably not until he found himself living in normal society in England that the full force of his experience at Deraa struck home.

Only three weeks after this degrading incident Lawrence was at Allenby's head-quarters in Palestine on the day that Jerusalem was captured. Allenby arranged for him to join the solemn procession which entered the city on foot. Lawrence was deeply moved. At Oxford he had steeped himself in the history of the Crusades, and he was now present at the moment when the Holy City returned to Christendom after 730 years of Moslem rule. In *Seven Pillars* he wrote that this was, for him, 'the supreme moment of the war.'[15]

During 1918, victory was secured both in Palestine and in the inland deserts. For Lawrence personally, however, the cost was very great. At Tafileh in January there was an incident for which the mobile guerrilla campaign had left him unprepared. When Turkish troops threatened to attack, he advised the Arabs to fight a conventional battle in the Wadi Hesa. He subsequently wrote : 'We could have won by refusing battle, foxed them by manoeuvring our centre as on twenty such occasions before and since : yet bad temper and conceit united for this time to make me not content to know my power, but determined to give public advertisement of it to the enemy and to everyone.'[16] Although Liddell Hart would describe the battle as 'a miniature masterpiece'[17], Lawrence was never to forget the aftermath : 'there was no glory

11. Suppressed introductory chapter to *Seven Pillars of Wisdom*, *Oriental Assembly*, pp. 144-6.
12. *SPW 1922*, ch. 51.
13. *SPW 1935*, epilogue, p. 661.
14. T. E. Lawrence to C. J. Kidston, 15.2.1919.
15. *SPW 1935*, ch. 81, p. 453.
16. *SPW 1935*, ch. 85, p. 476.
17. *Friends*, p. 183.

left, but the terror of the broken flesh, which had been our own men, carried past us to their homes.'[18]

The barbarism of this war confronted him again just before the fall of Damascus. The Arab army arrived at Tafas too late to stop a retreating Turkish column from slaughtering the villagers with hideous savagery. The Arab revenge was swift and virtually total. Even if Lawrence had wanted to prevent it, he could not have done so.

The Turks abandoned Damascus to the advancing Allied armies on 1 October 1918. Lawrence drove into the city with Colonel Stirling, another British liaison officer, in an army Rolls: 'Every man, woman and child in this city of a quarter-million souls seemed in the streets, waiting only the spark of our appearance to ignite their spirits. Damascus went mad with joy . . . and over the local cries and the shrilling of women came the measured roar of men's voices, chanting "Feisal, Nasir, Shukri, Urens"'.[19] Later he was to write: 'From this cup I drank as deeply as any man should do, when we took Damascus: and was sated with it.'[20]

By this time his attempts to match Bedouin endurance were failing. He had suffered months of ill-health, and his weight was down to six stone. He had been wounded several times and was suffering from nervous and physical exhaustion. Two days after Damascus fell he was on his way to England. Military victory in Syria was assured, but he knew that the battle for political victory still lay ahead.

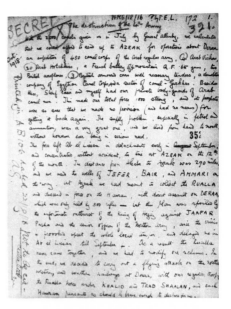

The Destruction of the 4th Army
Manuscript by T. E. Lawrence, 1918
(no. 166)

T. E. Lawrence at Damascus
By an unknown photographer, October 1918
Imperial War Museum (not exhibited)

18. *SPW 1935*, ch. 86, p. 482.
19. *SPW 1935*, ch. 119, p. 646.
20. *SPW 1922*, epilogue.

80

FRANK LAWRENCE
By an unknown photographer (1914)

While an undergraduate at Oxford Frank
Lawrence planned a military career. In
August 1914 he was immediately given a
commission as Second-Lieutenant in the 3rd
Gloucesters. He went to the front in
February 1915 and was killed three months
later at Richebourg l'Avoué.

Frank had been his mother's favourite son
and she was very distressed. Lawrence wrote
to his father: 'I hope that when I die there
will be nothing more to regret. The only
thing I feel a little is, that there was no need
surely to go into mourning for him? I cannot
see any cause at all − in any case to die for
one's country is a sort of privilege: Mother
and you will find it more painful and harder
to live for it, than he did to die: but I think
that at this time it is one's duty to show no
signs that would distress others: and to
appear bereaved is surely under this
condemnation. So please, keep a brave face
to the world: we cannot all go fighting: but
we can do that which is in the same kind.'[1]

He also told his mother: 'Frank's last
letter is a very fine one, and leaves no regret
behind it . . . I didn't go to say good-bye to
Frank because he would rather I didn't, and
I knew there was little chance of my seeing
him again; in which case we were better
without a parting.'[2]

1. T. E. Lawrence to his father, 4.6.1915, *Home Letters*,
p. 304.
2. T. E. Lawrence to his mother, June 1915, *Home
Letters*, p. 304.

81

WILL LAWRENCE
Photograph by Swaine (1914)

At the outbreak of war Will Lawrence had
been teaching in India; a sense of duty
compelled him to return to England in March
1915. Initially he joined the Oxford and
Bucks. Light Infantry, but he transferred to
the Royal Flying Corps in August and was
sent to France as an Observer. He was
reported missing on 23 October 1915, after
less than a week at the front. Although his
death was not confirmed for some time there
could be little hope that he had survived.

Lawrence was closer to Will than to any
of his other brothers, and was deeply affected
by his death. He wrote to E. T. Leeds: 'first
one and now another of my brothers has been
killed. Of course, I've been away a lot from
them, and so it doesn't come on one like a
shock at all . . . but I rather dread Oxford
and what it may be like if one comes back.
Also they were both younger than I am, and
it doesn't seem right, somehow, that I should
go on living peacefully in Cairo.'[1]

Private Collection

1. T. E. Lawrence to E. T. Leeds, 16.11.1915,
T. E. Lawrence, *Letters to E. T. Leeds*, ed. J. M. Wilson,
Whittington Press, 1988, p. 110.

82

*MILITARY REPORT ON THE SINAI
PENINSULA*
Prepared by the General Staff, War Office,
1914

Lawrence's first military posting was in the
Geographical Section of the War Office in
London, where he helped a very depleted
staff to prepare maps. When Turkey entered
the war at the end of October 1914 he
expected to leave immediately for
Intelligence and map work in Egypt.
However, the WO needed a road report on
Sinai, and he was asked to compile it, even
though he had visited only a small part of the
area it covered.

As he told a friend: 'I'm writing a report
from the military point of view of a country
I don't know, and haven't visited yet. One
of the minor terrors is, that later on I'm to
get my own book and guide myself over the
country with it. It will be a lesson in
humility, I hope.'[1]

It took Lawrence nearly a month to
complete the job. The result was a 190-page
book containing details of wells, gradients,
telephone lines, and Turkish police posts as
well as much other information. After the
capture of Akaba in July 1917 Lawrence
would make the 160-mile journey back to
Suez using the route described in the section
on display.

Public Record Office, London
(WO106/5976)

1. T. E. Lawrence to E. T. Leeds, 16.11.1914,
T. E. Lawrence, *Letters to E. T. Leeds*, ed. J. M. Wilson,
Whittington Press, 1988, pp. 104-5.

Printed book, 19.1
Literature: Introduction by J. M. Wilson to
T. E. Lawrence (compiler), *Military Report on the Sinai
Peninsula*, Castle Hill Press, 1989.
(not illustrated)

83
COLONEL STEWART FRANCIS
NEWCOMBE
By William Roberts, 1922

S. F. Newcombe (1878-1956) first met
Lawrence in January 1914 while serving as a
captain in the Royal Engineers. Lawrence had
been asked to accompany Newcombe's
survey party on a map-making expedition to
the Sinai Desert south of Beersheba. Later
that year, when Turkey entered the war,
Newcombe and Lawrence went out to Cairo

together to join the new Military Intelligence
Department. Newcombe remained Director
of the Department (under G. F. Clayton)
until the following September.

After the outbreak of the Arab Revolt
Newcombe was appointed head of a small
British Military Mission sent to the Hejaz in
December 1916. He arrived just in time to
join Lawrence for the final stages of the
march on Wejh. During the next few months
he became famous among the Arabs for the
wild daring of his attacks on the Hejaz Railway.

Lawrence commissioned this portrait for
Seven Pillars. He was particularly impressed
by the result and wrote promptly to Roberts:
'I liked your drawing of Newcombe . . . the
force and naturalism of this head took me by
surprise . . . you have improved on him by
putting into him a great deal of your spare
solidity.'[1] The following day he told a friend
that Roberts had 'done a wonderful study of
Newcombe, fierce almost to the point of
terror.'[2]

In 1935 Newcombe was one of the pall-
bearers at Lawrence's funeral.

S. L. Newcombe

1. T. E. Lawrence to William Roberts, 27.8.1922.
2. T. E. Lawrence to Robin Buxton, 28.8.1922.

Pencil, 35.5 × 33
Signed bl.: *William Roberts.*
Provenance: By descent.
Literature: *SPW 1926*, ill.; *SPW 1935*, ill. fp. 150.
Exhibitions: London, Chenil Galleries, *Paintings and
Drawings by William Roberts*, 1923.

84
AUBREY HERBERT
By an unknown photographer, c.1916
Vintage print

Aubrey Herbert (1880-1923) served in
Military Intelligence in Cairo for a few
months in 1914-15. In April 1916 he went
with Lawrence to negotiate with the Turkish
commanders outside Kut.

On their first meeting, in December
1914, Herbert thought Lawrence 'an odd
gnome, half cad – with a touch of genius'[1]
while Lawrence thought Herbert 'a joke, but
a very nice one.'[2]

Nevertheless they became close friends.
Lawrence's affection is apparent from
remarks made twelve years after Herbert's
death: 'Some friends of mine, in dying, have
robbed me. Hogarth and Aubrey Herbert are
two empty places which no one and nothing
can ever fill.'[3]

Private Collection

1. M. Fitzherbert, *The Man who was Greenmantle*, 1983,
p. 144.
2. T. E. Lawrence to his family, 12.2.1915, *Home Letters*,
p. 303.
3. T. E. Lawrence to Peter Davies, 28.3.1935.

12.8 × 9.5

COLONEL GILBERT CLAYTON
By Sir William Nicholson (c.1922)
Plate from *Seven Pillars of Wisdom*, 1935

In Autumn 1914 Colonel Gilbert Clayton (1875-1929) was appointed Director of Military Intelligence in Cairo. In his military and civil capacities he was personally responsible to the three most senior British officials in the Middle East: Major-General Maxwell, the GOC in Egypt, Sir Henry McMahon, the High Commissioner, and Sir Reginald Wingate, the Governor-General of the Sudan, whom he represented in Cairo.

Lawrence worked closely under Clayton in the Military Intelligence Department and later wrote that he 'made the perfect leader for such a band of wild men as we were. He was calm, detached, clear-sighted, of unconscious courage in assuming responsibility. He gave an open run to his subordinates. His own views were general, like his knowledge – and he worked by influence rather than by loud direction . . . He never visibly led – but his ideas were abreast of those who did: he impressed men by his sobriety, and by a certain quiet and stately moderation of hope. In practical matters he was loose, irregular, untidy, a man with whom independent men could bear.'[1]

J. M. Wilson

1. *SPW 1935*, ch. 6, p. 57.

Collotype, 18 × 12
Literature: *SPW 1926*, ill.; *SPW 1935*, ill. fp. 114.

GEORGE AMBROSE LLOYD, 1st BARON LLOYD
By William Roberts, 1925

George Ambrose Lloyd (1879-1941) served with Lawrence in Military Intelligence in Cairo from December 1914 to February 1915, and was involved in Arab Bureau work during 1916 and 1917 while Lawrence was engaged in the field.

Lawrence described his contribution in *Seven Pillars*: 'He gave us confidence, and with his knowledge of money, proved a sure guide through the subways of trade and politics . . . We would not have done so much so soon without his partnership.'[1]

In a letter to Roberts, Lawrence wrote: 'I want his very "British" head sweepingly painted in my gallery of human beings.'[2] On seeing the result, Lawrence thought that Roberts 'had been hard on Lloyd: deep in him is quite a decent fellow: thoughtful, considerate, well-read, charming. You haven't been subtle enough: yet it's a fine portrait, very like.'[3]

In June 1936 Lloyd named his new house 'Clouds Hill' in memory of Lawrence.

Harry Ransom Humanities Research Center, The University of Texas at Austin

1. *SPW 1935*, ch. 6, pp. 57-8.
2. T. E. Lawrence to William Roberts, 27.8.1925.
3. T. E. Lawrence to William Roberts, 2.10.1925.

Oil on canvas, 50.8 × 43.3
Signed br.: *William Roberts*
Provenance: The Estate of Eric Kennington, 1960; purchased from Hamill and Barker, 1962.
Literature: *SPW 1926*, ill.; *SPW 1935*, ill. fp. 392.
Exhibitions: Texas University, Humanities Research Center, *T. E. Lawrence/Fifty Letters: 1920-35*, 1962 (14c).

87
HANDBOOK OF THE TURKISH ARMY
Cairo, Government Press, second provisional
edition, 1 March 1915

Early in 1915 the Cairo Intelligence
Department took over production of the
Handbook of the Turkish Army from the War
Office in London. This was a secret manual
describing the disposition of enemy troops
throughout the Turkish Empire, and
required constant updating on the basis of the
latest intelligence reports. The department's
leading authority on the Ottoman Army was
Philip Graves, and he was chiefly responsible
for the contents of the *Handbook*. Other
members of the department contributed
from their own areas of knowledge,
however, and Lawrence also organised the
printing.

Trustees of the National Army Museum
Printed book, 16

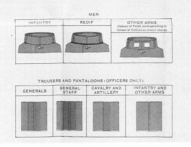

STAFF OFFICER wearing peaked cap or "ENVERIÉ."

88
T. E. LAWRENCE'S COPY OF *THE
STUDENT'S ARABIC-ENGLISH DICTIONARY*
By F. Steingass, London, 1884

Lawrence probably acquired this dictionary
before the war, and he almost certainly used
it during his time in the Cairo Intelligence
Department and later at the Peace
Conference.

In a letter to Robert Graves, Lawrence
wrote: 'In Oxford I picked up a little
colloquial grammar before I first went out [to
Syria]. In the next four years I added a
considerable (4,000 word) vocabulary to this
skeleton of grammar . . .

'Then for two more years I spoke hardly
a word of it: and as I've never learned the
letters to read or write naturally, almost it
all passed from me. So when I joined Feisal
I had to take it all up again from the
beginning, in a fresh and very different
dialect. As the campaign grew it carried me
from dialect to dialect, so that I never settled
down to learn one properly. Also I learned
by ear (not knowing the written language)
and therefore incorrectly . . .

'In the end I had control of some 12,000
words: a good vocabulary for English, but
not enough for Arabic which is a very wide
language: and I used to fit these words
together with a grammar and a syntax of my
own invention. Feisal called my Arabic "a
perpetual adventure" and used to provoke
me to speak to him so that he could enjoy it.'[1]

Lawrence did not tell Graves that he had
taken Arabic lessons between December
1910 and February 1911 at the American
Mission School in Jebail. His teacher Miss
Fareedeh el Akle wrote: 'Lawrence studied
Arabic for only three months . . . he was able
to read, write and speak very simple Arabic
in this short time.'[2] It is now certain that
Lawrence could both read and write simple
Arabic during the war (see no. 158).

Lawrence admitted that he 'could never
pass off as an Arab – but easily as some other
native speaking Arabic.'[3]

The dictionary was given by Lawrence to
Sir Gerald Clauson, presumably while they
were both working in the Eastern Department
of the Colonial Office. In this case the
probable date of the gift is 1921 or 1922, not
1920 as stated in the inscription.

Peter Hopkirk

1. T. E. Lawrence to R. Graves, 28.6.1927.
2. *Friends*, p. 79.
3. *Biographers* (Liddell Hart), p. 85.

Printed book, 1242 pp., 22.8
Inscribed on flyleaf in ink: *T. E. L.*; *Given to me in 1920
by T. E. Lawrence/Gerald Clauson*
Provenance: T. E. Lawrence; Sir Gerald Clauson,
?1920.
(not illustrated)

89

SIR RONALD STORRS
By Eric Kennington, 1921

Ronald Storrs (1881-1955) served as Oriental
Secretary to the British civil authorities in
Cairo from 1909 to 1917, first under Lord
Kitchener and later under Sir Henry
McMahon. It was he who in 1914 initiated
the secret correspondence between Cairo
and Mecca which eventually led to the Arab
Revolt.

Lawrence quickly made friends with the
urbane and highly-cultured Storrs, described
in *Seven Pillars* as 'the most brilliant
Englishman in the Near East . . . subtly
efficient, despite his diversion of energy in
love of music and letters, of sculpture,
painting, of whatever was beautiful in the
world's fruit.'[1] When Storrs visited Jidda in
October 1916 Lawrence went with him,
ostensibly for a 'joy-ride' but in reality to
report on the Arab Revolt for Clayton.

Storrs became Military Governor of
Jerusalem after the Holy City was captured
in December 1917. He remained Civil
Governor of Jerusalem and Judaea until 1926.

He was one of the pall-bearers at
Lawrence's funeral in 1935, and in his later
years wrote and lectured frequently on
Lawrence.

Kennington's drawing was one of two he
made of Storrs in Cairo; this one has been
reproduced in editions of *Seven Pillars*.

Dr J. F. Moor

1. *SPW 1935*, ch. 6, p. 57.

Pastel, 45.2 × 29.6
Provenance: By descent from the sitter.
Literature: *SPW 1926*, ill.; *SPW 1935*, ill. fp. 650;
R. Storrs, *Orientations*, 1943, p.445.
Exhibitions: Leicester Galleries 1921 (26); Leicester
Galleries 1927 (18, lent by Mrs Cust).

90

SIR RONALD STORRS
By John Singer Sargent (c.1918)
Annotated proof plate from *Seven Pillars of
Wisdom*, 1926

In a letter to Eric Kennington about
illustrations for *Seven Pillars*, Lawrence
described this as 'A loathesome drawing: put
in out of spite.'[1]

Lawrence's comment seems to reflect his
own ambivalent feelings about Storrs. In a
suppressed passage of *Seven Pillars* he gave a
very unflattering description of Storrs'
appearance: 'his eyelids were heavy with
laziness, and his eyes dulled with care of self,
and his mouth made unbeautiful by
hampering desires.'[2] Nevertheless he
acknowledged: 'Storrs sowed what we
reaped, and was always the first and greatest
of us. His shadow would have covered our
work and British policy in the East like a
cloak, had he been able to deny himself.'[3]

The original charcoal drawing is in the
collection of the University of Illinois.

The Curators of the Bodleian Library,
Oxford (MS.Res.b.55)

1. T. E. Lawrence to Eric Kennington, 7.7.1925.
2. *SPW 1922*, ch. 8, p. 23.
3. *SPW 1935*, ch. 6, p. 57.

Collotype, 25.5 × 19
Inscribed by T. E. Lawrence: *A darker shade/ like the
Wingate would?/ be less confusing*
Provenance: Given by A. W. Lawrence.
Literature: *SPW 1926*, ill.; *SPW 1935*, ill. fp. 62.

91
SIR HENRY McMAHON
By William Roberts (1922)
Annotated proof plate from *Seven Pillars of Wisdom*, 1926

Sir Henry McMahon was appointed High Commissioner in Egypt in 1914. He is now remembered chiefly for the controversial letters he exchanged with Hussein, the Grand Sherif of Mecca, before the outbreak of the Arab Revolt (the 'McMahon—Hussein correspondence'). He was abruptly recalled at the end of 1916, and replaced by Sir Reginald Wingate.

On seeing the portrait Lawrence wrote: 'It's absolutely splendid: the strength of it, and the life: it feels as though any moment there might be a crash in the paper and the thing start out.'[1]

The Curators of the Bodleian Library, Oxford (MS.Res.b.55)
1. T. E. Lawrence to William Roberts, 21.10.1922.

Collotype, 25.5 × 19
Inscribed by T. E. Lawrence: *No I don't like/this. Too pale/I think, compare/the Wingate*
Provenance: Given by A. W. Lawrence.
Literature: *SPW 1926*, ill.; *SPW 1935*, ill. fp. 60.

92
SHERIF HUSSEIN OF MECCA
(i) By an unknown photographer (1916)
(ii) By Colonel Cornwallis (?1919)

Hussein (*c.*1854-1931) was appointed Sherif and Emir of Mecca in 1908. Once in the Hejaz he extended his authority and opposed the Ottomanisation of the province. When Turkey entered the war he carefully distanced himself from the Constantinople Government, and finally declared the Arab Revolt on 5 June 1916. At the Peace Settlement of 1919 he was acknowledged as King of the Hejaz but not as King of the Arabs. He ruled the Hejaz until 1924 when he was defeated by Ibn Saud and abdicated in favour of his eldest son Ali.

According to Lawrence, Hussein was 'an obstinate, narrow-minded, suspicious character, little likely to sacrifice a pet vanity for unity of control.'[1]

(i) IWM Q59888 (ii) IWM Q59728
1. *SPW 1935*, ch. 57, p. 324.

93

THE SUEZ CANAL BY NIGHT
By James McBey, 1917

The Suez Canal was vital to Britain's communications with the Empire, and maintaining its security was the principal object of the British presence in Egypt. The idea of an Arab Revolt first became attractive to British officials in Cairo as a means of distracting the Turks from an attack on the Canal.

In the autumn of 1915 the vulnerability of the Canal became a matter of urgent concern. A British withdrawal from Gallipoli was already being discussed and the release of enemy troops from that front would pose an obvious threat to Egypt, especially now that Turkish communications were being improved in Palestine and Sinai. Anxiety about the Canal was a leading factor behind the British territorial offers to Sherif Hussein made through Sir Henry McMahon at this time.

Every ship sailing on the Canal by night had to carry a searchlight on the bow.

Trustees of the Imperial War Museum
(IWM 1413)

Charcoal and watercolour, 29.2 × 46.3
Signed and dated bl. : *James McBey 5 July 1917*
Provenance : War Artists Commission.

94

THE SIEGE OF KUT, CASUALTY BEING BROUGHT IN
By an unknown photographer (1915-16)

In late November 1915 General Charles Townshend's advance on Baghdad ran into serious difficulties. With a force of 17,000 men he retreated to the small town of Kut on the River Tigris, where he was quickly surrounded by a large Turkish army under Khalil Pasha. Despite costly relief efforts the main Indian army was unable to raise the siege during the months which followed. In late April a river steamer loaded with supplies (and manned entirely by volunteers) made a last vain attempt to break the Turkish blockade. By this time conditions in Kut had become desperate ; lack of food and the outbreak of disease made continuing resistance impossible.

Lawrence was a helpless spectator of the final stages of these events. The War Office had sent him to Mesopotamia hoping that he might be able to draw some of the pressure from Kut, either by stirring up disaffected Arabs behind enemy lines or by finding a Turkish officer susceptible to bribery. In the event, neither was possible but he arrived at advance headquarters in time to play a role in negotiations for Townshend's surrender. During the talks the British side offered the Turks money if they would allow the Kut garrison to go free on parole. But Khalil refused to accept anything short of unconditional surrender. Only those men the Turks pronounced sick were exchanged : the others were subjected to a long forced march and years in Turkish prisoner-of-war camps. Barely a quarter survived.

IWM Q92662

95

T. E. LAWRENCE'S COPIES OF THE
ARAB BULLETIN
Cairo, 1916-17

The Arab Bureau was set up in the spring of
1916. One of its first activities was to initiate
a secret bulletin dealing 'with any political
events in Turkey or elsewhere that affect the
Arab movement'. The idea originated with
Lawrence, who already had a great deal of
experience compiling the Cairo Intelligence
Bulletins. In Hogarth's absence, he helped to
assemble the first issue of the 'Arab Bureau
Summary' (dated 6 June 1916) and his name
appears on the title page. Later he sent the
Arab Bulletin many detailed reports of his
activities in the field. After the war
Lawrence made extensive use of *Bulletin*
material in writing *Seven Pillars of Wisdom*.

The *Bulletin* continued to appear
throughout the war and the final issue was
produced on 30 August 1919. Principal
contributors included D. G. Hogarth,
Gertrude Bell, George Lloyd, Harry St. John
Philby and Ronald Storrs. The set of which
this is the first volume was probably bound
up for Lawrence in Cairo. On the circulation
page of the first issue, he has written in
pencil: & *T.E.L. as Editor!*

The Houghton Library, Harvard University,
Gift of Bayard L. Kilgour Jr. (FEC9 L4388
916a)

Printed pamphlets, bound into one volume (of three),
27.5
Provenance: By descent to A. W. Lawrence; sold to
M. H. Mushlin, and by him to Bayard L. Kilgour Jr.;
given by Bayard L. Kilgour Jr., 1958-66.
Literature: *The Arab Bulletin*, ed. R. Bidwell, Archive
Editions, 1986.
(not illustrated)

96

A SHORT NOTE ON THE DESIGN AND ISSUE
OF POSTAGE STAMPS PREPARED BY THE
SURVEY OF EGYPT FOR HIS HIGHNESS
HUSEIN, EMIR AND SHERIF OF MECCA AND
KING OF THE HEJAZ
Survey of Egypt, Cairo, 1918

After Hussein's declaration of independence
in June 1916 Ottoman postage stamps could
no longer be used in the Hejaz. Lawrence
suggested that the issue of a new, distinctive
series of stamps would be one way of publicis-
ing the emergence of a new nation. Over the
coming months the Arab Bureau and the
Survey of Egypt collaborated on the project.

The task of choosing suitable illustrations
fell to Lawrence and Ronald Storrs. Their
principal objectives were spelt out in a
memorandum sent to the Sherif:

'(1) To make it self-evident to the world
that the series was not a survival or copy of
the Ottoman postage stamps in any form
whatsoever, but an entirely new and
independent national issue . . .

(2) That the design should in wording,
spirit, and ornament be, as far as possible,
representative and reminiscent of a purely
Arab source and inspiration.'

To achieve these aims 'designs never
adopted before for stamps were drawn from
beautiful existing specimens of Arabesque
ornament.' In his letters home Lawrence
mentioned many details of the project, which
he clearly found fascinating. In *Friends*,
A.W. Lawrence records how he wanted each
value to be backed with a gum of a different
taste, to help distinguish them in the dark
and to popularize use of the post.'[1] This was
found, however, to be impracticable.

The first stamps were produced during
September and issued by Hussein the
following month.

Trustees of the Imperial War Museum
(7444/IV(3))

1. *Friends*, p. 591.

Printed book, 22 pp. + 12 pls., 27.5
Provenance: Given by the Survey of Egypt, 1920.

97

ARAB BULLETIN No. 32
Cairo, 26 November 1916

During the summer and autumn of 1916 news
of Hussein's revolt had been sporadic and
contradictory, but it became increasingly
clear to the British in Cairo that things were
going badly wrong. Lawrence was therefore
sent to the Hejaz to bring back reliable
information about the present state of the
Arab campaign and an assessment of its
potential.

While there he met Hussein's sons, Ali,
Abdullah, and Feisal, who were each
commanding a separate army of tribesmen.
He quickly came to the conclusion that Feisal
was the most promising leader and that
Britain should back him more effectively.

About three-quarters of this issue of the
Bulletin is taken up with extracts from the
reports Lawrence wrote while waiting for his
passage back across the Red Sea (in five days
he produced some 17,000 words). His views
were considered particularly valuable
because he was the first British observer to
have been allowed inland. The reports are
remarkable for their detailed observation and
clarity of style.

Public Record Office, London
(WO106/1511)

Single issue, unbound pamphlet, 26.7 × 19.5
Literature: *The Arab Bulletin*, ed. R. Bidwell, Archive
Editions, 1986.
(not illustrated)

98
THE EMIR FEISAL
By Augustus John, 1919

The Emir Feisal (1883-1933) was the third
son of Sherif Hussein. Lawrence met him for
the first time at Hamra on 23 October 1916
and described him in the *Arab Bulletin* as
'almost regal in appearance . . . Far more
imposing personally than any of his brothers.
Looks . . . very like the monument of
Richard I, at Fontevraud . . . A popular idol,
and ambitious; full of dreams, and the
capacity to realize them'.[1]

Lawrence served as liaison officer
between Feisal and the British from late 1916
until the fall of Damascus in October 1918.
The posting would have come to an end after
only a few months if Feisal had not pressed
for Lawrence to continue in it.

Feisal was keenly aware of Lawrence's
value, and both men recognised the personal
affinity that had grown up between them. In
a letter to a friend after the war Lawrence
described Feisal as 'one of the most attractive
human beings I have ever met'.[2]

John painted this portrait during the Paris
Peace Conference of 1919 where Feisal was
Hussein's representative. It was the first of
many portraits Lawrence bought or
commissioned to illustrate *Seven Pillars of
Wisdom*. When the subscription edition was
printed, John's Feisal was reproduced in
colour as the frontispiece.

Feisal later became King of Syria (1920)
and first King of Iraq (1921-1933).

The Visitors of the Ashmolean Museum,
Oxford (A 449)

1. *Arab Bulletin*, 32, 1916.
2. T. E. Lawrence to C. F. Shaw, 18.10.1927.

Oil on canvas, 72 × 53
Signed and dated : A J 19
Provenance : Given by T. E. Lawrence to Mr and Mrs
Eric Kennington; presented in accordance with his
wishes to the Ashmolean, 1936.
Literature : *SPW 1926*, frontis.; *SPW 1935*, ill. fp. 50.
Exhibitions : Leicester Galleries 1927 (36, ill.)

99
THE EMIR ABDULLAH
By Eric Kennington (1921)
Plate from *Seven Pillars of Wisdom*, 1935

Abdullah was the second son of Sherif
Hussein. During the Arab Revolt he
commanded the southern army until Medina
fell in 1919.

Lawrence described his first impressions
of Abdullah in *Seven Pillars*: 'Astute he
certainly was, but not greatly enough to
convince us always of his sincerity. His
ambition was patent. Rumour made him the
brain of his father and of the Arab revolt; but
he seemed too easy for that . . . I became
more and more sure that Abdulla was too
balanced, too cool, too humorous to be a
prophet : especially the armed prophet who,
if history be true, succeeded in revolutions'.[1]

When Lawrence stayed in Abdullah's
camp in 1917 his opinion changed for the
worse : 'The leaven of insincerity worked
through all the fibres of his being. Even his
simplicity appeared false upon experience
. . . His brain often betrayed its intricate
pattern, disclosing idea twisted tightly over
idea into a strong cord of design ; and thus
his indolence marred his scheming, too. The
webs were constantly unravelling through his
carelessness'.[2]

In an essay on Kennington's Arab portraits
Lawrence wrote : 'the Emir Abdulla . . .
would not thank me for either praise or
blame of him. His complexity comes out in
this portrait.'[3]

Abdullah became Emir of Transjordan in
1921 and King of Jordan in 1948. He was
assassinated in 1951.

The original pastel is in the Harry Ransom
Humanities Research Center, University of
Texas at Austin.

J. M. Wilson

1. *SPW 1935*, ch. 8, p. 67.
2. *Ibid*, ch. 36, p. 213.
3. *Oriental Assembly*, p. 156.

Chromo-lithograph, 24.4 × 18.5
Literature : *SPW 1926*, ill.; *SWP 1935*, ill. fp. 68 ;
R. Storrs in E. Kennington, *Drawing the RAF*, 1942, pp.
13, 15, 16.

100

THE FOUR SONS OF SHERIF HUSSEIN

(i) Ali (1879-1935)
By an unknown photographer

Lawrence described Ali as 'a very
conscientious . . . gentleman, without force
of character, nervous and rather tired. His
physical weakness makes him subject to
quick fits of shaking passion with more
frequent moods of infirm obstinacy.
Apparently not ambitious for himself, but
swayed somewhat too easily by the wishes of
others. . . Shows his Arab blood more than
his brothers.'[1]

1. *Arab Bulletin*, no. 32, 1916, p. 481.

(ii) Abdullah (1882-1951) with officials at
Jidda
By an unknown photographer (October 1916)
Left to right: Rahia, Said Bey 'Ali', Colonel
Wilson, Aziz el Masri, Abdullah, Ronald
Storrs, J. A. H. Young.

For Abdullah see no. 99; for Storrs see
no. 89.

Aziz el Masri had served with distinction in
the Turkish army and played a role in the
Young Turk revolution of 1908. He had also
been a leading figure in Arab secret societies
before the war. After the outbreak of
Hussein's revolt he went to the Hejaz to
organise a force of Arab regulars: his
command of this force was confirmed at the
meeting recorded in this photograph, held at
Jidda in October 1916.

Colonel C. E. Wilson had been posted to
Jidda in July 1916 to improve British liaison
with Hussein. To dispel any suspicions that
the revolt was being run by infidels he was
given the title of 'Pilgrimage Officer'. Young
was his assistant.

(iii) Feisal (1885-1933) on his Arab charger
Photograph by Harry Chase (1917)

For Feisal see no. 98.

Literature: L.Thomas, *With Lawrence in Arabia*,
ill. fp. 205.

(iv) Zeid (1896-1972) at Tafileh with
captured 7.5 inch Austrian mountain guns
Photograph by T. E. Lawrence (1918)

Zeid was the fourth son of Sherif Hussein.
When they met in October 1916 Lawrence
found him 'a shy, white, beardless lad . . .
calm and flippant, no zealot for the revolt.
Indeed his mother was Turkish; and he had
been brought up in the Harem, so that he
could hardly feel great sympathy with an
Arab revival.'[1]

   In the *Arab Bulletin* Lawrence described
him as a little loutish, but not a bad fellow.
Humorous in outlook, and perhaps a little
better balanced because less intense, than his
brothers.'[2]

   In 1918 Zeid became nominal commander
of the Arab forces in the Dead Sea region (see
no. 155). Tafileh fell to the Arabs in January
and was successfully defended against a
Turkish counter-attack a few weeks later (see
no. 156 i). The gun in the picture is a 7.5 inch
Skoda Mountain Howitzer.

   After the war Zeid was educated at Balliol
College, Oxford. He was Iraqi Ambassador
to Great Britain from 1946 to 1958.

1. *SPW 1935*, ch. 10, p. 77.
2. *Arab Bulletin*, 32, 1916, p. 482.

(i) IWM Q59209 (ii) IWM Q58706 (iii)
copyright (iv) IWM Q59364

101
ADMIRAL SIR ROSSLYN ERSKINE WEMYSS
By Sir William Orpen, 1919

Lawrence returned from his first mission to the Hejaz in HMS *Euryalus* (see no. 125), the flagship of Admiral Wemyss (1864-1933), C-in-C of the East Indies and Egypt station. Wemyss and Lawrence then travelled to Khartoum where they took part in important discussions with Sir Reginald Wingate about the future strategy of the revolt.

Lawrence always spoke very gratefully of the practical and moral support that Wemyss had offered the Arab rising. Long after the war he wrote: 'Admiral Wemyss was in glorious contrast to the soldiers: no jealousy, no stupidity, no laziness: he was as keen to help as any two-year-old. His support in the mixed counsels and conferences was hearteningly useful . . . In practical affairs he did all the the Navy can do on the land . . . The Red Sea patrol-ships were the fairy-godmothers of the Revolt. They carried our men, our food, our arms, our ammunition, our stores, our animals, they built our piers, armed our defences, served as our coast artillery, lent us seaplanes, provided all our wireless communication: landed landing parties: mended and made everything. I couldn't spend the time writing down a tenth of their services.'[1]

National Portrait Gallery (NPG 4182)

1. T. E. Lawrence to Sir Henry McMahon, 18.10.1933.

Oil on canvas, 91.4 × 76.2
Signed tl.: *ORPEN*
Provenance: Commissioned by Viscount Wakefield and presented, 1960.
Literature: Sir W. Orpen, *An Onlooker in France 1917-1919*, pp. 106-7, ill. pl. LXXXIV.

102
SIR REGINALD WINGATE
By William Roberts, *c.*1922

Sir (Francis) Reginald Wingate (1861-1953) was Governor-General of the Sudan from 1899 to 1916 and subsequently High Commissioner in Egypt until 1919. In this last role he replaced Sir Henry McMahon and was in turn superseded by Lord Allenby.

Lawrence met Wingate for the first time in November 1916 at a conference held in Khartoum to discuss the progress of the Arab Revolt. Wingate had shown enthusiasm for the rising from its earliest days but his ideas

about future policy were very different from Lawrence's. He strongly favoured sending European troops to the Hejaz while Lawrence argued that such a measure would have a disastrous effect on Moslem opinion.

In 1922 when Lawrence commissioned this picture he wrote to Roberts: 'Do you think you could draw a courtly old man, broken and disappointed now because his career ended badly, a man who was never much more than a butter-merchant and great-man's friend, even in his best days, but whose administration was so successful that it gave him confidence, and for a while he believed himself great . . . please be very gentle with him, if you do him. He's not so much a butterfly as a ghost of one, a thing by no means to be broken on a wheel.'[1]

Harry Ransom Humanities Research Center, The University of Texas at Austin

1. T. E. Lawrence to William Roberts, 21.10.1922.

Sanguine, 34.4 × 29.9
Signed br.: *William Roberts*; inscribed below: *(General Sir Reginald Wingate) William Roberts*
Provenance: Purchased from Hamill and Barker, 1962.
Literature: *SPW 1926*, ill.; *SPW 1935*, ill. fp. 110.
Exhibitions: London, Chenil Galleries, *Paintings and Drawings by William Roberts*, 1923; Leicester Galleries 1927 (44); Texas University, Humanities Research Center, *T. E. Lawrence/Fifty Letters: 1920-35*, 1962 (14b).

103
SIR ARCHIBALD MURRAY
Photograph by Walter Stoneman (1919)

In January 1916 Sir Archibald Murray (1860-
1945) became Commander of the Suez Canal
Forces and two months later he replaced Sir
John Maxwell as GOC Egypt. Lawrence
served in Murray's Intelligence section
(under G.F. Clayton) for seven months.
Their first recorded meeting took place in
Cairo on Lawrence's return from the Hejaz
in November 1916.

Murray's second attempt to capture Gaza
ended in a serious defeat. He was replaced by
General Allenby in June 1917.

National Portrait Gallery (NPR 96685G)

104
SIR WILLIAM ROBERT ROBERTSON
By Francis Dodd, 1918

Sir William Robertson (1860-1933) was
appointed Chief of General Staff in January
1915 and succeeded Sir Archibald Murray as
Chief of the Imperial General Staff in
December. It was Robertson who suggested
sending Lawrence back to the Hejaz on a
temporary posting in 1916.

Robertson was a convinced 'Westerner'
opposed to wasting military resources on
'side-shows' such as the war in the East. He
strongly disapproved of Lloyd George's plan
for an offensive in Palestine in February 1918.

Trustees of the Imperial War Museum
(IWM 1822)

Charcoal and watercolour, 25.7 × 24.1
Signed and dated bl.: *Dodd/Jan/1918*
Provenance: War Artists Commission

105
ARAB UNDER-ROBE (*THOB*)

Lawrence had become accustomed to wearing Arab dress before the First World War. He had occasionally worn it when travelling in Syria during the intervals between seasons at Carchemish.

In October 1916, when Lawrence was first given permission to travel inland to visit Feisal's camp, Sherif Ali was horrified at the prospect of a Christian officer travelling uniformed in a holy Mohammedan province, and gave him an Arab cloak and headcloth to wrap around himself.

When Lawrence returned to Feisal some weeks later as a liaison officer, Feisal asked him to wear Arab dress. 'If I wore Meccan clothes, [the Arabs] would behave to me as though I were really one of the leaders; and I might slip in and out of Feisal's tent without making a sensation which he had to explain away each time to strangers. I agreed at once, very gladly; for army uniform was abominable when camel-riding or when sitting about on the ground; and the Arab things . . . were cleaner and more decent in the desert.'[1]

In his 'Twenty-seven Articles' (see no. 129) Lawrence gave advice on dress to British officers serving with the Arab forces: 'Wear an Arab headcloth when with a tribe. Bedu have a malignant prejudice against the hat, and believe that our persistence in wearing it . . . is founded on some immoral or irreligious principle. A thick headcloth forms a good protection against the sun, and if you wear a hat your best Arab friends will be ashamed of you in public . . .

'If you can wear Arab kit when with the tribes, you will acquire their trust and intimacy to a degree impossible in uniform. It is, however, dangerous and difficult. They make no special allowances for you when you dress like them . . . Complete success, which is when the Arabs forget your strangeness and speak naturally before you, counting you as one of themselves, is perhaps only attainable in character: while half success . . . is easier to win in British things . . . Also then the Turks will not hang you, when you are caught.'

'If you wear Arab things, wear the best. Clothes are significant among the tribes, and you must wear the appropriate, and appear at ease in them. Dress like a Sherif, if they agree to it.'[2]

The dress of the northern nomadic Arabs differs from tribe to tribe but is fairly uniform in essentials:

thob: an ankle-length white shirt with wrist-length sleeves. It is the basic male garment.

zebun: worn over the *thob* by the richer Arab. It is made of white or striped linen or silk, and is sometimes embroidered around the neck.

aba: this is a cloak worn over the *zebun*. It is usually made of fine wool or camel-hair, but is sometimes partly cotton.

The headcloth, measuring more than a yard square, covers a round soft cap. It is bound on the outside by a decorative rope (an *agal*) which keeps it in place.

See also nos. 106, 108, 112, 113, 114 and 151.

The Visitors of the Ashmolean Museum, Oxford (1966/84)

1. *SPW 1935*, ch. 20, p. 126.
2. Extracts from 'Twenty-seven Articles'(17-19) in *Arab Bulletin*, no. 60, 1917.

Undyed silk, blue embroidery, 129.6 × 142.2 with detachable collar and belt
Provenance: Given by Dr M.R.Lawrence, 1966.

106
ARAB CEREMONIAL ROBE (*ZEBUN*)
See no. 105.

The Warden and Fellows of All Souls College, Oxford

Silk brocade, cotton and gold thread, 134.6 × 134.6
Provenance: Given by Sarah Lawrence, 1938

107
WHITE SAPPHIRE RING

A white sapphire set in a pierced gold mount, carried by Lawrence during the Arab Revolt.

The Warden and Fellows of All Souls College, Oxford

Gold with inset stone, 2.5 diameter
Provenance: Given by Sarah Lawrence, 1938.

108
HEAD-CLOTH AND *AGAL*

Lawrence bought this head-dress in Aleppo
on 24 June 1912 as a present for Haj Wahid.
He described it as 'a most lovely weave of
rolled gold over silver wire entwined in
scarlet silk: the most noble material I have
ever handled: it's about 5 feet square and
local stuff: one man and his son alone of all
Syria know how to make it . . . it is perfectly
royal'.[1]

The head-cloth and *agal*, which were
given by Lawrence to his mother in 1913 and
later presented to All Souls College, are kept
in a box specially made by Herbert Baker and
Laurence Turner.

Good quality head-cloths were not easy to
obtain during the war. In late 1916 Lawrence
wrote to his mother asking 'If that silk
headcloth with the silver ducks on it – last
used I believe as a table-cloth – still exists,
will you send it out to me? Such things are
hard to get here now.'[2]

The Warden and Fellows of All Souls
College, Oxford

1. T. E. Lawrence to his mother, 24.6.1912, *Home
Letters*, p. 219.
2. T. E. Lawrence to his mother, 14.12.1916, *Home
Letters*, p. 332.

Agal: silver gilt wire and red silk; head-cloth: patterned
red silk; not measured
Provenance: Given by T. E. Lawrence to his mother,
1913; presented by Sarah Lawrence, 1938.

109
T. E. LAWRENCE'S LEE ENFIELD SHORT MAGAZINE RIFLE MARK 3

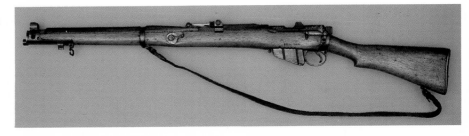

Lawrence learned to shoot at Oxford while
a member of the Officers Training Corps, and
later practised at Carchemish as his letters
home proudly relate.

This rifle was given to Lawrence by Feisal.
It is inscribed on the butt *TEL 4.12.16*,
presumably the date on which he received it.
The notches near the magazine each
represent a shot Turk.

In *Seven Pillars* Lawrence stated that the
rifle had been presented to Feisal by Enver
Pasha (one of the Turkish ruling triumvirate)
before the Arab Revolt. There is a gold
inscription in Arabic characters damascened
on the receiver. Lawrence explained the
significance of this in a letter to E.T. Leeds:
'The Turks took four of the short Lee Enfield
rifles taken at Gallipoli, and engraved them
in gold on the chamber "Part of our booty

in the battles for the Dardanelles" in a most
beautiful Turkish script. Deeply cut by hand,
and then gold wire beaten in. Four of these
rifles were sent, one to each of the sons of
the Sherif of Mecca.'[1]

By the time he wrote this letter Lawrence
knew that C. J. ffoulkes was collecting
materials for a new Imperial War Museum.
He suggested to Leeds that ffoulkes might be
interested in the rifles: 'I carry Feisul's,
which he gave me (it's a 1st Essex gun) and
I'm trying to get Zeid's, which I'll send to
C. J. ff. if I win . . . Ali has one, but
Abdulla's has been given to Ronald Storrs'.[2]

Trustees of the Imperial War Museum

1. T. E. Lawrence to E. T. Leeds, 15.12.1917, T. E.
Lawrence, *Letters to E. T. Leeds*, ed. J. M. Wilson,
Whittington Press, 1988, p. 115.
2. *ibid.*

113 long
Inscribed on fore-end: *TEL 4. 12. 16*; gold inscription
in arabic script damascened on the receiver.
Serial no. M6594
Provenance: Given by T. E. Lawrence to H.M. King
George V; presented by The King to Imperial War
Museum.

110

SILVER DRINKING CUP MADE FOR T. E. LAWRENCE IN JIDDA, ?1917

The silver canteen that Lawrence used in his campaigns originally comprised a cup, two bowls, a plate, and a spoon. The set was made for him at Jidda. The bowls and the mug were made to his own design from Indian rupees. When Lawrence gave away his silver, the cup went to Charles Bell, the larger bowl went to Mrs Hogarth, and the smaller to E. T. Leeds.

The larger of the two bowls is also exhibited (see no. 111); the location of the smaller is not recorded. The plate and spoon are now at All Souls College, Oxford.

Private Collection

10.5 × 14.5
Provenance: Given by T. E. Lawrence to C. F. Bell; presented by him to present owner.

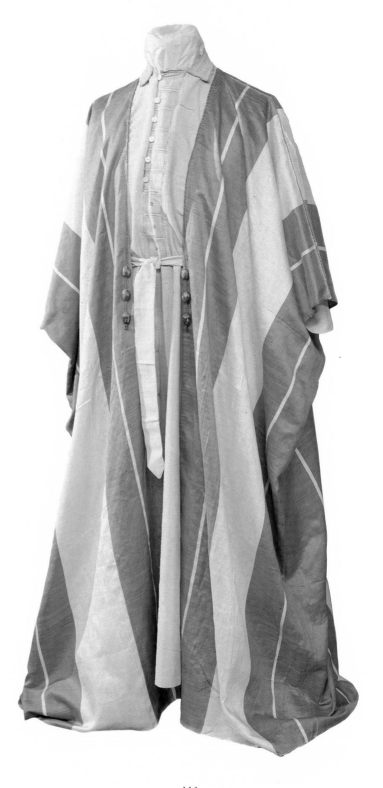

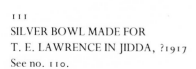

111

SILVER BOWL MADE FOR T. E. LAWRENCE IN JIDDA, ?1917
See no. 110.

Dr Caroline Barron

22 diameter
Incised on base: O/TEL (in monogram)
Provenance: Given by T. E. Lawrence to D. G. Hogarth; by descent.

112

ARAB UNDER-ROBE (THOB)
See no. 105.

Museum of Costume, Bath

Tussore, blue and white embroidery, pearl buttons, 134 × 136
Provenance: Said to have been given to T. E. Lawrence by The Emir Feisal; by descent to Dr M. R. Lawrence; presented by him, 1964.

113

ARAB ROBE (ZEBUN)
See no. 105.

Museum of Costume, Bath

Striped cream and brown silk, 135 × 123.7
Provenance: Said to have been given to T. E. Lawrence by The Emir Feisal; by descent to Dr M. R. Lawrence; presented by him, 1964.

114
AGAL

115
T. E. LAWRENCE
By Augustus John, 1919

By the end of the war Lawrence had collected some fine examples of contemporary Arab dress, which returned to Europe with him. These are often referred to in letters to artists and he is seen wearing them in portraits by Augustus John, Kathleen Scott, and William Rothenstein.

This particular *agal*, or circlet, is made of purple silk wire. It was given to Mrs Clare Sydney Smith, the wife of Lawrence's commander at RAF Cattewater on Plymouth Sound.

Dr Lionel Dakers CBE

Purple silk and silver wire, 76.5 long
Provenance : Given by T. E. Lawrence to Mrs Clare Sydney Smith; by descent to her daughter Mrs Maureen Hews; given by her to present owner.

This portrait of Lawrence is the best known of several painted by Augustus John during the Paris Peace Conference of 1919. It was exhibited at the Alpine Club Gallery in London during March and April 1920. Lawrence came to see the picture on many occasions and was keen to acquire it; it was, however, beyond his means.

When the work was sold to the Duke of Westminster (who shortly afterwards donated it to the Tate Gallery) Lawrence wrote to the artist: 'Really, I'm hotter stuff than I thought : the wrathful portrait went off at top speed for a thousand to a Duke ! Of course I know you will naturally think the glory is yours but I believe it's due to the exceeding beauty of my face'.[1]

The Trustees of the Tate Gallery (TG 3566)

1. T. E. Lawrence to Augustus John, 19.3.1920.

Oil on canvas, 80 × 59.7
Unsigned
Provenance : Purchased by the Duke of Westminster from the Alpine Club Gallery, 1920; presented 1920.
Literature : *SPW 1935*, ill. fp. 126; A. John, *Chiaroscuro*, 1952, pp. 238, 244-7; M. Chamot, D. Farr & M. Butlin, *The Modern British Paintings, Drawings and Sculpture I*, Tate Gallery, 1964, p. 323; M. Holroyd, *Augustus John*, 1974-5, II, p.86.
Exhibitions : London, Alpine Club Gallery, 1920 (8).
(illustrated in colour p. 49)

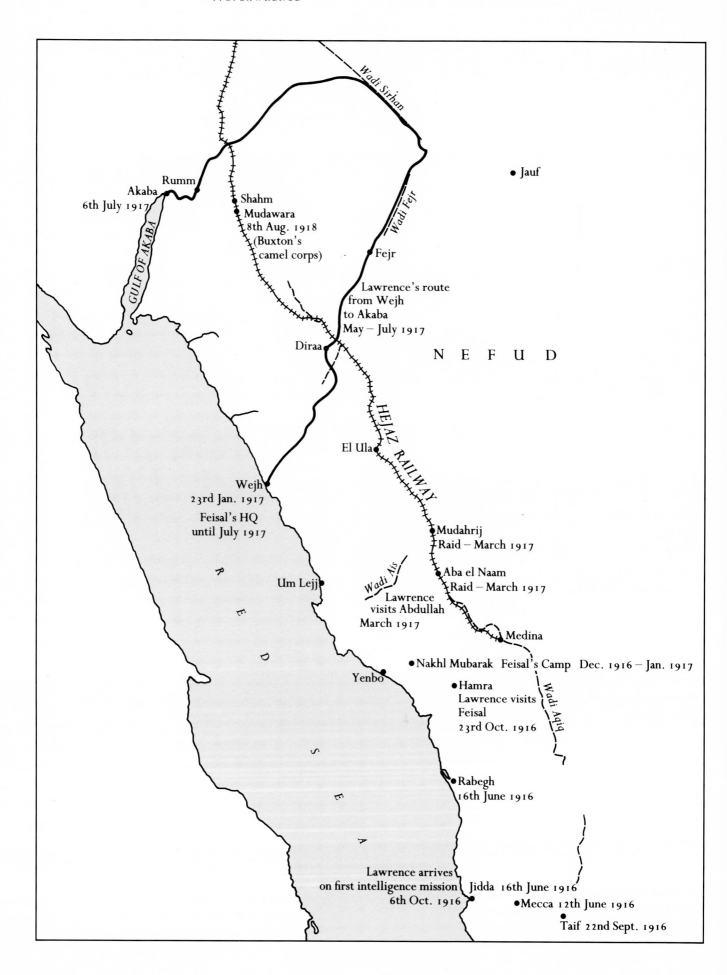

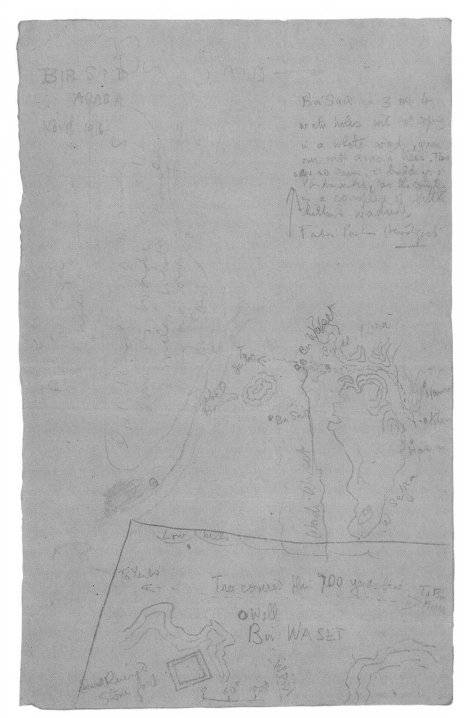

116

SKETCH MAP OF BIR SAID
By T. E. Lawrence, 1916

In December 1916 Feisal's army was trapped in the Red Sea port of Yenbo (see no. 117 i). HMS *Raven II*, a former German merchant ship converted into an aircraft carrier, was one of several British warships which had been assembled nearby to protect the town. The ship's seaplanes carried out a number of bombing raids on Turkish forces near Bir Said which seemed poised to advance on Yenbo. Calling on his detailed knowledge of the area, Lawrence drew this map of Bir Said to help the pilots find their targets.

Trustees of the Imperial War Museum

Pencil on paper, 18.6 × 12.1
Provenance : unrecorded.

Facing page
*Map of the Hejaz campaigns to the capture
of Akaba, 6 July 1917*

117
THE WAR IN THE DESERT: THE HEJAZ
CAMPAIGN, DECEMBER 1916 – MAY 1917
Photographs from T. E. Lawrence's
collection

(i) Feisal's Army falling back on Yenbo
Photograph by T. E. Lawrence
(December 1916)

In early December 1916 a vigorous Turkish
campaign was pushing Feisal back towards
Yenbo on the Red Sea coast. Captain Boyle,
the Commander of the Red Sea Patrol
Squadron, had already provided a number of
British warships to cover the town. Feisal
entered Yenbo with a depleted tribal army on
9 December. In his memoirs Boyle described
the spectacle:

'Being on deck early one morning I saw
a blaze of colour on the shore horizon
looking rather like the lower end of a
rainbow moving towards the harbour.

'As it got nearer I saw what looked like
trunks of tall trees underneath the colour,
and it was not until some minutes later that
with my glasses I made it out to be a large
force of Arabs on camels moving in the shape
of a 'V' towards the town.

'At the apex of the 'V' rode the two
Sherifs (Feisal and Zeid) . . . and the phalanx
was made up of Feisal's retainers and escort,
all wearing robes of brilliant colours. The
effect had a striking though not a warlike
appearance, but the actual fighting men were
holding off the Turks who were pursuing the
retreating Arabs down to the hills bordering
the coastal plain, about six miles inland.'[1]

1. W. H. D. Boyle, *My Naval Life*, 1942, pp. 99-100.

(ii) Nakhl Mubarak, scene in camp at dawn
Photograph by T.E. Lawrence

From mid December 1916 to early January
1917 Feisal's army was camped at Nakhl
Mubarak, a date grove close to Yenbo.
Lawrence later sent home some photographs
that he had taken of the site and in the
accompanying letter he wrote: 'One of the
prints to appear, showing the Sherifian camp
at dawn, in Wadi Yenbo, was taken by me
at 6 a.m. in January last, and is a very
beautiful picture. Most sunrise pictures are
taken at sunset, but this one is really a
success.'[1]

1. T. E. Lawrence to his family, 8.1.1918, *Home Letters*,
p. 347.

(iii) Wejh, looking east
Photograph by T.E. Lawrence

By 4 January 1917 Feisal was ready to move
his force 200 miles up the coast to Wejh.
From here the Arabs would be able to mount
a large-scale attack on the Hejaz Railway out
of range of the Turkish garrison in Medina.

Wejh was captured on 23 January 1917 by
Arab troops with British naval assistance. It
became Feisal's headquarters until the
capture of Akaba in July 1917.

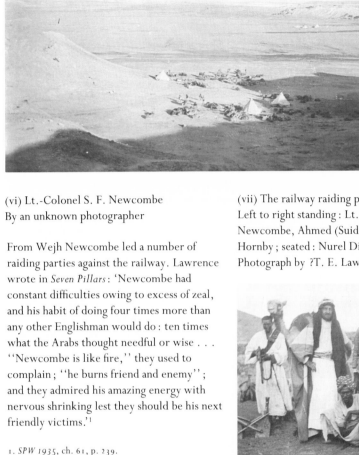

(iv) Bedouin tents in the desert near Wejh
Photograph by Captain R.G. Goslett

Lawrence described the camp at Wejh in
Seven Pilllars: 'Feisal pitched his tents (here
an opulent group: living tents, reception
tents, staff tents, guest tents, servants') about
a mile from the sea, on the edge of the coral
shelf which . . . ended in a steep drop facing
east and south over broad valleys radiating
star-like from the land-locked harbour. The
tents of soldiers and tribesmen were grouped
in these sandy valleys, leaving the chill height
for ourselves; and very delightful in the
evening we northerners found it . . .
Immediately beneath us were the Ageyl, an
irregular close group of tents . . . The
scattered tents and shelters of the tribesmen
filled each gully or windless place. Beyond
the last of them lay open country, with camel
parties coming in or out.'[1]

1. *SPW 1935*, ch. 29, p.170.

(v) T. E. Lawrence
By an unknown photographer (February 1917)

(vi) Lt.-Colonel S. F. Newcombe
By an unknown photographer

From Wejh Newcombe led a number of
raiding parties against the railway. Lawrence
wrote in *Seven Pillars*: 'Newcombe had
constant difficulties owing to excess of zeal,
and his habit of doing four times more than
any other Englishman would do: ten times
what the Arabs thought needful or wise . . .
''Newcombe is like fire,'' they used to
complain; ''he burns friend and enemy'';
and they admired his amazing energy with
nervous shrinking lest they should be his next
friendly victims.'[1]

1. *SPW 1935*, ch. 61, p. 239.

(vii) The railway raiding party
Left to right standing: Lt.-Colonel
Newcombe, Ahmed (Suida), Aziz, Lt
Hornby; seated: Nurel Din, Abdu
Photograph by ?T. E. Lawrence, 1917

In *Seven Pillars* Lawrence described the
tenacity of Newcombe and Hornby in their
attacks on the railway: 'The persistent pair
would cling for weeks to the railway edge,
almost without helpers, often without food,
till they had exhausted either explosives or
camels, and had to return for more . . .
Arabs told me Newcombe would not sleep
except head on rails, and that Hornby would
worry the metals with his teeth when gun-
cotton failed. These were legends, but
behind them lay a sense of their joint
insatiate savagery in destroying till there was
no more to destroy.'[1]

1. *SPW 1935*, ch. 61, p. 239.

(i) IWM Q58754; (ii) IWM Q58837; (iii)
IWM Q58816; (iv) IWM 59015; (v) IWM
Q58816; (vi) IWM Q60209A; (vii) IWM
Q48912

118

T.E. LAWRENCE
Photograph by B. E. Leeson, 1917
Vintage print

A note written on the back of this
photograph states that it was taken at Wejh
aerodrome shortly before Lawrence set off
with the Akaba expedition. Another print is
marked: 'taken at Rabegh aerodrome on 17
March 1917',[1] but this combination of date
and place is impossible. B. E. Leeson joined
the RFC squadron at Rabegh in January and
moved up to Wejh some weeks later.

In spring 1917 Leeson and Lawrence went
on a seven-day car journey in the Wadi
Hamdh (not mentioned in *Seven Pillars*)
looking for an RFC machine that had
crashed. Leeson was later invalided out of
Arabia, and although Lawrence wanted him
to run mechanical transport at Akaba he was
not allowed to return.

National Portrait Gallery (NPG P324)

1. Bodleian Library, MS. Res. c.54.

11.7 × 11.7
Provenance : Purchased, 1987.
Literature : *Secret Despatches*, ill. frontis.

119

T. E. LAWRENCE'S ARMY FIELD
SERVICE CORRESPONDENCE BOOK,
1917

One of a series of correspondence books used
by Lawrence during the Arab campaign. This
survived among the Arab Bureau papers at
the end of the war, and he consulted it and
transcribed part of its contents when he
visited Cairo in 1919. The book came back
into Lawrence's possession when Dr W.E.
Marshall (formerly the medical officer at

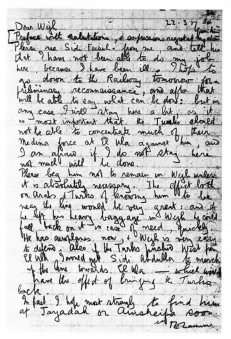

Akaba) brought it back to England. Lawrence
later presented it to Charlotte Shaw. He lost
a number of similar books with the
manuscript of *Seven Pillars* in 1919.

In the spring of 1917 Lawrence spent a
few weeks at Abdullah's camp in Wadi Ais.
The page displayed contains the draft of a
letter which he sent back to Wejh on 22
March 1917.

The letter is addressed simply to 'Wejh'
because Lawrence did not know which
British officer was in charge of liaison work
there during his absence.

The British Library Board (Add.MS 45914)

Paper bound booklet, squared paper, 20 × 15.8
Provenance : Given by T. E. Lawrence to Charlotte
Shaw ; presented to the British Museum by
G. B. Shaw, 1944.

120

LETTER FROM EMIR FEISAL TO
T. E. LAWRENCE
Wejh, 30 March 1917

This letter, in imperfect French, translates as
follows : 'I was very sorry to learn that you
were ill. I hope that you are already better
and that you would like to come back to us
in a short time, as soon as possible. Your
presence with me is very indispensable, in
view of urgency of questions and the pace of
affairs. It was not at all your promise to stay
there so long. So I hope that you will return
as soon as you receive this letter.'

Lawrence had been away from Feisal's
camp for three weeks. This urgent request

for his return was prompted by Feisal's
perplexity in the face of contradictory advice
from his Arab and British counsellors. The
Arabs counselled an immediate rising in
Syria, hoping to catch the Turks unprepared.
The British, however, could not support this
impetuous scheme as they knew that lines of
supply and communication had not been
properly established. They thought that
Feisal should concentrate his attentions on
the Hejaz Railway.

By the end of March 1917, when the
letter was written, Feisal had begun to be
swayed by the Syrian enthusiasts. This
reflected one of the weaknesses in his
character. As Lawrence later admitted,
Feisal 'always listened to his momentary
adviser, despite his own better judgment.'[1]

On receipt of this letter, Lawrence
returned immediately from Wadi Ais,
arriving in Wejh on 14 April.

The Warden and Fellows of All Souls
College, Oxford

1. *Biographers* (Liddell Hart), pp. 188-9.
Single sheet squared paper, with envelope, 27 × 21
Provenance : Given by Lionel Curtis.
(not illustrated)

121

AUDA ABU TAYI
By Eric Kennington (1921)
Annotated plate from *Seven Pillars of Wisdom*,
1926

Auda was leader of the Abu Tayi Howeitat,
a tribe based to the north of the Hejaz.
Lawrence met him for the first time in April
1917 at Feisal's camp in Wejh.

'The inimitable Auda' is described in a

report Lawrence sent to the *Arab Bulletin*:
'He must be nearly fifty now (he admits
forty) and his black beard is tinged with
white, but he is still tall and straight, loosely
built, spare and powerful, and, as active as
a much younger man. His lined and haggard
face is pure Bedouin: low forehead, high
sharp hooked nose, brown-green eyes,
slanting outward, large mouth . . . pointed
beard and moustache, with the lower jaw
shaven clean in the Howeitat style . . . He
has married twenty-eight times, has been
wounded thirteen times . . . He has only
reported his "kill" since 1900, and they now
stand at seventy-five Arabs; Turks are not
counted . . . He sees life as a saga and all
events are significant and all personages
heroic.'[1]

In *Seven Pillars* Lawrence also described an
incident which took place at their first
meeting: 'Suddenly Auda scrambled to his
feet with a loud "God forbid", and flung
from the tent. We stared at one another, and
there came a noise of hammering outside. I
went after to learn what it meant, and there
was Auda bent over a rock pounding his false
teeth to fragments with a stone. "I had
forgotten," he explained, "Jemal Pasha gave
me these. I was eating my Lord's bread with
Turkish teeth!" Unfortunately he had few
teeth of his own, so . . . he went about half-
nourished till we had taken Akaba, and Sir
Reginald Wingate sent him a dentist from
Egypt to make an Allied set.'[2]

Auda helped Lawrence plan the
expedition to Akaba and played an important
role in its success.

Ian D. Struthers

1. *Arab Bulletin*, no. 57, 1917.
2. *SPW 1935*, ch. 38, p. 222.

Chromo-lithograph, 25 × 18.5
Inscribed and signed by Eric Kennington in ink b.: *Auda
abu Tayi Amman, 1922/Eric H. Kennington*
Provenance: By descent from the artist.
Literature: *SPW 1926*, ill.; *SPW 1935*, ill. fp. 222.;
R.Storrs in E. Kennington, *Drawing the RAF*, 1942, p.16.

122
NAWAF SHALAAN
By Eric Kennington, 1921

Nawaf Shalaan was the eldest son of Sheikh
Nuri Shalaan, the Paramount Emir of the
Ruwalla. Lawrence met Nawaf and Nuri at
Azrak in June 1917 on the way back from his
secret journey behind Turkish lines in Syria.

In a letter of December 1917 Lawrence
raised the question of Nawaf's motivation in

the revolt: 'Nawaf aimed at the eventual
conquest of Hail, for himself, with the help
of the Sherif and an overlordship for his
family over the combined Rualla-Shammar
blocks. It is, I think understood that this is
the price of his assistance.'[1]

Kennington thought that this was the best
of his Arab portraits.

Miss Susan Mary Kennington

1. T.E. Lawrence to C.E. Wilson, 5.12.1917.

Pastel, 75 × 50
Inscribed bl.: *Nawaf Shalaan*
Provenance: By descent.
Literature: *SPW 1926*, ill.; *SPW 1935*, ill. fp. 174;
R.Storrs in E. Kennington, *Drawing the RAF*, 1942, p.13.
Exhibitions: Leicester Galleries 1927 (20).

123
THE CAPTURE OF AKABA, JULY 1917
Photographs from T.E. Lawrence's collection

(i) Sherif Nasir
Photograph by T. E. Lawrence (July 1917)

Sherif Nasir of Medina was Feisal's cousin and one of the great leaders of the Arab Revolt. He was the formal head of the Akaba expedition. When Lawrence first met him in January 1917: 'Nasir made a splendid impression . . . He was the opener of roads, the forerunner of Feisal's movement, the man who had fired his first shot in Medina, and who was to fire our last shot at Muslimieh beyond Aleppo on the day that Turkey asked for an armistice, and from beginning to end all that could be told of him was good.'[1]

1. SPW 1935, ch. 26, p. 160.

(i)

(ii) Left to right: Auda abu Zaal, Mohammed abu Tayi, unknown, Auda abu Tayi, Zaal ibn Motlog
Photograph by T. E. Lawrence, Amman (1921)

(ii)

For Auda abu Tayi see no. 121. Mohammed was Auda's son.

Zaal ibn Motlog was Auda's nephew, 'a lithe metallic man, with a bold appraising look, cruel lips, and a thin laugh, full of the brutality which these nomad Howeitat had caught from the peasantry.'[1] Auda used him as the chief scout of the Howeitat.

In June 1917 Zaal accompanied Lawrence on a train-wrecking expedition designed to draw Turkish attention away from Akaba. He was one of the leaders of the Howeitat force which defeated the Turks at Aba el Lissan on the Akaba road in July.

In the Arab Bulletin Lawrence described Auda abu Zaal as 'the fourth great man of Abu Tayi . . . the Howeitat flock to his side when there is a raid, and say that in action for concentrated force he is second only to Auda'.[2]

Lawrence took this photograph when he revisited the scenes of his wartime campaigns in 1921.

1. SPW 1935, ch. 45, p. 259.
2. Arab Bulletin, 57, 1917.

(iii) Guweira
Photograph by T. E. Lawrence (May 1917)

Guweira is in the Wadi Itm about twenty-five miles inland from Akaba. Lawrence described it as: 'a map of pink sand, brushed over with streaks of watercourses, in a mantle of scrub . . . out of this, and bounding this, towered islands and cliffs of glowing sandstone, wind-scarped and rain-furrowed, tinted celestially by the early sun.'[1]

In the later stages of the war, Feisal and Colonel Joyce (see no. 132 iv) had their headquarters at Guweira.

1. SPW 1935, ch. 54, pp. 308-9.

(iii)

(iv)

(iv) In Wadi Itm, near Resafe, while discussing terms of Turkish surrender
Photograph by T.E. Lawrence (5 July 1917)

'The narrows of Wadi Itm increased in intricate ruggedness as we penetrated deeper. Below Kethira we found Turkish post after Turkish post empty. Their men had been drawn into Khadra, the entrenched position (at the mouth of Itm), which covered Akaba . . .

'In the afternoon we were in contact with this main position, and . . . only a last three hundred men barred us from the sea . . . the enemy were resisting firmly, in bomb-proof trenches with a new artesian well. Only it was rumoured that they had little food . . .

(v)

'We sent the Turks summonses, first by white flag, and then by Turkish prisoners, but they shot at both . . . We had a third try to communicate with the Turks, by means of a little conscript, who said that he understood how to do it. He undressed, and went down the valley in little more than boots. An hour later he proudly brought us a reply, very polite, saying that in two days, if help did not come from Maan, they would surrender . . .

'We gave our little man a sovereign as earnest of reward, walked down close to the trenches with him, and sent in for an officer to speak with us. After some hesitation this was achieved, and we explained the situation on the road behind us; our growing forces; and our short control over their tempers. The upshot was that they promised to surrender at daylight.'[1]

On the following day (6 July), the Turks duly surrendered, and Akaba lay in Arab hands.

1. SPW 1935, ch. 54, pp. 310-12.

(v) Triumphal entry into Akaba
Photograph by T. E. Lawrence (6 July 1917)

After the surrender of the Turkish troops in Wadi Itm, the Arab forces 'raced through a driving sand-storm down to Akaba'.[1]

Through the whirling dust we perceived that Akaba was all a ruin. Repeated bombardments by French and English warships had degraded the place to its original rubbish. The poor houses stood about in a litter, dirty and contemptible, lacking entirely that dignity which the durability of their time-challenging bones conferred on ancient remains.

'We wandered into the shadowed grove of palms, at the very break of the splashing waves, and there sat down to watch our men streaming past as lines of flushed vacant faces without message for us. For months Akaba had been the horizon of our minds, the goal: we had had no thought, we had refused thought, of anything beside. Now, in achievement, we were a little despising the entities which had spent their extremest effort on an object whose attainment changed nothing radical either in mind or body.'[2]

1. SPW 1935, ch. 54, p. 312.
2. SPW 1935, ch. 55, p. 314.

(vi) Akaba fort from the land side
By an unknown photographer (18 January 1918)
See no. 123 (v).

(vi)

(vii) T.E. Lawrence on his camel, Akaba
By an unknown photographer

For Lawrence the camels of Egypt and Sinai did not bear comparison with the 'rich mounts of the Arabian princes.' He was conscious that 'It was easy to sit on a camel's back without falling off, but very difficult to understand and get the best out of her so as to do long journeys without fatiguing either rider or beast.'[1]

But there were drawbacks when the camels ate stubble grass: 'The camels loved this grass, which grew in tufts, about sixteen inches high, on slate-green stalks. They gulped down great quantities of it until the men drove them in and couched them by me. At the moment I hated the beasts, for too much food made their breath stink; and they rumblingly belched up a new mouthful from their stomachs each time they had chewed and swallowed the last, till a green slaver flooded out between their loose lips over the side teeth, and dripped down their sagging chins.'[2]

1. SPW 1935, ch. 10, p. 80.
2. SPW 1935, ch. 32, p. 184.

(i) IWM Q59157 (ii) IWM Q60169
(iii) IWM Q59199 (iv) Q59207 (v) IWM
Q59193 (vi) IWM Q59393 (vii) IWM
Q60212

(vii)

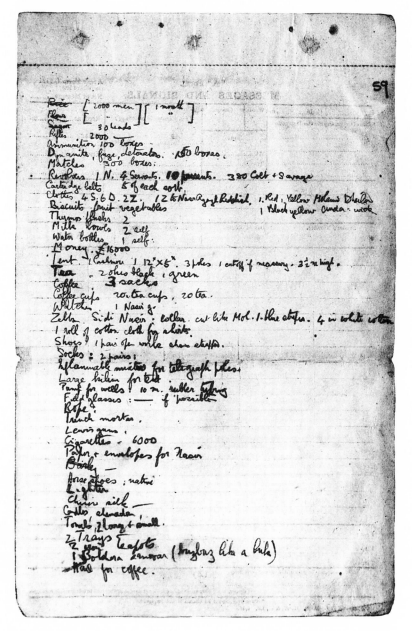

124

'SHOPPING LIST'

Facsimile of notes made by T.E. Lawrence in pencil on the back of an army messages and signals pad (July 1917)

There was very little in Akaba to feed the Arab force and their Turkish prisoners. Lawrence therefore rode across Sinai to the Suez Canal with a small party to arrange for the immediate dispatch of supplies and money. The requirements of the occupying force are listed in the notes displayed. These included 2,000 rifles, 'rice for 2,000 men for one month', three sacks of coffee, 6,000 cigarettes, 300 boxes of matches, presents for Nasir and the Howeitat leaders, and two pairs of socks.

The list also mentions the sum of £16,000. Lawrence explained the need for this money in *Seven Pillars*: 'Clayton drew sixteen thousand pounds in gold and got an escort to take it to Suez by the three o'clock train. This was urgent, that Nasir might be able to meet his debts. The notes we had issued at Bair, Jefer and Guweira were penciled promises, on army telegraph forms, to pay so much to bearer in Akaba . . . no one had dared issue notes before in Arabia, because the Beduins had neither pockets in their shirts nor strong-rooms in their tents, and notes could not be buried . . . So there was an unconquerable prejudice against them, and for our good name it was essential that they be early redeemed.'[1]

British Library (Add. MS 45915)

1. *SPW 1935*, ch. 56, p.321.

125

THE CAMP AT ISMAILIA

By Frank Mason, 1916

After the capture of Akaba Lawrence rode across the desert to Ismailia, very anxious that stores and naval support should be provided for the newly-taken town. To his relief, Admiral Wemyss instantly dispatched a storeship with money and food. When the dangerous weakness of the Arab position was confirmed Wemyss sent his own flagship HMS *Euryalus* to lie off Akaba as a guardship. Lawrence later commented on this episode: 'the *Euryalus* . . . was a four-funnel boat, and as such made an indelible impression on tribal opinion. Obviously, the more funnels the greater the ship.'[1]

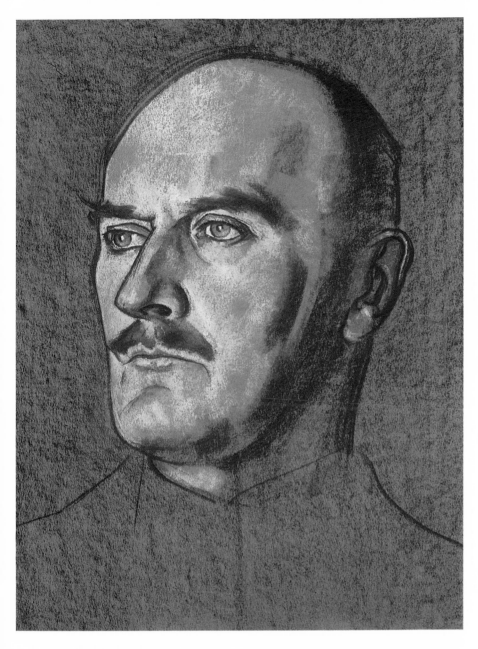

Mason's etching shows the same ship off Ismailia in May 1916. The other warship shown is the French cruiser *Requin*.

Trustees of the Imperial War Museum (IWM 2821)

1. T. E. Lawrence to Sir Henry McMahon, 18.10.1933.

Etching, 12.7 × 19.7
Signed br.: *Frank H. Mason*
Provenance: Given by the artist, 1920.

126
FIELD MARSHAL LORD ALLENBY
By Eric Kennington, 1921

Sir Edmund Allenby (1861-1936) took command of the Egyptian Expeditionary Force in June 1917. Under his direction the Force broke through the Turkish defences at Gaza in October and drove northward beyond Jaffa, capturing Jerusalem in December. A further offensive in September 1918 led to the capture of Damascus a month later.

Lawrence first met Allenby on his return to Cairo after the capture of Akaba. From this point onwards Arab operations were planned to synchronise with Allenby's projected advance in Sinai and Palestine.

Feisal was made an army commander under Allenby's orders, with Lawrence as the link between them. This position would give Lawrence a decisive influence on Arab action in the north.

Lawrence wrote in *Seven Pillars* that Allenby was 'physically large and confident, and morally so great that the comprehension of our littleness came slow to him.'[1]

In 1927 Edward Garnett was surprised to receive a copy of the subscribers' *Seven Pillars* from Lawrence as a gift. In return, he bought this portrait of Allenby from the Leicester Galleries exhibition of *Seven Pillars* illustrations and promised it to Lawrence, who was deeply touched. He knew that Garnett was not a wealthy man, and wrote: 'Your gift of the Allenby pastel is an irresistible thing: but rather overwhelming . . . I'm most grateful, for as a portrait of Allenby the drawing is unusually rich, and Allenby is an admiration of mine.'[2]

On 10 August 1933 Lawrence wrote telling Garnett that he was at last ready to have the portrait at Clouds Hill: 'You know I already possess John's picture of Feisal . . . so thanks to your goodness in reserving me the Allenby I shall have my dual mastership preserved in my cottage for all my time. It will be a queer, rich feeling. In the flesh that double allegiance was difficult: but the two quiet heads on the wall will let me do what I please.'[3]

National Portrait Gallery (NPG 2906)

1. *SPW 1935*, ch. 56, p. 321.
2. T. E. Lawrence to E. Garnett, 1.3.1927, *Letters*, p. 510.
3. T. E. Lawrence to E. Garnett, 10.8.1933, *Letters*, p. 774.

Pastel, 44.5 × 33.7
Provenance: Purchased from the Leicester Galleries by Edward Garnett for T. E. Lawrence, 1927; by descent to A. W. Lawrence; given by him, 1936.
Literature: *SPW 1926*, ill.; *SPW 1935*, ill. fp.322.
Exhibitions: Leicester Galleries 1921 (14); Leicester Galleries 1927 (14); London, Picture Hire Limited, *Eric Kennington Exhibition*, 1936 (32).

127

GOLD DAGGER MADE FOR T. E. LAWRENCE IN MECCA, 1917

In July 1917 Lawrence had to visit Jidda for discussions with Sherif Hussein, and he seems to have made a secret journey to Mecca specifically to order this gold dagger. He had it made 'in the third little turning to the left off the main bazaar, by an old Nejdi goldsmith whose name I fancy was Gasein'.[1]

The dagger was especially small because Lawrence found a full-size weapon too cumbersome. He wore it for the rest of the war except when it was being repaired or re-belted. The story that this dagger and its scabbard were made from melted-down coins is probably no more than popular conjecture.

In 1923 Lawrence sold the dagger for £125 to Lionel Curtis who later presented it to All Souls College. Lawrence used the money to repair his newly-rented cottage at Clouds Hill.

The Warden and Fellows of All Souls College, Oxford

1. T. E. Lawrence to S. C. Cockerell, 27.5.1927.

Dagger: 22.8; belt: 78.5
Provenance: T.E.Lawrence; sold through Spinks to Lionel Curtis 1923; given to All Souls, 1938.
Exhibitions: Leicester Galleries 1927 (82).

128

SILVER-GILT DAGGER

In the summer of 1917, while Lawrence was waiting for a gold Meccan dagger to be made (see no. 127), he wore this silver gilt weapon. It was presented to him by Sherif Nasir as a replacement for an earlier one – a gift from the Emir Abdullah – which Lawrence had given to a Howeitat chief.

Lawrence found this dagger too heavy and was delighted when his smaller gold dagger was ready.

The belt shown is not the original.

Private Ownership

30 long
Provenance: Presented to T. E. Lawrence by Sherif Nasir 1917; left by T. E. Lawrence with the family of present owner.

129

'TWENTY-SEVEN ARTICLES'
By T.E. Lawrence, 1917
Facsimile of autograph manuscript

By August 1917 Lawrence had been on active
service with the Arabs longer than any other
British officer. He had also been uniquely
successful, as demonstrated by the capture of
Akaba in July. Other British officers had
found great difficulties in directing the
irregular warfare of the Bedouin to useful ends.

Lawrence's 'Twenty-seven Articles',
published in the *Arab Bulletin* in August 1917,
is a compendium of advice for British officers
working with the Arabs for the first time. He
insisted on the need for infinite tact and
patience, and the importance of adapting to
local customs and conditions. Pre-conceived
military ideas based on experience elsewhere
had to be abandoned from the start. He
wrote: 'Do not try to trade on what you
know of fighting. The Hejaz confounds
ordinary tactics. Learn the Bedu principles of
war as thoroughly and as quickly as you can,
for till you know them your advice will be
no good to the Sherif.'

The 'Articles' also reveal a great deal
about Lawrence's own role in Feisal's camp,
which was now one of unacknowledged
leadership. He advised other officers: 'Your
ideal position is when you are present and not
noticed. Do not be too intimate, too
prominent, or too earnest . . . Let your name
. . . be coupled always with a Sherif's . . .
When the moment comes for action put
yourself publicly under his orders . . . Wave
a Sherif in front of you like a banner and hide
your own mind and person. If you succeed,
you will have hundreds of miles of country
and thousands of men under your orders, and
for this it's worth bartering the outward
show.'

Public Record Office, London (FO882/7)

Literature: *Arab Bulletin*, no. 60, 1917; T. E. Lawrence,
Secret Despatches from Arabia, 1937, pp. 126-133;
B. Liddell Hart, *'T. E. Lawrence'*, 1934, pp. 142-7;
J. E. Mack, *A Prince of Our Disorder*, 1976, pp. 463-7.
(not illustrated)

130
T. E. LAWRENCE
By an unknown photographer (c.1917)

Lawrence rarely wore British uniform in
Arabia. This photograph may have been taken
during a brief visit to Akaba at the beginning
of August 1917, when he travelled up by ship
with other British officers. The three shoulder
pips indicate his rank of Captain. A few days
later, on 5 August, he was promoted Major.

Arab head-dress was worn by most British
officers attached to the Arab forces.

IWM Q59314A

131
TUNIC AND HEAD-DRESS OF OFFICER
IN HEJAZ REGULAR ARMY

The Hejaz Regular Army was based at Akaba
from August 1917 (see no. 132 i). This
uniform is representative of the type worn by
officers. It was presented by T.E. Lawrence
to the Imperial War Museum after the war.
Troops wearing similar uniforms are
shown in photograph no. 132 (i).

Trustees of the Imperial War Museum

Tunic: 78 × 50; head-dress 20 × 17
Provenance: Given by T. E. Lawrence.

132
THE WAR IN THE DESERT, AKABA,
AUGUST 1917 – JANUARY 1918
Photographs from T.E. Lawrence's
collection

(ii) Representatives of tribes coming in under
cover of the white flag to swear allegiance to
Sheikh Feisal, Akaba

The capture of Akaba meant the end of the
Hejaz campaign, and the beginning of a new
northern offensive. Feisal arrived in Akaba in
late August and began recruiting men for the
projected campaign in Syria. The tribal
nature of Arab irregulars meant that new
troops had to be enrolled in each different
region.

In this photograph representatives of the
tribes are shown coming in to arrange the
enlistment of men and to swear allegiance to
Feisal. Lawrence reported to Clayton: 'The
slide of Arabs towards the Sherif . . . has
become immense, almost impossible, since
Feisul arrived. He is unable even to see all
the head sheikhs of the newcomers.'[1]

IWM Q59061

1. T. E. Lawrence to G. F. Clayton, 27.8.1917.

(i) Sherifian troops, Akaba
Photograph by Captain R.G. Goslett

The Arab Regular Army under Jaafar Pasha
proved to be of limited use during the
campaigns. According to a British officer
who visited Akaba in August 1917, 'the men
are quite untrained and have little discipline
. . . and their one desire (which they have no
hesitation in expressing) is to be left alone to
eat and sleep . . . Something, however,
might be made of them in time, especially
the cavalry (mule and camel), machine
gunners and artillery, as long as they are not
asked to fight any pitched battle with the
Turk, but are used entirely as irregulars, and
only used for minor operations.'[1]

Lawrence replied to these criticisms by
arguing that the real object of these troops
was 'not so much to engage Turkish forces
on equal terms, as to stiffen the Beduin
resistance, by providing the comforting
spectacle of a trained reserve, and to impress
the Turks with the fact that behind the
Beduin screen lies an unknown quantity.'[2]

IWM Q59304

1. Capt MacIndoe, 'Report on Situation at Akaba',
27.8.1917, WO158/634.
2. T.E. Lawrence to G.F. Clayton, 27.8.1917,
FO882/7.

(iii) HMS Humber, Akaba
Photograph by T. E. Lawrence

The monitor HMS Humber was sent to Akaba
in August 1917 to act as guardship. Lawrence
frequently went aboard to visit Captain
Snagge and to enjoy the ship's facilities:
'Snagge was fortunate in his ship, which had
been built for Brazil, and was much more
comfortably furnished than British monitors;
and we were doubly fortunate in him and in
this, for he was the spirit of hospitality. His
inquiring nature took interest in the shore,
and saw the comic side even of our petty

disasters . . . and always for a good story he
gave me a hot bath, and tea with civilized
trappings, free from every suspicion of blown
sand. His kindness and help served us in lieu
of visits to Egypt for repairs, and enabled us
to hammer on against the Turks through
month after month of feckless
disappointment.'[1]

IWM Q60193

1. SPW 1935, ch. 59, p.343.

(iv) Jaafar Pasha, Feisal and Lt.-Colonel
Joyce, Wadi Kuntilla
Photograph by Colonel S. F. Newcombe
(August 1917)

In August 1917 a Turkish force left Maan and
threatened the Arab camp at Guweira, which
lay on the direct route to Akaba. In order to
defend the new Arab base, the RFC set up
a temporary landing ground at Kuntilla and
used it for long-distance air raids on Maan
and the Turkish positions. These raids were
carried out after consultation with
Lawrence, who was able to supply detailed
geographical information and even to point
out the house of a Turkish notable in Maan
(on which a direct hit was scored).

For Lt.-Colonel P.C. Joyce, Commandant
of the Akaba base from August 1917, see
no. 153.

IWM Q59011

(v) T. E. Lawrence in Arab robes
Photograph by Captain R.G. Goslett

This photograph was taken at Akaba where
Captain Goslett was Supply Officer.

IWM Q59314

(vi) T. E. Lawrence's camel Ghazala and foal
Photograph by Captain R.G. Goslett (1918)

In *Seven Pillars* Lawrence described Sherif
Nasir (see no. 123 i) 'riding his Ghazala – a
camel vaulted and huge-ribbed as an antique
ship; towering a good foot above the next of
our animals, and yet perfectly proportioned,
with a stride like an ostrich's – a lyrical
beast, noblest and best bred of the Howeitat
camels.'[1]

In July 1917 Lawrence managed to
persuade King Hussein to grant Nasir a
month's leave to Mecca, his first since the
outbreak of the revolt. In gratitude, Nasir
sold Lawrence 'the regal camel'[2] Ghazala.

IWM Q59390

1. *SPW 1935*, ch. 49, p. 281.
2. *SPW 1935*, ch. 57, p. 326.

(vii) Wadi Rumm
Photograph by T. E. Lawrence

Lawrence was overawed by the 'vast and echoing and God-like'[1] Wadi Rumm, a spectacular gorge in the mountains behind Akaba. In *Seven Pillars* he described his first entry into Rumm : 'We looked up on the left to a long wall of rock, sheering in like a thousand-foot wave towards the middle of the valley ; whose other arc, to the right, was an opposing line of steep, red broken hills. . . . They drew together until only two miles divided them : and then, towering gradually till their parallel parapets must have been a

thousand feet above us, ran forward in an avenue for miles . . . The Arab armies would have been lost in the length and breadth of it, and within the walls a squadron of aeroplanes could have wheeled in formation. Our little caravan grew self-conscious, and fell dead quiet, afraid and ashamed to flaunt its smallness in the presence of the stupendous hills.'[2]

IWM Q59363A
1. *SPW 1935*, ch. 75, p. 414.
2. *SPW 1935*, ch. 62, p. 351.

(viii) T. E. Lawrence in Wadi Itm
Photograph by Captain Lloyd (October 1917)

In October 1917 Lawrence left Akaba with a party of Bedouin to make an ill-fated attack on the Yarmuk railway bridges (see no. 156 iii and iv). He was accompanied for part of the way by George Lloyd. In a diary account of the journey Lloyd mentions reaching the well at the the foot of Wadi Itm on the evening of 24 October 1917.

See also no 138.

IWM Q60097

(ix) Wadi Zubara and Abu Khasaf Hill, looking west
Photograph by T. E. Lawrence
(30 December 1917)

In the last days of 1917 Lawrence accompanied Colonel Joyce on an armoured car expedition from Guweira. They had considered mining a train, but finally decided to attack a small Turkish entrenchment near Mudawara.

The operation, which began on New Year's morning, is described in *Seven Pillars* : 'Joyce was in charge, and for the first time I was at a fight as spectator. The novelty was most enjoyable. Armoured car work seemed fighting de luxe, for our troops, being steel-covered, could come to no hurt. Accordingly we made a field-day of it like the best regular generals, sitting in laconic conference on our hill-top and watching the battle intently through binoculars.' The skirmishing was inconclusive, but Lawrence and Joyce were 'contented with having prowled up and down the line, and proved the surface hard enough for car-operations at deliberate speed.'[1]

IWM Q59434
1. *SPW 1935*, ch. 82, p. 459.

Facing page
*Map of the Syrian Campaign,
July 1917–October 1918*

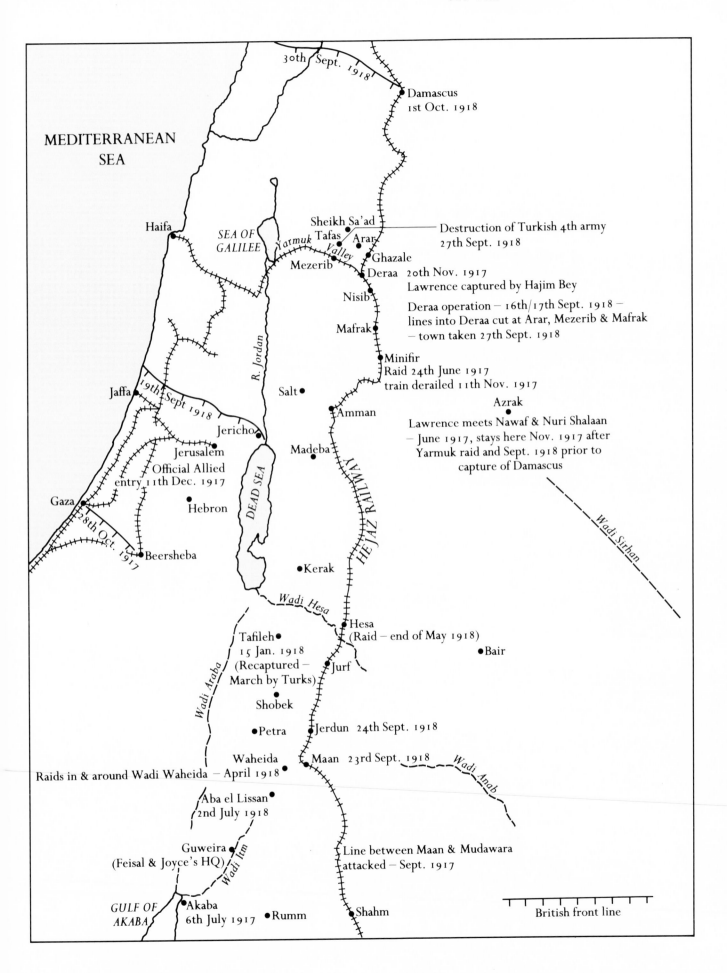

MEDITERRANEAN
SEA

*SEA OF
GALILEE*

Haifa

30th Sept. 1918

Damascus
1st Oct. 1918

Sheikh Sa'ad
Tafas Arar
Ghazale
Mezerib Deraa
Yarmuk Valley

Destruction of Turkish 4th army
27th Sept. 1918

Deraa 20th Nov. 1917
Lawrence captured by Hajim Bey

Nisib

Mafrak

Deraa operation – 16th/17th Sept. 1918 –
lines into Deraa cut at Arar, Mezerib & Mafrak
– town taken 27th Sept. 1918

Minifir
Raid 24th June 1917
train derailed 11th Nov. 1917

R. Jordan

Salt

Jaffa

19th Sept 1918

Jericho

Jerusalem
Official Allied
entry 11th Dec. 1917

Amman

Madeba

Azrak

Lawrence meets Nawaf & Nuri Shalaan
– June 1917, stays here Nov. 1917 after
Yarmuk raid and Sept. 1918 prior to
capture of Damascus

DEAD SEA

Gaza

28th Oct. 1917

Hebron

Beersheba

Kerak

HEJAZ RAILWAY

Wadi Sirhan

Wadi Hesa

Hesa
(Raid – end of May 1918)

Bair

Tafileh
15 Jan. 1918
(Recaptured –
March by Turks)

Jurf

Shobek

Petra

Jerdun 24th Sept. 1918

Waheida

Maan 23rd Sept. 1918

Wadi Araba

Raids in & around Wadi Waheida – April 1918

Aba el Lissan
2nd July 1918

Wadi Anab

Guweira
(Feisal & Joyce's HQ)

Wadi Itm

Line between Maan & Mudawara
attacked – Sept. 1917

*GULF OF
AKABA*

Akaba
6th July 1917

Rumm

Shahm

British front line

133
THE WAR IN THE DESERT: ATTACKS
ON THE RAILWAY 1917-18
Photographs from T. E. Lawrence's
collection

(i) The Hejaz line at Abu Taka
GHQ photograph

The narrow gauge Hejaz railway ran from
Damascus southward through the desert for
800 miles. It was the only easy line of
communication and supply for the Turkish
garrison in Medina, and an obvious target for
Arab raiding parties.

IWM Q59684

(ii) A 'tulip' exploding on the Deraa line
Photograph by T. E. Lawrence

Lawrence used various methods of
demolition in his attacks on the railway. In
Seven Pillars he described the effect of one of
them: 'Thirty ounces of gun-cotton were
planted beneath the centre of the central
sleeper of each ten-metre section of the
track. The sleepers were steel, and their
box-shape left an air-chamber which the gas
expansion filled to blow the middle of the
sleeper upward. If the charge was properly
laid, the metal did not snap, but humped
itself . . . two feet in the air. The lift of it
pulled the rails three inches up: the drag of
it pulled them six inches together; and, as
the chairs gripped the bottom flanges,
warped inward seriously. The triple
distortion put them beyond repair.'[1]
    'The appearance of a piece of rail treated
by this method is most beautiful, for the
sleepers rise up in all manner of varied forms,
like the early buds of tulips.'[2]

IWM Q60020

1. *SPW 1935*, ch. 109, pp. 594-5.
2. *The Essential T. E. Lawrence*, ed. D. Garnett, 1951,
p. 211.

(iii) Wrecked railway trucks at Ghadir el Haj
Photograph by ?T.E. Lawrence

In *Seven Pillars* Lawrence describes a number
of occasions on which he destroyed Turkish
locomotives: 'at that moment the engines,
looking very big, rocked with screaming
whistles into view around the bend. Behind
them followed ten box-wagons, crowded
with rifle-muzzles at the windows and doors;
and in little sand-bag nests on the roofs Turks
precariously held on, to shoot at us. I had not
thought of two engines, and on the moment
decided to fire the charge under the second . . .
    'Accordingly, when the front "driver"
of the second engine was on the bridge I
raised my hand to Salem. There followed a
terrific roar'.[1]

IWM Q60032
1. *SPW 1935*, ch. 66, p. 367.

(iv) Repairing the railway track near Maan
Photograph by ?T.E. Lawrence

Lawrence appreciated the difficulties that the
Turks faced in defending the Hejaz Railway:
'we were able, till the end of the war, to
descend upon the railway when and where
we pleased, and effect the damage we
wished, without great difficulty. At the same
time our ways and means had constantly to
be improved. We began with small parties of
ten or fifteen Beduins, and we ended with
mobile columns of all arms, including
armoured cars'.[1]

IWM Q60116

1. *The Essential T. E. Lawrence*, ed. D. Garnett, 1951,
pp. 209-10.

134
FRAGMENTS FROM THE HEJAZ
RAILWAY

These fragments include sections of track,
axle box covers with the emblem of the
Hejaz railway, a brake wheel, a fireman's
stoking firelight, and a Belgian locomotive
maker's nameplate (1907).

Hugh Leach OBE
Provenance: Collected by the lender, c.1967.

135
HEJAZ RAILWAY
Photographs by Hugh Leach, 1967

(i) Wrecked train near Weiban

(ii) Abandoned train at Hadiya

Hugh Leach photographed these Turkish
First World War locomotives some fifty
years after they had been abandoned. The
trains had not rusted owing to the arid
Arabian climate.

Weiban and Hadiya were on a section of
the Hejaz line menaced by Abdullah's forces
from 1917 to the end of the war. Lawrence
carried out his first experiments in train-

wrecking in this area during the spring of
1917. In (ii) the Turkish fort at Hadiya can
be seen in the background.

By courtesy of Hugh Leach OBE

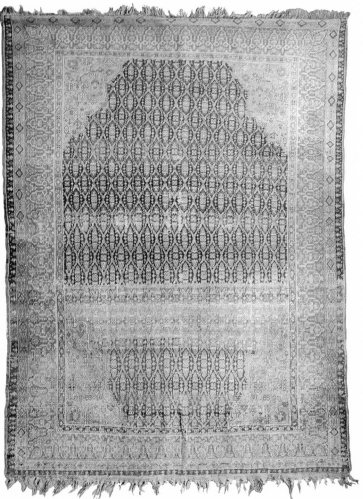

136
BALUCH PRAYER CARPET

Lawrence gave this carpet to Lady Allenby when he passed through Egypt on his way to England in October 1918. It was accompanied by the following letter:

'I do wish it was first-class, but it is all I have, and the very best Baluch are rare. Perhaps you will think it good enough to enter your house.

'It was the prayer carpet of Ayesha, the daughter of Jelal el Leyl of Medina, and of her mother before her. The mother was a Sherifa of Mecca and almost a saint. Ayesha herself was famous for her wealth and liberality. After war broke out the Turks expelled her from Medina to Syria, and I happened to stop her train one day (with a charge of blasting gelatine). I was then able to render her a service, which she acknowledged a few months later from Damascus just before she died (aged 84), by sending me a very delightful letter, and the rug. The letter I want to keep.

'It ought to have been loot, of course, but I must confess that in spite of all the stories I've never looted anything in my life!'[1]

His account of how this particular prayer rug came into his hands is repeated in *Seven Pillars*. However two letters written by Lawrence just after returning from the train attack also mention a fine red Baluch prayer rug, which he *had* taken as loot. It is possible that two rugs were involved, and that the Lady Ayesha, having seen that Lawrence appreciated such things, later sent him the one exhibited here.

The Warden and Fellows of All Souls College, Oxford

1. T. E. Lawrence to Lady Allenby, 14.10.1918.

158 × 120.4
Provenance: Given by T.E.Lawrence to Lady Allenby 1918; bequeathed to the sister of Miss Norah Fearn, by whom presented, 1967.

137
STATION BELL FROM THE HEJAZ RAILWAY

This bell was acquired by Major Hubert Young (see no. 157) during the Arab campaign. It probably came from Mezerib, a station on the Deraa-Palestine line. On 16 September 1918, with a small detachment of Arabs under Nuri Shaalan, Lawrence and Young managed to storm the station, disable the line and cut the main telegraph between Syria and Palestine.

Lawrence also took station bells as trophies. In *Seven Pillars* he describes an attack on the station at Shahm in April 1918: 'We cranked up our Rolls tenders; the Arabs leaped on to their camels . . . and the force converged wildly upon the station. Our car won; and I gained the station bell, a dignified piece of Damascus brass-work. The next man took the ticket punch and the third the office stamp, while the bewildered Turks stared at us'.[1]

He kept the station bell from Deraa in his rooms at All Souls after the war. Its present location is not recorded.

Nicholas Young

1. *SPW 1935*, ch. 94, p. 523.

Bronze, 31.2 h., 15.5 diam.
Provenance: Collected by Major Hubert Young, 1918; by descent.

139
IRISH TROOPS IN THE JUDEAN HILLS
SURPRISED BY A TURKISH
BOMBARDMENT
By Henry Lamb, 1919

138
T. E. LAWRENCE AND GEORGE LLOYD
By an unknown photographer, 1917
Vintage print

The inscription on the back of this photograph
(which has been crossed through) states that
it was taken in 1917 shortly after 'torpedoing'
a train.

The photograph was almost certainly
taken in late October 1917 during the first
stage of the Yarmuk bridges expedition (see
no. 132 viii). Although Lloyd and Lawrence
succeeded in damaging the line on 29 October
they did not blow up a train. This may be why
the inscription was subsequently deleted.

Lady Lloyd

9.2 × 14.5
Inscribed in pencil on reverse and deleted: *Self and
T. E. L. after torpedoing/a train. Hejaz 1917*
Provenance: By descent.
Literature: J. Charmley, *Lord Lloyd and the Decline of the
British Empire*, 1987, ill.

Chosen by Lawrence as an illustration for
Seven Pillars of Wisdom.

In March 1919, Henry Lamb was
commissioned to paint a "Palestine subject"
by the Ministry of Information as part of a
plan to form a special gallery of war pictures.
When this painting was exhibited at the
Royal Academy in December it attracted
large crowds.

The physical features of the Judean
highlands strongly influenced the campaign
that was fought there in the second half of
November 1917, prior to the capture of
Jerusalem. The picture shows several
bivouacs and a bell tent spread along the
rocky terraces. Men of the 10th Irish
Division, surprised by the first few shells of
a high-explosive bombardment, are hastily
taking cover under the walls of the terraces.

Lamb apparently had difficulty in finding
suitable models for the canvas. He asked for
soldiers other than Irish Guards, as he
wanted his sitters 'to look as little spick and
span as they dare be seen'.[1] Guardsmen,

however, were all that could be found in
London except for a few Australians in the
military hospital near Lamb's Hampstead
studio. Eventually, he was forced to settle for
three men from a Salvation Army Hostel in
the Euston Road. The painting has been
unkindly dubbed 'dossers surprised in the
Vale of Health'.[2]

Trustees of the Imperial War Museum
(IWM 2746)

1. M. & S. Harries, *The War Artists*, 1983, p. 109.
2. *ibid*.

Oil on canvas, 182.9 × 218.4
Unsigned
Provenance: War Artists Commission.
Literature: *Studio*, 182, 1921, p. 181, ill. p. 97; G. L.
Kennedy, *Henry Lamb*, 1924, pp. 11, 18-24, ill. pl. 10;
SPW 1926, ill.; *Studio*, Dec. 1939, ill. p. 233;
Fergusson, *The Arts in Britain, World War 1*, pp. 106,
112; M. & S. Harries, *The War Artists*, 1983, p. 109,
ill. fp. 134.
Exhibitions: RA, *War Paintings*, 1919; Manchester City
Art Gallery, *The Nation's War Pictures*, 1920 (125);
Leicester Galleries 1927 (16); Venice, British Pavilion,
1932; Manchester City Art Gallery (and tour), *Henry
Lamb*, 1984 (54).
(illustrated in colour p. 57)

140
WATER TRANSPORT
By James McBey, 1917

The picture shows water in *fanatis* being
conveyed to the men in the trenches. *Fantasse*
(plural *fanatis*) was an Arabic word adopted
by the Army to describe a small metal water
tank with a capacity of twelve gallons. Two
were usually carried by each camel.

Trustees of the Imperial War Museum
(IWM 2930)

Pen and watercolour, 38 × 64.2
Signed and dated bl. : *James McBey 21 September 1917*
Provenance : War Artists Commission.

141
THE ENTRY OF THE ALLIES INTO JERUSALEM
By James McBey, 1917

Jerusalem fell to the British early in December 1917, and Allenby made his official entry on the 11th. For Lawrence, who was present, the entry 'was the most memorable event of the war, the one which, for historical reasons, made a greater appeal than anything on earth.'[1]

In this picture the representatives of the Allied Powers (General Allenby, Colonel de Piépape commanding the French Detachment, and Lt.-Colonel d'Agostino commanding the Italian Detachment) are entering the city on foot through the Jaffa gate. To the left is the Tower of David and the breach in the walls made by the Turks for the entry of the Kaiser in 1898.

An oil painting depicting this scene was later worked up from this watercolour sketch.

Trustees of the Imperial War Museum
(IWM 2929)

1. *SPW 1935*, ch. 88, p. 195.

Pen and watercolour, 41.2 × 59.7
Signed and dated br.: *James McBey/Jerusalem December 1917*
Provenance: War Artists Commission.
Literature: M. & S. Harries, *The War Artists*, 1983, p.25.

142
THE PRESENTATION OF THE NOTABLES, JERUSALEM
By James McBey, 1917

Sir Edmund Allenby, the Allied Commander-in-Chief, was met at the Jaffa Gate by the Military Governor of Jerusalem and led to the steps of the Citadel, where the chief inhabitants of the city were presented to him. A proclamation was read to the citizens in English, French, Arabic, Hebrew, Greek, Russian and Italian. This put the city under martial law and promised protection for the customs and beliefs of Jews, Christians, and Muslims.

After the ceremony, Allenby left again through the Jaffa Gate. In the picture he is seen shaking hands with the Mayor of Jerusalem.

See also no. 141.

Trustees of the Imperial War Museum
(IWM 1525)

Pencil and watercolour, 42.5 × 61
Signed and dated b.: *James McBey 11 December 1917.*
Provenance: War Artists Commission.

143

T. E. LAWRENCE WITH HIS
BODYGUARD OF ARAB TRIBESMEN,
AKABA

Photograph by R.G. Goslett (summer 1918)

When Lawrence returned to Akaba he began
to form a personal bodyguard. This decision
reflected the high price the Turks were now
putting on his head, and his recent experience of
Turkish captivity at Deraa. In *Seven Pillars*
Lawrence described how he recruited:
'such lawless men as I found, fellows
whose dash had got them into trouble
elsewhere. I needed hard riders and hard
livers; men proud of themselves, and
without family . . . Fellows were very proud
of being in my bodyguard, which developed
a professionalism almost flamboyant. They
dressed like a bed of tulips, in every colour
but white; for that was my constant wear,
and they did not wish to presume . . . In my
service nearly sixty of them died.'[1]

IWM Q59576

1. *SPW 1935*, ch. 83, pp. 462-7.

144

MAHMAS

By Eric Kennington (1921)
Annotated plate from *Seven Pillars of Wisdom*,
1926

Mahmas was a Horani, of a clan of the Ateiba,
a nomad tribe based inland of Medina. In
Seven Pillars Lawrence described him as 'not
properly of my guard, but a camel-driver'.[1]

When Lawrence first saw Kennington's
portrait he mused: 'Mahmas. That means
coffee-spoon. Called so, probably, because
the parents happened to notice one during his
birth . . . cannot endure to be worsted in
argument. When it happens he leans forward
with his little knife and kills the other party.
Three times he did it before people learnt to
respect his convictions, however ill
expressed.'[2]

Kennington doubtless appreciated these
remarks. When he had tried to wake Mahmas
during a sitting for this portrait the Arab had
'leapt over me with his dagger ready about
a foot from my eyes . . . I turned away and
began selecting chalks, thinking "It will go
in just above the collar bone". But nothing
happened, so I soon asked him to sit down
again. He did, but kept the dagger ready, and
it came out so in the drawing.'[3]

The location of the original is not
recorded.

Ian D. Struthers Esq.

1. *SPW 1935*, ch. 87, p. 486.
2. E.H. Kennington, *Drawing The RAF*, 1942, p. 14.
3. *ibid.*, p. 16.

Chromo-lithograph, 25 × 18.5 (sight)
Inscribed and signed by Eric Kennington in ink, t.:
Mahmas. (the coffee spoon) Amman 1922/Eric H. Kennington
Provenance: By descent from the artist.
Literature: *SPW 1926*, ill.; *SPW 1935*, ill. fp. 292.

145
MUTTAR IL HAMOUD MIN BENI
HASSAN
By Eric Kennington, 1921

Muttar served in Lawrence's bodyguard. In
Seven Pillars Lawrence described him in
grotesque terms: 'Matar, a parasite fellow of
the Beni Hassan, attached himself to us. His
fat peasant's buttocks filled his camel-saddle,
and took nearly as large a share in the lewd
or lurid jokes which, on march, helped pass
my guards' leisure . . . His unblushing greed
made us sure of him, till his expectations
failed.'[1]

The Trustees of the Tate Gallery (TG 3637)

1. *SPW 1935*, ch. 71, p. 391.

Pastel, 76.8 × 55.9
Inscribed tr.: *Muttar il Hamoud/min Beni Hassan/(ibn
Gallat/Section)/14*
Provenance: Given by T. E. Lawrence, 1922.
Literature: *SPW 1926*, ill.; *SPW 1935*, ill. fp. 432;
J. Rothenstein, *British Art since 1900*, 1962, ill. pl. 43;
M. Chamot, D. Farr & M. Butlin, *The Modern British
Paintings, Drawings and Sculpture*, I, Tate Gallery, 1964,
pp. 354-5, ill. pl. 52.
Exhibitions: Leicester Galleries 1921 (2); Leicester
Galleries 1927 (32).

146
ALAYAN
By Eric Kennington, 1921

Commenting on Kennington's portrait,
Lawrence wrote of Alayan: '[he] was our
most excellent informant in the War, but is
looked down upon by his fellows because he
took money for his work. He lost the money
in a bad trading venture after the armistice,
and now without either friends or substance
must serve as a donkey-boy where he once
walked free. His face shows his sense of the
broken world about him: but when he was
sent for to be drawn he ran home and put on
his best clothing. It was not very good, but
evidently he still has hope and self-respect.'[1]

Anthony Mould Ltd.

1. *Oriental Assembly*, p. 156.

Pastel, 88.2 × 73.3
Unsigned
Provenance: Leicester Galleries; W. H. Haslam; sold
Sotheby's, 19 November 1980 (260).
Literature: *SPW 1926*, ill.; *SPW 1935*, ill. fp. 260.
Exhibitions: Leicester Galleries 1921 (8); Leicester
Galleries 1927 (55).

147
ABD EL RAHMAN
By Eric Kennington, 1921

Abd el Rahman was a 'runaway slave from
Riyadh'[1] whom Lawrence enrolled in his
bodyguard in October 1917.

Royal Academy of Arts, London

1. *SPW 1935*, ch. 71, p. 391.

Pastel, 49 × 55.5
Signed and dated br.: *E.H.Kennington 1921*
Provenance: Deposited as diploma work by the
artist, 1959.
Literature: *SPW 1926*, ill.; *SPW 1935*, ill. fp. 360.
Exhibitions: London, Picture Hire Limited, *Eric
Kennington Exhibition*, 1936 (31).

148
ALI IBN EL HUSSEIN
By Eric Kennington, 1921

Sherif Ali ibn el Hussein of the Harith tribe
was one of Feisal's lieutenants. He had
distinguished himself in the early days of the
rising, and accompanied Lawrence on the
unsuccessful raid on the Yarmuk bridges in
1917 (see no. 156 ii and iii).

Lawrence thought highly of Ali : 'His
courage, his resource, and his energy were
proven. There had never been any adventure,
since our beginning, too dangerous for Ali to
attempt, nor a disaster too deep for him to
face with his high yell of a laugh.

'He was physically splendid : not tall nor
heavy, but so strong that he would kneel
down, resting his forearms palm-up on the
ground, and rise to his feet with a man on
each hand. In addition, Ali could outstrip a
trotting camel on his bare feet, keep his
speed over half a mile and then leap into the
saddle.'[1]

A note on the back of the picture states
that Kennington drew the portrait at Amman
in May 1921, when Ali was twenty-three.

Reading Museum and Art Gallery

1. SPW 1935, ch. 70, p. 388.

Pastel, 76.2 × 50.8
Provenance : William Chappell ; sold Sotheby's,
14 November 1979 (54) ; private collection.
Literature : SPW 1926, ill. ; SPW 1935, ill. fp. 178.
Exhibitions : Leicester Galleries 1921 (7) ; Leicester
Galleries 1927 (57).

149

SS *OZARDA* AT SUEZ
Photograph by Harry Chase (1918)

In the spring of 1918 Lowell Thomas, an
American journalist, and Harry Chase, a
photographer, came out to the Middle East
looking for material which would stimulate
enthusiasm for the Allied cause in America.

SS *Ozarda* was the ship that brought
Thomas and Chase to Akaba at the end of
May. This visit had been arranged by
Lawrence, who had met the pair in
Jerusalem a few weeks earlier (see no. 150).
According to the inscription by Lowell
Thomas on the back of this photograph, the

Ozarda was loaded with 200 Sudanese sheep,
100 Missouri mules, 100 Argentine horses,
ninety deserters from the Turkish army,
fifteen Scots Highlanders, six British officers
and one aeroplane, as well as the two
Americans.

Bodleian Library (MS.Res.c.52)

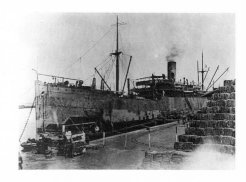

150

T. E. LAWRENCE
Three photographs by Harry Chase (1918)

(i) On the Governor's balcony in Jerusalem,
May 1918
(ii) In Arab dress
(iii) Seated in Arab robes

(i) IWM Q46093 (ii) copyprint (iii) IWM
Q73535

Literature: L. Thomas, *With Lawrence in Arabia*,
(i) ill. fp. 16; (ii) ill. fp. 304.

151

ARAB OVER-GARMENT (*ABA*)

See no. 105. This appears to be the outer
garment Lawrence is seen wearing in several
photographs taken by Harry Chase (see no.
150 ii). After the war it was converted into
a dressing gown and lined with yellow
cotton.

Museum of Costume, Bath

Woven paisley cloth, 119 × 132
Provenance: By descent to Dr M. R. Lawrence;
presented by him, 1964.

152
GENERAL JAAFAR PASHA
Photograph by Harry Chase (1918)

General Jaafar Pasha (1885-1936),
commander of the Hejaz Northern Regular
Army under Feisal, was a Mesopotamian
Arab who had served with distinction in the
Turkish army. He was captured by the
British in 1915 and later given parole.
According to Lawrence: 'one day [Jaafar]
read in an Arabic newspaper of the Sherif's
revolt, and of the execution by the Turks of
prominent Arab Nationalists – his friends –
and realized that he had been on the wrong
side. Feisal . . . wanted him as commander-

153
COLONEL PIERCE JOYCE
Photograph by Harry Chase (1918)

Lt.-Colonel Pierce C. Joyce was appointed
senior British officer at Akaba in 1917, and
for a time Lawrence was nominally under his
command. In reality their work ran parallel:
Lawrence advised Feisal on the operations of
the Bedouin irregulars, and Joyce on the
Arab Regulars. This was given official
recognition when Lawrence was promoted to
Joyce's rank of Lt.-Colonel in March 1918.

Lawrence wrote in *Seven Pillars*: 'Joyce
was a man in whom one could rest against the
world: a serene, unchanging, comfortable

154
ARAB LEADERS INCLUDING NESIB EL
BEKRI WITH T. E. LAWRENCE
Photograph by Harry Chase, 1918
Vintage print

in-chief of his regular troops . . . Jaafar was
one of the few men with enough of
reputation and personality to weld their
difficult and reciprocally disagreeable
elements into an army.'[1]

After the war Jaafar Pasha became
Military Governor of Aleppo (1919) and
Minister of Defence, Baghdad (1920-22). In
1923 he became Prime Minister and served
in successive Iraqi governments until his
assassination in 1936.

1. *SPW 1935*, ch. 28, pp. 166-7.

Literature: L. Thomas, *With Lawrence in Arabia*,
ill. fp. 229.

spirit. His mind, like a pastoral landscape,
had four corners to its view: cared-for,
friendly, limited, displayed.'[1]

1. *SPW 1935*, ch. 57, p. 323.

Literature: L. Thomas, *With Lawrence in Arabia*, 1925,
ill. fp. 222.

Lawrence is seen conferring with Arab
nationalist leaders from Baghdad and
Damascus. Nesib el Bekri (centre), an
influential adviser on Feisal's staff, was a
Damascus landowner who had been deeply
involved in secret Arab independence
movements before the war. He had been
exiled with a death sentence over him. Like
other Syrian politicians in Feisal's entourage,
he was constantly urging an early uprising in
his country while the Turks were unprepared.
This enthusiasm for immediate action carried
little weight with Lawrence, who knew that
the logistics of such an enterprise would be
extremely difficult.

According to Lawrence 'Nesib had brains
and position . . . his cheerful endurance of
adventure, rare among Syrians, marked him
out as our fellow, as much as his political
mind, his ability, his persuasive good-
humoured eloquence, and the patriotism
which often overcame his native passion for
the indirect.'[1]

The figure in the background, between
Lawrence and Nesib, is Ali ibn el Hussein
(see no. 148).

Malcolm Brown

1. *SPW 1935*, ch. 39, p. 228.

39 × 30
Literature: L.Thomas, *With Lawrence in Arabia*,
ill. fp. 312.

155
THE DEAD SEA
By Sydney Carline, 1920

In late 1917 the Arab forces tried to advance
northwards from Akaba to the Dead Sea and
beyond in order to join up with General
Allenby's army in Palestine. Progress
through the hills on the south-eastern shores
of the Dead Sea between December 1917 and
March 1918 was slow, and despite some
successes the original objective was not fully
attained. It was important, however, to clear
this region of Turkish forces so that Arab
supply lines leading inland from Akaba were
not threatened.

The brothers Sydney and Richard Carline
(see also nos. 167, 173), who had themselves
been RAF pilots, were rushed out to the
Middle East in January 1919 as war artists.
Their task was to record something of the
RAF's involvement in Palestine and the
Lebanon before the squadrons dispersed.

Trustees of the Imperial War Museum
(IWM 3079)

Oil on canvas, 76.2 × 108
Signed and dated bl.: *Sydney W. Carline 1920*
Provenance: War Artists Commission.
Exhibitions: Imperial War Museum, *Richard and Sydney
Carline: First World War Aerial Pictures*, 1973 (54).

156
THE WAR IN THE DESERT: MARKING
TIME, JANUARY – MAY 1918
Photographs from T.E. Lawrence's
collection

(i) Tafileh, Turkish prisoners defiling
Photograph by T. E. Lawrence (January
1918)

Tafileh was taken with little resistance on
15 January 1918 as part of the Arab Dead Sea
campaign. On 25 January, in the first set
battle of Lawrence's campaigns, a Turkish
expedition attempting to recapture the town
was heavily defeated in the Wadi Hesa.
Tafileh proved easy to occupy but difficult to
hold because of powerful factional interests
there. Through the improvidence of Zeid,
Feisal's half-brother, it was retaken by the
Turks on 10 March.

Lawrence was astonished by Turkish
persistence: 'Tafileh was an obscure village
of no interest. Nor did we value it as a
possession; our desire was to get past it
towards the enemy. For men so critically
placed as the Turks to waste one single
casualty on its recapture appeared the rankest
folly.'[1]

IWM Q59367
1. *SPW 1935*, ch. 85, p. 474.

(ii) Before Tell esh Shahab, the 7th tunnel in
the Yarmuk valley
GHQ photograph

The Yarmuk valley which carried the railway
line from Deraa to Palestine was of great
strategic importance. Despite the fact that it
was often a target, Lawrence's attacks in this
area were unsuccessful.

IWM Q59644

(iii) Train after leaving the Jordan plain,
entrance to the Yarmuk valley.
GHQ photograph

IWM Q59614

(iv) Entering Wadi Waheida
Photograph by T. E. Lawrence (?April 1918)

Wadi Waheida is to the south-west of Maan.
This photograph is believed to have been
taken in the spring of 1918, presumably
during the operations against Maan by Arab
regular troops.

IWM Q60019

157

MAJOR HUBERT YOUNG
By R.M.Young, c.1923

Hubert Young (1885-1950) had stayed with
Lawrence at Carchemish in 1913. In March
1918, at Lawrence's request, Young was
transferred from service in Mesopotamia to
join the British liaison staff with Feisal's
northern army. He took over transport and
supplies for the Arab forces.

Lawrence asked Young if he would sit for
a portrait for *Seven Pillars*. Young at first
declined until Lawrence told him 'that a page
was reserved in the *Seven Pillars* for my
picture, and that if I persisted in my refusal
to sit he would leave it blank, all but a footnote to say ''This page was for a portrait of
Young, but he refused to sit because he was
afraid of what I might have said about him.''
''All right,'' I said, ''you can do that if you
like. I don't know which of us will look the
bigger fool.'' Nothing more happened for
nearly two years, when, having married an
artist, I agreed to sit to her, but only if he
showed me the proofs. He gave way then and
sent them to me.'[1]

Young worked in the Eastern Department
of the Foreign Office (1919-21), and then in
the Middle East Department of the Colonial
Office (1921-6). He was knighted in 1932.

Nicholas Young

1. *Friends*, p. 124.

Pencil, 31.5 × 21.5
Signed br.: *RMY*; inscribed by Eric Kennington b.:
*colour: the same/size: just cover the lines + it will be full
page/ — / can you send me a list of titles of everyone you are/
doing? If you do not know titles invent some so that I shall/be
able to place them?/E. K.*
Provenance: By descent.
Literature: *SPW 1926*, ill.; *SPW 1935*, ill. fp. 526;
Friends, p. 124; Sotheby's, sale catalogue, 'English
Literature and History', 22/23 July 1985 (300).
Exhibitions: Leicester Galleries 1927 (23).

158

T. E. LAWRENCE, D. G. HOGARTH AND COLONEL ALAN DAWNAY, CAIRO HQ
Photograph by Harry Chase (1918)

Lawrence is seen with Commander Hogarth
and Colonel Alan Dawnay. For Hogarth see
no. 50. Alan Dawnay (1888-1938) served
with distinction in Europe before taking over
responsibility on Allenby's staff for liaison
with Feisal's Arab forces. Lawrence wrote:
'Dawnay was Allenby's greatest gift to us . . .
His was an understanding mind, feeling
instinctively the special qualities of
rebellion: at the same time, his war-training
enriched his treatment of this antithetic
subject. He married war and rebellion in
himself . . . From his teaching we began to
learn the technique of fighting in matters we
had been content to settle by rude and
wasteful rules of thumb.'[1]

Dawnay was later a member of the
Charitable Trust established to distribute the
profits from *T. E. Lawrence by His Friends*.

IWM Q59595

1. *SPW 1935*, ch. 92, p. 507.

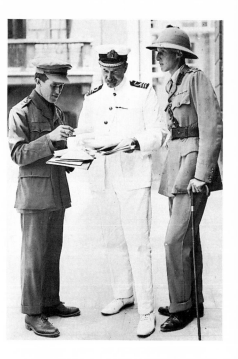

159

LETTER FROM T. E. LAWRENCE TO
KING HUSSEIN
'Ramadan 17, 1336 – June 25, 1918'
Facsimile of autograph letter in Arabic,
signed by Lawrence in Arabic and English.

This letter concerns the movements of
Feisal's forces and Turkish troops around
Maan. It cannot be proved absolutely that it
was written in Arabic by Lawrence, but for
several reasons this seems very likely. It was
certainly written by a European who had
learned colloquial Arabic in the areas
Lawrence had lived in. Furthermore it was
written or dictated by someone experienced
in British military communications.
Lawrence was one of the few people who
knew the facts referred to, and the issue was
so sensitive that he would probably have
preferred not to use a clerk.

The letter is in colloquial Arabic, and
cannot have been drafted by anyone who
knew the written language. It is
inconceivable that it was the work of an Arab
or Arabic-speaking clerk, not least because it
lacks all the formalities that would normally
have been employed by someone addressing
the Sherif of Mecca. Moreover, some words
are misspelt in ways that suggest that the
writer has never seen them in writing, nor
established the correct form of the word
from hearing it spoken. By contrast, in other
places the writer employs shortcuts in script
which would only be taught to the most
experienced students of Arabic.

On learning of Allenby's plans for an
advance in Palestine during the autumn of
1918, Lawrence had decided to ask Sherif
Hussein to reinforce Feisal's northern army
by transferring there the Arab regulars still
attached to the armies led by Sherif Ali and
Sherif Abdullah in the Hejaz. When
Lawrence reached Jidda, however, he was
only able to speak to Hussein by telephone,
and he was unable to get a satisfactory reply.
The letter exhibited seems to have been
Lawrence's final attempt to put the case for
reinforcing Feisal. It points out that Jaafar
Pasha's Arab force outside Maan was smaller
than the defending garrison and therefore
unable to capture the town; unless decisive
action was taken, there was a risk that the
Turks would be able to reinforce Maan and
raise the siege. The letter seems to have had
no more effect than Lawrence's telephone
calls, and he returned to Akaba empty
handed.[1]

It is fortuitous that this sample of
Lawrence's written Arabic survives. He
enjoined Hussein: 'I beg you, Sir, to burn
this letter after reading it because I am
writing to you about matters which I should
have disclosed orally.'

Private Collection

1. See *SPW 1935*, ch. 97, p. 534.

Provenance: Sold Sotheby's, 13 July 1976 (668).

160

MAJOR ROBIN BUXTON
By William Roberts (1922)
Annotated proof plate from *Seven Pillars of
Wisdom*, 1926

Robert ("Robin") Buxton (1883-1953)
served in the Imperial Camel Corps and spent
several weeks operating behind Turkish lines
during the Arab Revolt. It was his Camel
Corps unit which finally succeeded in
capturing the important station at Mudawara
in August 1918.

After the war Buxton was Lawrence's
bank manager, and he helped finance the
subscribers' edition of *Seven Pillars*. He then
served as one of the Trustees of *Revolt in the
Desert*.

In August 1922 Lawrence wrote to
Buxton: 'Dear Robin, I've finished my book
on the Arab Revolt . . . What I'm writing to
you about is your head . . . I'm now having
a small batch of Englishmen drawn in London
. . . For you I'd like William Roberts . . .
I think he might do something rather subtle
of you, because you don't look like an officer.'[1]

Two months later Lawrence wrote again,
more apologetically: 'Dear Robin, It must

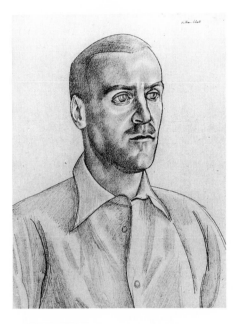

have been an effort: and the result is
astonishing: you have become severe,
abstracted, slightly sorry: with the laughter
gone from your face . . . A wonderful
drawing. Did Roberts bother you very much
with sittings and sitting still?'.[2]

The location of the original is not
recorded.

The Curators of the Bodleian Library,
Oxford (MS.Res.b.55)

1. T. E. Lawrence to R. V. Buxton, 28.8.1922.
2. T. E. Lawrence to R. V. Buxton, 27.10.1922.

Collotype, 25.5 × 19
Inscribed by T. E. Lawrence: *try a warmer tint*
Provenance: Given by A. W. Lawrence.
Literature: *SPW 1926*, ill.; *SPW 1935*, ill. fp. 544.

161
LIEUTENANT JUNOR
By Gilbert Spencer, 1923

The RFC (which became the RAF in April 1918) provided invaluable assistance during the Arab Revolt in reconnaissance, bombing, and communication. Lieutenant Junor was one of the pilots involved in this work.

On 16 September 1918, while the Arabs under Lawrence were attempting to destroy the Yarmuk section of the Palestine line, Junor arrived to provide air cover in a BE 12, 'a type so out of date that it was impossible for fighting and little use for reconnaissance.'[1]

Nevertheless, Junor kept the Turkish aircraft away from Lawrence's exposed forces. Finally he reappeared, 'still alive, though attended on three sides by enemy machines, spitting bullets. He was twisting and slipping splendidly, firing back.'[2]

Eventually he was forced to make a crash landing on a hastily cleared strip of ground. Junor had scarcely got out of his aircraft when one of the Turkish planes dropped a bomb on it.

Harry Ransom Humanities Research Center, The University of Texas at Austin

1. *SPW 1935*, ch. 108, p. 589.
2. *SPW 1935*, ch. 109, pp. 596-7.

Pencil, 31.2 × 24.9
Signed and dated br.: *Gilbert Spencer/1923*
Provenance: Purchased from Hamill and Barker, 1962.
Literature: *SPW 1926*, ill.; *SPW 1935*, ill. fp. 596.
Exhibitions: University of Texas, Humanities Research Center, *T. E. Lawrence/Fifty Letters: 1920-35*, 1962 (14a).

162
REMAINS OF LIEUTENANT JUNOR'S BE12 AEROPLANE
Photograph by T. E. Lawrence (September 1918)

See no. 161.

IWM Q60019

163
DERAA
By Stuart Reid, *c*.1918-19

On 22 September 1918 a Handley Page bombing biplane flew to the Sherifian headquarters behind Turkish lines with stores of petrol and spare parts for two Bristol Fighter biplanes. These had been attached to the Sherifian forces operating against Deraa to hold in check the activities of enemy aircraft.

When Lawrence, Feisal and Nuri Shaalan went to see the Handley Page land, they 'perceived a single Bedawi, running southward all in a flutter, his grey hair and grey beard flying in the wind, and his shirt . . . puffing out behind him. He altered course to pass near us, and, raising his bony arms, yelled ''The biggest aeroplane in the world'', before he flapped on into the south, to spread his great news among the tents.

'At Um el Surab the Handley stood majestic on the grass, with Bristols and 9.A like fledglings beneath its spread of wings. Round it admired the Arabs, saying, ''Indeed and at last, they have sent us THE aeroplane, of which these things were foals''.'[1]

Stuart Reid's painting shows the Arabs welcoming this plane.

Trustees of the Imperial War Museum (IWM 3198)

1. *SPW 1935*, ch. 114, p. 619.

Oil on panel, 76.2 × 91.4
Signed br.: *STUART REID*
Provenance: War Artists Commission.

164
'AN HISTORIC LAWRENCE'
Facsimile of a newspaper article,
25 September 1918

By the autumn of 1918 the War Cabinet was
well aware of Lawrence's work, but he was
still unknown to the public at large. On 24
September, however, the *Echo de Paris* ran a
short report which was translated a day later
by several London newspapers.

AN HISTORIC LAWRENCE.

PARIS, Tuesday, Sept. 24.
The Echo de Paris says: " Side by side
with General Allenby and the French
Colonel de Piepape we must mention Colonel
Lawrence as having played a part of the
greatest importance in the Palestine victory.
The name of Colonel Lawrence, who placed
at the disposal of the British leader his
experience of the country and his talent for
organisation, will become historic in Great
Britain.
At the head of the cavalry force which he
had formed with Bedouins and Druses he
cut the railway at Deraa, thus severing the
enemy communications between Damascus
and Haifa and the eastern side of the
Jordan."—Reuter.

165
ADMIRALTY, WAR OFFICE AND PRESS
COMMITTEE NOTICE, 26 SEPTEMBER
1918
Facsimile of document

On the day after the first British Press
mention of Lawrence's wartime role (see no.
164) the matter was discussed by the War
Cabinet. There was some concern that his
work had been publicised in France and not
in England. However, it was suggested that
'the reason for not giving wide publicity to
the services rendered by Colonel Lawrence
was, perhaps, regard for that officer's own
personal safety.'[1] That evening the notice
exhibited here was issued by the Admiralty,
War Office, and Press Committee, the
official organisation through which guidance
was given to newspaper editors during the
First World War.

Imperial War Museum

1. Minute of War Cabinet meeting 447, 25.9.1918,
CAB23/7.

166
THE DESTRUCTION OF THE 4th ARMY
By T.E. Lawrence, 1918
Facsimile of autograph manuscript

On 26 October 1918 the Arab army took
Ghazale, cutting the line between Deraa and
Damascus. The Turks were panic-stricken by
this move and sent out two columns (one
from Deraa of six thousand men, the other
from Mezerib of two thousand). The Arabs
decided to attack the latter and marched to
meet it to the north of Tafas. On arrival at
this village, however, the Arabs found that
the Turks had raped 'all the women they
could catch. We attacked them with all arms
. . . and bent the head of their column back
towards Tell Arar. When Sherif Bey, the
Turkish Commander of the Lancer rearguard
in the village, saw this he ordered that the
inhabitants be killed. These included some
twenty small children (killed with lances and
rifles), and about forty women. I noticed
particularly one pregnant woman, who had
been forced down on a saw-bayonet.'
The Arab army split the Turkish column
into three. The third section managed to
escape with heavy casualties, but the first and
second were 'wiped out completely.'
Exceptionally, an order had been given that
no prisoners should be taken. In a
contemporary report Lawrence stated that
250 enemy soldiers had, nevertheless, been
captured alive. Later, however, an Arab was
found bayonetted to the ground : 'we turned
our Hotchkiss on the prisoners and made an
end of them, they saying nothing. The
common delusion that the Turk is a clean and
merciful fighter led some of the British
troops to criticise Arab methods a little later
– but they had not entered Turaa or Tafas,
or watched the Turks swing their wounded
by the hands and feet into a burning railway
truck, as had been the lot of the Arab army
at Jerdun. As for the villagers, they and their
ancestors have been for five hundred years
ground down by the tyranny of these Turks.'
Lawrence too had experienced Turkish
brutality.
The other column from Deraa did not fare
much better. It was harrassed by irregular
Arab forces and then attacked by British

artillery and cavalry, and was destroyed.
'This ended the history of the Fourth Army.'[1]

Lawrence's anger and revulsion at the
butchery in Tafas was so deep that he
indicated both in this contemporary report
to the Arab Bureau and in *Seven Pillars* that
he had approved the order to take no
prisoners. In reality rather more Turks
survived than his account would suggest;
British units arrived at the close of the
engagement and rounded up about 1,000
prisoners.

Public Record Office, London (FO882/7)

1. *Arab Bulletin*, 106, 1918.
(illustrated p. 59)

167
DAMASCUS AND THE LEBANON
MOUNTAINS FROM 10,000 FEET
By Richard Carline, 1920

During the closing stages of the Syrian
campaign great use was made of aerial
reconnaissance. Lawrence received almost
daily reports and messages from Palestine.

Trustees of the Imperial War Museum
(IWM 3082)

Oil on canvas, 143.5 × 105.4
Signed and dated bl.: *Richard Carline Feb 1920*
Provenance: War Artists Commission.
Literature: M. & S. Harries, *The War Artists*, 1983,
pp. 139-41.
Exhibitions: Imperial War Museum, *Richard and Sydney
Carline: First World War Aerial Pictures*, 1973 (21).

168

T. E. LAWRENCE AT DAMASCUS IN HIS ROLLS-ROYCE TENDER

By an unknown photographer (1 October 1918)

During the closing stages of the campaign Lawrence often travelled in this Rolls-Royce tender. Despite harsh treatment for eighteen months, driving over rough terrain, there was only one structural breakdown. Lawrence concluded: 'A Rolls in the desert was above rubies'. With improvised repairs this car survived to enter Damascus: 'Great was Rolls, and great was Royce! They were worth hundreds of men to us in these deserts.'[1]

On 4 October Lawrence left Damascus again in this same Rolls-Royce 'Blue Mist'.

Rolls-Royce Motor Cars Ltd

1. *SPW 1935*, ch. 108, pp. 591-2.

169

THE BODYGUARD TO EMIR SHERIF FEISAL

By James McBey, 1918

Feisal's bodyguard was described by McBey as 'a gigantic Abyssinian negro, his kit consisting of innumerable weapons of all epochs, from the Saracenic scimitar to the latest Mauser automatic.' He also appears in no. 183.

Trustees of the Imperial War Museum
(IWM 1567)

Pencil and watercolour, 48.2 × 36.2
Signed and dated b.: *James McBey Damascus 11 October 1918*
Provenance: War Artists Commission.
Literature: M. & S. Harries, *The War Artists*, London, 1983, p.27.
Exhibitions: Imperial War Museum, *James McBey*, 1977.

170

THE HEADQUARTERS OF THE HEJAZ
ARMY, DAMASCUS
By James McBey, 1918

The Hejaz army had fought for two years in
the hope of taking Damascus. This view of
their headquarters was painted by James
McBey, the first war artist to reach the city,
on 6 October.

Trustees of the Imperial War Museum
(IWM 1565)

Pen and watercolour, 25.4 × 38.7
Signed and dated br.: *James McBey/Damascus/6 October
1918*
Provenance: War Artists Commission.

171

BRONZE WREATH FROM SALADIN'S
TOMB, DAMASCUS
German, 1898

Lawrence considered that the Kaiser had
been presumptuous in laying this wreath on
Saladin's tomb in Damascus. He had it
removed, and brought it to England as a war
trophy. It was among the gifts he
subsequently made to the Imperial War
Museum.

   According to Charles ffoulkes, then
Curator of the Imperial War Museum, 'when
a photograph of this trophy . . . appeared in
the Press, I received anonymous letters
threatening Lawrence and myself for this
piece of iconoclasm.'[1]

Trustees of the Imperial War Museum

1. *Friends*, p. 66.

Gilt bronze, 73 × 59
Provenance: Given by T. E. Lawrence.

172
T.E. LAWRENCE
By James McBey, 1918

James McBey (1883-1959) was an official war
artist with Allenby's Egyptian Expeditionary
Force (1917-18), and met Lawrence in
Damascus in October 1918, immediately
after the city was taken. The painting was
executed at the Victoria Hotel, probably on
3 October.

The portrait captures something of
Lawrence's physical and emotional condition
during these final weeks of the campaign.
Fifteen years later he wrote to his biographer
Liddell Hart that the portrait seemed
'shockingly strange to me.'[1]

Trustees of the Imperial War Museum
(IWM 2473)

1. *Biographers* (Liddell Hart), p. 153.

Oil on canvas, 53.3 × 38.1
Signed and dated r.: *James McBey/Damascus/October, 1918.*
Provenance: War Artists Commission.
Literature: R.Storrs, *Orientations*, 1937, p.473;
Grosvenor, no.42.
Exhibitions: Imperial War Museum, *James McBey*, 1977.

173

THE DESTRUCTION OF THE TURKISH
TRANSPORT IN THE GORGE OF THE
WADI FARA, PALESTINE
By Sydney Carline, 1920

Sydney Carline (1888-1929) was appointed a
war artist in the Mesopotamian sector in
1919, and painted this picture in 1920. It was
chosen by Lawrence as an illustration to the
subscribers' *Seven Pillars*, and was also used
in the English edition of *Revolt in the Desert*.
The latter had no text concerning the
Turkish retreat north of Damascus, and
Lawrence wrote the following passage to
provide a context for Carline's picture: 'the
climax of air attack, and the holocaust of the
miserable Turks, fell in . . . [Wadi Fara] . . .
The modern motor road, the only way of
escape for the Turkish divisions, was
scalloped between cliff and precipice in a
murderous defile. For four hours our
aeroplanes replaced one another in series
above the doomed columns: nine tons of
small bombs or grenades and fifty thousand
rounds of S.A.A. were rained upon them.
When the smoke had cleared it was seen that
the organization of the enemy had melted
away. They were a dispersed horde of
trembling individuals, hiding for their lives

in every fold of the vast hills. Nor did their
commanders ever rally them again. When
our cavalry entered the silent valley next day
they could count ninety guns, fifty lorries,
nearly a thousand carts abandoned with all
their belongings. The R.A.F. lost four killed.
The Turks lost a corps.'[1]

When Carline arrived at the Wadi Fara
early in 1919, he found the gorge still
littered with the skeletons of horses and even
of men.

Trustees of the Imperial War Museum
(IWM 3138)

1. *Revolt*, 1927, ch. 33, pp. 392-3

Oil on canvas, 121.9 × 121.9
Signed and dated tr.: *Sydney W.Carline – 1920*
Provenance: War Artists Commission.
Literature: *SPW 1926*, ill.; *Revolt*, ill. fp. 392; *SPW
1935*, ill. fp. 618; M. & S. Harries, *The War Artists*,
1983, pp. 139-40, ill. between pp. 134-5.
Exhibitions: Lincoln, Usher Gallery, 1929; Imperial
War Museum, *Richard and Sydney Carline: 1st World War
Aerial Pictures*, 1973 (67).

174
BOMBING OF THE WADI FARA, 20
SEPTEMBER 1918
By Stuart Reid, 1918

The subject of this painting is the same as that
of no. 173. It is known that Reid met
Lawrence in the Middle East, and the artist
subsequently professed that 'among his most
cherished paintings is one he did of Lawrence
riding his ''racing camel''.'[1] The present
location of that portrait is not recorded.

Trustees of the Imperial War Museum
(IWM 3196)

1. *The Australian Magazine*, November 1950, p. 46.

Oil on canvas, 101.6 × 101
Signed bl.: *STUART REID*
Provenance: War Artists Commission.
Literature: See 'He always draws good horses' in *The
Australian Magazine*, November 1950, p. 46, for Reid
and T. E. Lawrence.

175
T.E. LAWRENCE
By Augustus John, 1919

One of the oil portraits of Lawrence known
to have been painted by Augustus John
during the Paris Peace Conference. It was
included in the Alpine Club Gallery
exhibition of March 1920, and was the first
picture sold. Lawrence remarked that this
proved him to be 'a good selling line.'[1] He
referred to the portrait as the 'little one' and
the 'goody-goody one.'

It was purchased by William Pancoast
Clyde who gave it to the Yale University Art
Gallery in 1947.

Yale University Art Gallery, Gift of William
P. Clyde Jr. (B.A. 1901), Courtesy of Yale
Center for British Art.

1. T. E. Lawrence to Augustus John, 1920, A. John,
Chiaroscuro, 1952, p. 245.

Oil on canvas, 45.8 × 38.2
Unsigned
Provenance: Purchased, 1920, by William Pancoast
Clyde; given by him, 1947.
Literature: A. John, *Chiaroscuro*, 1952, p. 236;
Grosvenor, no. 2.
Exhibitions: London, Alpine Club, *Augustus John*, 1920
(29); New York, Anderson Galleries, *Augustus John*,
1928 (3 or 5); New York, Museum of Modern Art, *20th
Century Portraits*, 1942 (43).

176
T. E. LAWRENCE
By Sir William Rothenstein, 1920-2

177
T. E. LAWRENCE
By John Cosmo Clark, 1922

William Rothenstein (1872-1945) worked on this portrait in a number of sittings between June 1920 and the spring of 1922. He subsequently wrote that Lawrence 'seemed to like being painted'[1] and was generous with his time: 'he never seemed to object to standing for hours together – once, when I was painting the folds of his outer garment, he remained standing for two hours without a rest!'[2]

John Cosmo Clark was introduced to Lawrence by Eric Kennington, who suggested that Clark might contribute some illustrations to *Seven Pillars*.

Lawrence sat for this portrait in late 1922. The head rope, or *agal*, that he is wearing is quite different from that in other paintings. The drawing was apparently intended for the subscribers' edition of *Seven Pillars*, but not used.

National Museum, Beograd (Istr.761)

1. W. Rothenstein, *Men and Memories 1900-1922*, 1932, p. 367.
2. *Friends*, p. 253.

Oil on canvas, 122 × 71.5
Provenance: Lord Esher (?); Lord Duveen; Prince Paul of Yugoslavia; presented by him to National Museum.
Literature: A. Rutherston, gen.ed., *Contemporary British Artists: William Rothenstein*, 1928, ill. pl. 28;
W.Rothenstein, *Men and Memories 1900-1922*, 1932, p.367, ill. fp.366; *Friends*, pp.253-4; *The Saturday Review of Literature*, 7 January 1939, p.7; W.Rothenstein, *Since Fifty: Men and Memories 1922-1938*, 1940, pp. 225, 265; *Grosvenor*, no. 48.
Exhibitions: ? Leicester Galleries, 1923.

Private Collection

Conté, 37 × 27.6
Signed and dated br.: *T.E.L. – 1922/Sketch for Seven Pillars./COSMO CLARK/1922*.
Provenance: By descent from the artist.
Literature: *Grosvenor*, no. 39.
Exhibitions: London, Bankside Gallery, *Cosmo Clark/Jean Clark*, 1983 (99).

INTERNATIONAL
DIPLOMACY
1918-22

With the approach of the Versailles Peace Conference, Britain needed a defined policy towards the Middle East. Lawrence reached London before the end of October 1918 and was immediately summoned to discussions with the Eastern Committee of the Cabinet. His contribution during the Revolt was well known to the Committee's members, who included influential figures such as Balfour, Cecil, Curzon and Smuts. He compiled for them a detailed report called 'The Reconstruction of Arabia', which indicated possible areas of conflict in the Arab world. It also warned that Arab claims for self-determination would inevitably be heard if the powers admitted an Arab delegation to the Peace Conference.

His deep personal misgivings over British intentions towards the Arabs were expressed at a private audience with George V on 30 October during which he refused to accept the insignia of the CB and DSO he had been awarded. He found it impossible to receive such honours from a Government which seemed to him on the point of betraying its former Arab allies. Stories about this interview were soon circulating, and a gesture which Lawrence doubtless meant sincerely was used by political opponents to discredit him.

When the European war ended on 11 November 1918 Lawrence's exploits were already attracting comment in the British and French press. The closing weeks of 1918 were hectic as he made contacts with those whose influence might help the Arab cause. He was frequently invited to dinners, and met a number of people who were to become lasting friends, among them Winston Churchill, Siegfried Sassoon, and the American publisher F. N. Doubleday, through whom he also met Rudyard Kipling.

At Christmas, he told Charles Doughty of his intention to write a history of the desert campaigns. For the moment, however, he was too busy preparing a case for the Arabs, whose political expectations were now threatened by French ambition and British indifference. Lawrence hoped that America's President Wilson would make good his wartime promise that 'nationalities which are now under Turkish rule should be assured an undoubted security of life and an absolutely unmolested opportunity of autonomous development.'

In January 1919 Lawrence went with the British delegation to the peace negotiations in Paris. With Foreign Office blessing he would act as adviser and interpreter to the Emir Feisal, who was representing Sherif Hussein. This was the most important gathering of the Great Powers since the Congress of Vienna in 1815. The victorious leaders were preoccupied with immense questions such as German reparations and a political settlement which would reshape the nation states of Europe. Arab claims took a very low priority, and were vulnerable to bargaining between the Powers on matters which they thought more important. Lawrence found the atmosphere deeply depressing and later described these months in Paris as the worst he ever lived through. He put the Arab case as best he could to anyone who had influence and was prepared to listen. This included British and American journalists, who were happy to interview 'one of the most remarkable men produced by the war'.

He also did the social rounds, attending countless functions where he mixed easily with everyone from presidents to portrait painters. But though he talked to several of the most important figures in Paris, he could only look on as the European leaders struck their deal. As we now know, the Treaty of Versailles sowed the seeds of the Second World War and would prove disastrous for Europe. But to Clemenceau and Lloyd George it represented simple justice in the imperial tradition. Lawrence wrote bitterly: 'We lived many lives in those whirling campaigns, never sparing ourselves:

T. E. Lawrence
Photograph by Harris and Ewing, Paris,
1919
(no. 180)

yet when we achieved and the new world dawned, the old men came out again and took our victory to re-make in the likeness of the former world they knew.'[1]

In March 1919 the Powers, unable to reach agreement on the Arab question, decided to send an international commission (the King-Crane Commission) to Syria to assess local feeling. The French refused to take part, as did the British. Lawrence's mood was now one of increasing frustration and anger.

During the many periods of inaction in Paris he had started work on his account of the desert campaigns, *Seven Pillars of Wisdom*. Before the war he had been looking for a great theme upon which he could write a book to rank with Doughty's *Travels in Arabia Deserta*. The Arab Revolt had provided the subject matter he was seeking: 'the story I have to tell is one of the most splendid ever given a man for writing'.[2]

Friends who knew of the project now offered to put him up for a fellowship at All Souls College, Oxford, which would enable him to complete the book. The All Souls common room would also be a welcome release from the cynicism and duplicity of international politics, and he readily accepted the prospect of a base in Oxford's academic community.

Before this was settled his family suffered another loss. In April he learned that his father had contracted pneumonia at the age of seventy-three. Lawrence left Paris as soon as he could, but arrived in Oxford to find his father already dead. The house in Polstead Road where five brothers had grown up together was now strangely empty.

Lawrence travelled back to Paris from the funeral in time to witness an acrimonious meeting between Feisal and Clemenceau. Although a final decision on the Arab question had been postponed until the King-Crane commission reported, French designs on Syria were as firm as ever. Feisal left Paris with feelings of bitterness and anger at this treatment from his former allies. Lawrence had hoped to fulfil the promises he had made to the Arabs in the field through his advocacy in the council-chamber. This hope had now come to nothing, and he therefore regarded the outcome of the Paris Conference as a personal failure.

In May he took the opportunity to escape temporarily from Paris, travelling to Cairo with a flight of Handley-Page bombers. While there he looked through the Arab Bureau papers and made notes for *Seven Pillars*. Near Rome the aircraft in which he was travelling crashed, killing the pilot and co-pilot. Lawrence was lucky to escape with broken ribs and concussion; he did not reach Cairo until the end of June.

He returned to Paris almost at once and moved into the Arab delegation headquarters. *Seven Pillars* was now taking up most of his time; by the end of August he had completed about 200,000 words of the first draft. When there was nothing left for him to do in Paris, he went to Oxford where his All Souls Fellowship had been confirmed. In the leisurely atmosphere of All Souls he was free to contemplate a new career. He had no taste for public life, and archaeology in French-controlled Syria was out of the question. Yet two of his pre-war ambitions remained. One, his hope of becoming a writer, would depend on the success of *Seven Pillars*. The other was fine printing, and he now revived the scheme to set up a private press with Vyvyan Richards, first mooted ten years before. Richards had become a schoolteacher in Chingford on the edge of Epping Forest, and was renting land nearby at Pole Hill. Lawrence bought the land, and they planned to build a press there. During these first post-war years he collected outstanding examples of book production, including work from presses such as Kelmscott, Doves and Ashendene.

Another scheme was to get Doughty's *Travels in Arabia Deserta* republished. Only 500 copies had been printed in 1888 and Lawrence tackled various publishers with a view to bringing out a new edition. The book was eventually reprinted at the beginning of 1921 by a new firm, Jonathan Cape, in association with the Medici Society. Lawrence contributed an introduction which helped Cape recover his risk on the 500-copy reprint. Though priced at nine guineas it sold quickly, and the book was reprinted several times during the next few years. Lawrence withdrew his introduction after Cape's first printing: 'to introduce a classic is a silly performance . . . like scribbling your name on a ruined building.'[3]

With the task of revising *Seven Pillars* ahead, he wanted to improve his own literary style as much as possible. He carefully studied the work of contemporary authors,

Facing page
T. E. Lawrence
By Sir William Orpen, 1919
(not exhibited, see no. 186)

1. *Oriental Assembly*, p. 142.
2. T. E. Lawrence to V. Richards, undated (1922).
3. T. E. Lawrence to S. C. Cockerell, 31.1.1921.

and met a good many of them in Oxford through friends such as Robert Graves. These new literary acquaintances included Joseph Conrad, Ezra Pound and Robert Bridges.

After the Peace Conference, Lawrence had turned down offers of further government work in the East. He was busy with *Seven Pillars* and showed little interest in the many invitations from society hostesses, requests to write for newspapers and periodicals, and opportunities to lecture at Oxford, Princeton and elsewhere. This flood of interest was in large part due to the popularity of Lowell Thomas's Covent Garden travelogue, 'With Allenby in Palestine', which for the first time brought 'Lawrence of Arabia' before the British public. His fame guaranteed an introduction to anyone he wished to meet, but he chose his new friends among poets, painters and intellectuals.

Although he no longer held any kind of official position he had not ceased to campaign, privately and publicly, against the Middle Eastern settlement. Taking advantage of his popular reputation and status as a Fellow of All Souls, he submitted a series of hard-hitting articles to the press.

Events moved swiftly during 1920. Arab leaders, angry and impatient with both France and Britain, took matters into their own hands by claiming Syria for Feisal and Iraq for his brother Abdullah. They had no means to enforce this, but it was a direct challenge to the imperial powers, who had now taken control of Arab territories under League of Nations mandates. Britain was to be responsible for Palestine, Transjordan and Iraq, while France at last achieved her ambition to govern Syria, effectively as a colony.

In the summer of 1920 Britain faced a serious rising in Iraq, while the French for their part drove Feisal out of Damascus. Lawrence was not surprised by these developments. He wrote to *The Times*: 'The Arabs rebelled against the Turks during the war not because the Turk Government was notably bad, but because they wanted independence. They did not risk their lives in battle to change masters, to become British subjects or French citizens, but to win a show of their own.'[4]

Though he could not help Feisal in any formal capacity, his articulate and informed outbursts in the press won over public opinion; they also carried increasing political weight as the costs of containing the revolt in Iraq began to mount. Despite opposition from some quarters, the Cabinet began to take Lawrence's suggestions seriously.

In December there came a chance to help steer British policy towards fulfilment of its wartime promises to the Arabs. Partly as a result of Lawrence's press campaign, but more particularly because of continuing unrest in Iraq, the Cabinet decided to set up a Middle East Department under a new Colonial Secretary, Winston Churchill. Lawrence was invited to become an adviser on Arab affairs. The Government also hoped that this appointment would silence one of its sternest critics.

Lawrence no longer had any belief in old-fashioned imperialism. He joined Churchill in the hope of writing 'a new page in the loosening of the Empire tradition'[5] by giving the Arabs dominion rather than colonial status. The recasting of British policy in the Middle East might also provide an opportunity to give Feisal a proper reward for his part in the Arab Revolt, now that the French had expelled him from Syria. A conference was planned to decide the future of the Arab areas under British mandate: this was set for March 1921 and would take place in Cairo.

Lawrence was to attend the talks, but his reputation as an independently minded pro-Arab worried many of the old-style imperialists in the Government and civil service. Lord Curzon, the Foreign Secretary, told Churchill, 'Lawrence will be very useful if he will cease to intrigue.'[6] Before the Cairo Conference opened he spent several weeks in London advising Churchill on the agenda. He also met Feisal with instructions from Churchill to explain Britain's idea of putting a Sherifian candidate on the throne of Iraq.

The Conference opened on 12 March and lasted ten days. It was attended by almost all the officials responsible for British policy in the Middle East. Together, they agreed that Feisal should be offered Iraq, provided that the people there accepted him. Lawrence was delighted at this outcome: 'We're a very happy family: agreed upon everything important.'[7] He also supported the idea of using the RAF to police Iraq

4. T. E. Lawrence to the Editor of *The Times*, 22.7.1920, *Letters* p. 307.
5. T. E. Lawrence to R. Graves, undated (January 1921), *Biographers* (Graves), p. 12.
6. Lord Curzon to Winston Churchill, 16.2.1921, in Martin Gilbert, *Winston S. Churchill*, companion vol. IV, part 2, p. 1359.
7. T. E. Lawrence to his family, 20.3.1921, *Home Letters*, p. 353.

from the air, which was put forward at the Conference by Sir Hugh Trenchard, the Air Force chief. This would be much cheaper than using conventional ground forces, and would provide the young service with a training area for its pilots. At this time the continued independent existence of the RAF was in doubt, and Lawrence, who had learned the military value of aircraft during the desert campaign, was keen that the new force should be properly developed. Trenchard welcomed his support.

In Cairo, unlike Paris, the process of diplomacy worked in Lawrence's favour. The negotiations – or, rather, the acceptance of the new Colonial Office policy – went ahead at breakneck speed. But he found time to see his old chief, Allenby, who was now High Commissioner in Egypt. He also visited the Pyramids with Churchill and Gertrude Bell, and enjoyed the sight of the Colonial Secretary being unceremoniously dumped by his camel.

The decisions arrived at in Cairo had now to be put formally to the Arabs themselves. In particular, Abdullah was creating difficulties. While the Conference was going on he had appeared in Transjordan, threatening, in a bold if quixotic gesture, to liberate Syria from the French and restore Feisal to its throne. Doubtless he still harboured ambitions to the throne of Iraq himself. Britain viewed Abdullah's intervention with alarm, and Churchill dispatched Lawrence to meet the two brothers and secure their acceptance of the new British plan. This was an important and a delicate task, and Lawrence remained in Palestine and Transjordan throughout April, urging the settlement on them both. Abdullah was invited to remain in Transjordan for six months and use his influence to help Britain keep the region quiet.

Lawrence was satisfied that the settlement in Iraq and Transjordan was the best that could be obtained: it was, indeed, a remarkable concession from an imperial power. He returned to England in May and resumed work at the Colonial Office. For several months he had put all his energy into getting favourable terms for the Arabs, but once back in London he realised again how little he relished the prospect of a career in public service. He felt increasingly impatient to put the Middle East behind him, writing to Robert Graves, 'the Arabs are like a page I have turned over: and sequels are rotten things.'[8]

Churchill, however, had another job in store for him. On 30 June 1921 'Our most trusty and well-beloved Thomas Edward Lawrence Esquire, Lieutenant Colonel in Our Army, Companion of Our Most Honourable Order Of The Bath, Companion of Our Distinguished Service Order' was appointed a plenipotentiary under the Great Seal of England to treat with the King of the Hejaz. Lawrence had no liking whatsoever for the task, which would involve negotiating an agreement with the ageing and difficult Hussein. If accepted, however, this treaty would complete the British settlement in the Middle East.

Lawrence arrived in Jidda at the end of July 1921, and remained in the East until Christmas. Negotiations with Hussein went badly from the start. The old man was reasonable and intransigent by turns; at his worst he made absurd demands, like the cession to himself of all Arab states, or called for a massive increase in his subsidy from the British. By this time he had become something of an embarrassment even to his sons. Neither Feisal, who was crowned in Baghdad during August, nor Abdullah in Transjordan were prepared to submit to their father's control. The other sons, Ali and Zeid, did their best to salvage the negotiations.

Faced with theatrical gestures from Hussein, who at times threatened abdication and even suicide, Lawrence grew impatient. He knew that an independent Hejaz could not survive without British support. To the east there was a constant danger of invasion by the great desert leader Ibn Saud, who wanted control of the Islamic Holy cities. Hussein's obduracy continued; ultimately he lost British support, and with it, in 1924, his kingdom.

Having failed to get a satisfactory agreement, Lawrence left Jidda at the end of September, recommending angrily that Hussein's subsidy should be cut off. He went to Palestine where he spent a few weeks working with the High Commissioner. While in Jerusalem he was visited by his mother and brothers: Bob, the eldest, was on his way to China to work as a medical missionary.

In October 1921 he left Palestine to act as British representative with Abdullah

Delegates from the Cairo Conference on a visit to the Pyramids
Photograph by G. M. Georgoulas, 20 March 1921
(detail, no. 201)

8. T. E. Lawrence to R. Graves, 21.5.1921, *Biographers* (Graves), p. 15.

in Transjordan. Returning to the scene of his wartime campaigns, he was still disappointed with the final outcome in Syria and Palestine. He wrote to Newcombe: 'I thank what Gods I have that I'm neither an Arab nor a Frenchman – only the poor brute who has to clean up after them.'[9]

There was much to clean up in Transjordan. It was theoretically a part of the Palestine mandate, and as such was to be governed from Jerusalem. At the end of his six month stewardship, seeing no more attractive prospect, Abdullah wanted to be named Emir of the country. Lawrence backed him against strong opposition in London and got crucial support from Churchill. A friendly Sherifian regime in the Transjordan would save enormous costs in administration and policing.

Lawrence was glad when he was replaced as British representative in Amman after only two months. His successor, St. John Philby, gave an appreciative account of what Lawrence had achieved in his short time there. Transjordan was more stable than Palestine (where planned Jewish settlement was causing increasing friction) and Feisal was established in Iraq: Lawrence now felt he had done all that could reasonably be expected of him, and that Britain was 'quit of the war-time Eastern adventure, with clean hands'.[10] He returned to England in December 1921, hoping to leave public service at the end of February.

In the meantime he took leave and spent days on end revising *Seven Pillars* in the attic of his friend Sir Herbert Baker's offices in Barton Street, London. By the spring of 1922 he was clearly in a strange state of mind. He had become a celebrity; yet he loathed the wartime role for which everyone praised him. The Cairo settlement had gone some way towards honouring Britain's ambiguous pledges to the Arabs. Yet to his strict sense of morality, that did not in any way excuse the lies he had told on Britain's behalf throughout the campaign. He had valued fame as long as it helped in his political struggle, but that was over now. He had no wish to spend the rest of his life acting the part of Lowell Thomas's 'Uncrowned King of Arabia'.

To the annoyance of friends such as John Buchan who were trying to place him in a promising career, Lawrence continued to refuse all offers. Most people in his position would have taken up a diplomatic post, but he had very different plans. With his release from the Colonial Office now due, he wrote to Trenchard, Chief of Air Staff, asking to join the ranks of the RAF.

The war, the diplomatic battle, and the writing of *Seven Pillars* had all taken their toll on Lawrence's health and nervous energy. He gave different friends many reasons for his enlistment, but one of the most important conscious factors was a desperate need to get away from further mental strain. He described enlistment as a 'brain sleep'.

Ever since the war he had despised the plaudits of society, and now found it equally hard to stomach the congratulations he had earned for making the best of a bad job. By contrast his experience with the armoured car units and Flying Corps pilots at the close of the war had left him with a very favourable impression of service life. In the ranks he would find safety; he felt an 'inclination towards ground-level . . . a despairing hope that I'd find myself on common ground with men . . . a little wish to make myself a little more human than I had become in Barton Street.'[11]

Also, as he said to Trenchard, he was interested in writing another book. *Seven Pillars* was temporarily stalled, but his literary ambition was as strong as ever. The evolution of the Air Force might provide worthy subject matter, and Lawrence thought of describing it as seen from the ranks.

Trenchard was surprised by Lawrence's plans, but nonetheless co-operated. Churchill, however, was extremely reluctant to let him go; he had hoped to send him to Baghdad in order to make further use of his influence with Feisal. It was not until July that Lawrence finally escaped from the Colonial Office.

Between 1918 and 1922 he had moved in the highest social, political and academic circles. He had security as a Fellow of Oxford's most prestigious college. His book, *Seven Pillars*, was pronounced a great success by all who read it. In politics, too, he could claim considerable achievement, notably for his part in the creation of two Arab kingdoms. He was famous, and could have been rich. Yet his only wish now was to become a serving airman.

9. T. E. Lawrence to S. F. Newcombe, 8.11.1921, *Letters*, p. 336.
10. *SPW 1935*, ch. 48, p. 276 n.
11. T. E. Lawrence to R. Graves, 12.11.1922, *Biographers* (Graves), p. 23.

178
VISIT OF EMIR FEISAL TO GLASGOW
Photograph by *The Bulletin* (16 December 1918)

On 16 December 1918 Feisal arrived in Glasgow for a four day visit. Seen in this photograph, taken at Queen Street Station, are : (left to right) Sir James Watson Stewart, the Lord Provost of Glasgow; (behind) Captain Hassan Kadri; Brigadier General Nuri Pasha Said; (front) Feisal; Lawrence; Sir John Samuel, Official Secretary to the Lord Provost; and R. F. Synge from the Foreign Office. On the following day the Lord Provost gave a banquet at the City Chambers. The *Glasgow Herald* reported: 'Prince Feisal acknowledged the toast, speaking in Arabic. His speech was interpreted by Colonel Lawrence, who said that his Royal Highness was deeply grateful for the welcome they had accorded him . . . the Arabs had been indebted more perhaps to Glasgow than to any other city except London during the war . . . Without exception His Royal Highness thought that all the ships that took part in the campaign were built and engined on the Clyde.'[1]

David Ransley

1. *Glasgow Herald*, 17.12.1918.

Literature: *The Bulletin*, Glasgow, 17 December 1918, ill. p.1.

179
EMIR FEISAL AND T. E. LAWRENCE ON BOARD HMS *ORION*
By an unknown photographer, 1918
Vintage print

This photograph was taken during Feisal's visit to Scotland in December 1918. It shows: (front row, left to right) unidentified RN officer; Lawrence; Feisal; Rear-Admiral W.E. Goodenough; R.F. Synge; (back row, left to right) unidentified naval officer; Nuri Said; Captain Hassan Kadri.

R. S. Atterbury

26.6 × 34.5
Inscribed in Arabic on an attached leaf of ship's notepaper: *I present my respect to the great British fleet/ 15 December 1918 Feisal bin Hussein* (transl.)

180
T. E. LAWRENCE
Photograph by Harris and Ewing, Paris, 1919
Vintage print

Lawrence's role as British liaison officer with
Feisal continued during the Peace Conference.
The Foreign Office recognised Feisal as a key
Arab leader, and regarded Lawrence as
indispensable. He acted as Feisal's personal
adviser throughout the Conference, and lost
no opportunity to campaign for Syrian
independence. In reality, however, he was
fighting for a lost cause, and he found the
work abhorrent: 'Those five months in Paris
were the worst I have lived through'.[1]

The Warden and Fellows of All Souls
College, Oxford
1. T. E. Lawrence to C. F. Shaw, 18.10.1927.
25 × 20

181
A PEACE CONFERENCE AT THE QUAI
D'ORSAY
By Sir William Orpen, 1919

William Orpen (1878-1931) served with the
British army as an official war artist from
April 1917. After the war he spent nine
months working as a portrait painter at the
Paris Peace Conference. The Conference
opened on 18 January 1919 as a discussion
between all the victorious and defeated
nations, but the proceedings were dominated
by the big 'three' Allied Powers, Britain,
France, and America. Their leaders, seen in
this painting, were President Wilson (seated
third from left), Clemenceau (seated fourth
from left), and Lloyd George (seated fifth
from left). Other British representatives
were Arthur Bonar Law and A. J. Balfour
(seated, respectively sixth and seventh from
left).

Despite French objections, Feisal
(standing third from left) was allowed to
represent his father's interests, and defend
the Arab case.

Trustees of the Imperial War Museum
(IWM 2855)

Oil on canvas, 124.5 × 101.6
Signed br.: ORPEN
Provenance: War Artists Commission.
Literature: W. Orpen, *An Onlooker in France 1917-1919*,
1921, pp. 102-4, ill. pl. LXXXIII; B. Arnold, *Sir
William Orpen, Mirror to an Age*, 1981, pp. 359-63, ill.;
M. & S. Harries, *The War Artists*, 1983, p. 146.
Exhibitions: Ireland, National Gallery, *William Orpen
1873-1931*, 1978 (117).

182
THE EMIR FEISAL
By an unknown photographer, 1919
Vintage print

Feisal did not find the Peace Conference an
enjoyable experience, and by temperament
he was ill-suited to it. Lawrence wrote that
he was: 'Very gentle . . . and very kind, and
very considerate, and outrageously generous
to his friends, and mild to his enemies, and
cleanly and honest and intelligent: and full of
wild freakish humour'.[1] This photograph was
taken in the garden of the American Club in
Paris, possibly by Mrs Woodrow Wilson,
wife of the American president.

The Liddell Hart Centre for Military
Archives, King's College London
1. T. E. Lawrence to C. F. Shaw, 18.10.1927.

25.2 × 20.2
Provenance: T. E. Lawrence; given to Basil Liddell
Hart; acquired 1973.

183
THE HEJAZ DELEGATION TO THE PARIS
PEACE CONFERENCE
By an unknown photographer (1919)

From left to right: Rustum Haidar, (Feisal's
personal secretary; Nuri Said; Capitaine
Pisani, commander of the French gunnery
detachment with Feisal's army; Feisal;
Lawrence; Feisal's slave; and Captain Hassan
Kadri.

Feisal put the Arab case as strongly as he
could, but the French position was too
strong. All previous agreements affecting
Syria and Mesopotamia were swept aside to
make way for the League of Nations Mandate
scheme. In effect this gave France imperial
power in Syria, while the Anglo-Indian lobby
took Mesopotamia. Only America could have
put a stop to this convenient deal, but
President Wilson lacked the authority to do
so. Feisal left France in April 1919, to a
precarious stewardship of his inland Kingdom
in Syria. It took little more than a year for
the French authorities to supersede him.

IWM Q55581

T. E. LAWRENCE
By Augustus John, 1919

John was one of the artists appointed by
Lloyd George to make a permanent memento
of the Peace Conference. He travelled to
Paris in January 1919 and met Lawrence
shortly afterwards. During the Conference
John painted three studies of Lawrence in oil
(see no. 115), and a series of four pencil
drawings, all of them in Arab robes.
Lawrence was delighted with the drawings,
and remarked that on the strength of them
'posterity will call me beautiful'.[1] See also
no. 238.

The Warden and Fellows of All Souls
College, Oxford

1. T. E. Lawrence to Mrs L. Curtis, 1.8.1933, *Letters*,
p. 771.

Pencil, 63 × 53
Signed in blue crayon, br.: *John/1919*
Provenance: ? Acquired by Lionel Curtis at Alpine Club
Gallery, 1923; presented by the Executors of the Estate
of Mrs Lionel Curtis, 1966.
Literature: *Grosvenor*, no. 7.
Exhibitions: London, Alpine Club Gallery, *Augustus
John*, 1923 (48).

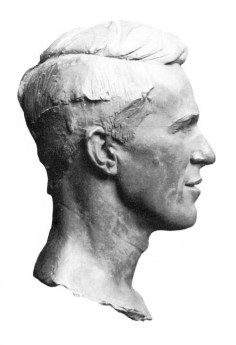

185
T. E. LAWRENCE
By Francis Derwent Wood, 1919

Derwent Wood was commissioned by Lord Rothermere in March 1919 to execute busts of various notables at the Peace Conference, among them Lawrence. The original study was done in plaster and two bronze casts were made from it. One of these was exhibited in the Royal Academy Summer Exhibition of 1920, where Lawrence came upon it by chance: 'I met it suddenly in the Academy, and felt like the man in Rossetti who met himself in a wood!'[1] The meeting may not have been a happy one, for Lawrence later described the bust as 'a strained joke'.[2]

The Trustees of the Tate Gallery (TG 3602)

1. T. E. Lawrence to Lady Scott, 2.2.21, *Letters*, p. 325.
2. T. E. Lawrence to Eric Kennington, 15.2.1927, *Letters*, p. 507.

Bronze, 36 h.
Inscribed: *Derwent Wood – Paris 1919*
Provenance: Given by the artist, 1921
Literature: M. Chamot, D. Farr & M. Butlin, *The Modern British Paintings, Drawings and Sculpture I*, Tate Gallery, 1964, p. 781; *Grosvenor*, no. 56.
Exhibitions: RA, 1920 (1465); RA, *Works by the late Sir Hamo Thornycroft RA and F. Derwent Wood RA*, 1927 (58).

186
T. E. LAWRENCE
Colour print from original painting by
Sir William Orpen (1919)

Early in 1919 Sir William Orpen (see no. 181) painted a portrait of Lawrence in two ninety-minute sittings. Looking back on the work fourteen years later, Lawrence found it lacking in conviction: 'The portrait is not great shakes. I remember it as better than that'.[1] He thought that the fault lay in the artist's character: 'Orpen is not a man who paints with *all* his soul and strength and mind';[2] he was merely 'a bright surface and that's all'.[3] Lawrence's mother, however, greatly admired the painting and tried to buy it shortly after his death.

The painting is now in a private collection in the USA.

J. M. Wilson

1. T. E. Lawrence to Blanche Patch, 20.2.1933, in B. Patch, *30 Years With G.B.S.*, 1951, p. 76.
2. T. E. Lawrence to C. F. Shaw, 20.7.1926.
3. T. E. Lawrence to Blanche Patch, 20.2.1933, in B. Patch, *30 Years With G.B.S.*, 1951, p. 76.

Literature: *Grosvenor*, no.45.
(illustrated in colour p. 123)

187
T. E. LAWRENCE'S VISITING CARD
*c.*1919-22

In 1910, after securing a First Class honours degree, Lawrence tried unsuccessfully to win one of the two All Souls Fellowships offered that year in the annual competitive examination. When he returned to England in the autumn of 1918, he received a letter from Geoffrey Dawson, editor of the *Manchester Guardian* and himself a Fellow of All Souls, suggesting that a place might be available if he were interested.

He was elected to a Fellowship on 18 June 1919, and during the next three years spent a certain amount of time at his rooms there. He preferred London, however, and the only writing he is known to have done at All Souls was his introduction to Doughty's *Travels in Arabia Deserta* (see no. 195).

Dr Lionel Dakers CBE

Printed card, 3.8 × 7.5

188
LIONEL CURTIS
Photograph by Ramsey and Muspratt,
c.1935-40
Vintage print

Lionel Curtis (1872-1955) was an influential
adviser and lecturer in politics and
international relations. He first met Lawrence
at the Versailles Conference in 1919, and
they became close friends at All Souls. His
ideas undoubtedly had an influence on
Lawrence's political thinking.

Curtis became a trusted confidant of
Lawrence's, and between March and June
1923 Lawrence sent him a series of deeply
personal and desperate letters (see no. 262).
'They are', David Garnett wrote, the most
revealing letters of Lawrence's I know'.[1]

In early December 1923 Curtis,
collaborating with Hogarth and Dawnay,
managed to persuade Lawrence to produce a
subscribers edition of *Seven Pillars*.

National Portrait Gallery (NPG X7086)

1. *Letters*, p. 410.

10 × 7.5
Provenance: Given by the sitter, 1949.

189
VYVYAN RICHARDS
Detail from school photograph (1921)

Vyvyan Richards befriended Lawrence in
1908 when they met at Jesus College,
Oxford. As a result Richards came to share
Lawrence's interest in William Morris and in
fine printing. When Richards graduated in
1909 he took up a teaching post at Bancroft's
School in Chingford, Essex, and rented land
nearby at Pole Hill. The following year he
and Lawrence agreed to set up a private press
there.

At first Lawrence hoped that his father
would lend money to buy the Pole Hill land
and finance buildings for the press; but his
parents were unsympathetic to the project.
They recognised that Richards had a difficult
personality, and no doubt suspected that his
interest in their son was homosexual (a fact
confirmed many years later by Richards
himself). In any case, Lawrence was engaged
in archaeological work overseas.

In 1919, shortly after he was discharged
from war service, Lawrence bought Pole
Hill, and he later purchased several adjoining
pieces of land. He now intended to set up the
press he had planned with Richards eight
years earlier; their first project was to be an
edition of poems by the Gadarene poet
Meleager. In 1920, however, Lawrence
abruptly backed out of the scheme, and their
relationship thereafter seems to have been
more distant. He nevertheless continued to
add to the Pole Hill land where Richards had
built a wooden 'hall' and cloister, and a small
swimming pool. Lawrence later hired an

independent printer to produce *Seven Pillars*,
and at much the same time Richards printed
one book, a small collection of William
Caxton's *Prologues and Epilogues*. Later, when
Richards had moved to Wales, Lawrence sold
Pole Hill to Epping Forest.

After Lawrence's death Richards wrote
two biographies: *Portrait of T.E. Lawrence*,
1936, and *T.E. Lawrence*, 1939.

Bancroft's School and the Old Bancroftians'
Association

190
LOWELL THOMAS
Photograph by Harry Chase (1918)

The popular image of Lawrence as a romantic
military hero was largely created by Lowell
Thomas. He had originally come to Europe
looking for the kind of material which would
help swing American opinion behind the
Allied war effort. By the time he returned
the war was nearly over, but he went on to
make a personal fortune, largely from his
lectures, books and articles about Lawrence.

Lawrence was fairly blunt about Thomas:
'He's a born vulgarian, who does the best
that is in him. If the victim was other than
myself I'd praise him. But it rankles in my
mind to be called proud names for qualities

which I'd hate to possess . . . or for acts of which I'm heartily ashamed. Would you like to be known only by your inferior work?'.[1]

1. T. E. Lawrence to C. F. Shaw, 26.3.1924.

Literature: L. Thomas, *With Lawrence in Arabia*, ill. fp. 104.

191

'WITH ALLENBY IN PALESTINE'
Programme for Lowell Thomas' travelogue at the Royal Opera House, 1919

Lowell Thomas used film, slides, music, and dance as well as narration in his 'travelogues' about the First World War, and his account of the Arab and Palestine campaigns proved to be extremely popular. The show first opened in New York in March 1919, where it was seen by Percy Burton, an English impresario. He persuaded Thomas to bring it to England, and it opened at Covent Garden on 14 August 1919 for a two week run. The demand for seats was so great that it ran for six months, moving successively to the Royal Albert Hall, the Philharmonic Hall and Queen's Hall.

Thomas turned Lawrence into a marvellous and exotic figure, the central figure in a story whose romantic embellishments had little or no basis in fact. It was, however, just what the British public wanted. The *Daily Telegraph* reviewer wrote: 'I can conceive of a no more invigorating tonic than two hours spent in the company of Mr. Lowell Thomas. What is modestly and prosaically described as "an illustrated travelogue" of the British campaigns in Palestine and Arabia is in reality an heroic epic capable of inspiring a dozen modern emulators of Homer or Plutarch . . . Now, thanks to Mr. Lowell Thomas, Thomas Lawrence is definitely marked as one of the elect. In the opinion of the young American lecturer, the name Thomas Lawrence will go down to remotest posterity beside the names of half a dozen men who dominate history.'[1]

Lowell Thomas subsequently claimed that Lawrence courted publicity, although he came to hate its consequences. In *T.E. Lawrence by his Friends* Thomas suggested that Lawrence 'had a genius for backing into the limelight'.[2] Lawrence's own judgement was

ROYAL OPERA HOUSE,
COVENT GARDEN.

PROPRIETORS · THE GRAND OPERA SYNDICATE, LTD.

Twice Daily until October 14th.
Matinees Every Day at 2.30.   Nightly at 8.30.

PERCY BURTON
(by arrangement with the Grand Opera Syndicate)
presents
AMERICA'S TRIBUTE TO BRITISH VALOUR
IN THE PERSON OF
LOWELL THOMAS
in
His Illustrated Travelogue of the British Campaigns:

With Allenby in Palestine
including
THE CAPTURE OF JERUSALEM
and
THE LIBERATION OF HOLY ARABIA.

The motion pictures used in this travelogue were taken by Mr. Harry A. Chase and Captain Frank Hurley. Still photographs by Mr. Chase. Art work by Miss Augusta A. Heyder. Projection by Mr. Chase.

Business Manager (for Lowell Thomas and Percy Burton) W. T. Cunningham.

With authority from the Secretary of War and the Secretary of the Navy of the United States Government, Mr. Lowell Thomas, accompanied by Colonel W. C. Hayes and a staff of photographers, journeyed over sixty thousand miles gathering material for a series of travelogues. Mr. Lowell Thomas was attached to the Allied forces in Europe, Asia and Africa, and was with them from the Orkney Islands to the forbidden deserts of Holy Arabia, from New York to Jerusalem, from Rome to Khartoum, from Paris to Salonika, and from Cairo to Berlin. He was the first pilgrim to tour the Holy Land by airplane, and the first person to go into the holy land of the Mohammedans with a cinema camera. After the signing of the armistice he was the first to visit Kiel, Hamburg, Berlin and other parts of Germany, and bring back the pictorial story of the German Revolution.

By arrangement with Mr. Percy Burton, Mr. Thomas cancelled a number of his engagements in America in order to appear at Covent Garden Royal Opera House for a limited period, under the auspices of the English-Speaking Union.

His travelogue on Allenby's crusade in Palestine and the liberation of Holy Arabia, is not a tale of Jules Verne, but the story of the reality of the present, surpassing the dreams of the imagination of the past.

(Under the auspices of *THE ENGLISH-SPEAKING UNION*.)
President: Rt. Hon. A. J. BALFOUR, O.M.
Hon. President: The AMERICAN AMBASSADOR to England.
Vice-Presidents:

Field-Marshal Sir DOUGLAS HAIG, O.M.
Rt. Hon. WINSTON CHURCHILL, M.P.
Earl CURZON of KEDLESTON, O.M.
The ARCHBISHOP of YORK.
Sir ROBERT S. S. BADEN POWELL, K.C.B.
Rt. Hon. Sir ROBERT BORDEN, K.C.M.G.
Viscount BURNHAM

Rt. Hon. J. R. CLYNES, M.P.
The ARCHBISHOP of CANTERBURY.
BISHOP of LONDON, K.C.V.O.
Viscount BRYCE, O.M.
Earl of READING, G.C.B.
Rt. Hon. W. M. HUGHES.
Viscount NORTHCLIFFE, &c

more stoical: 'For Lowell Thomas: I don't bear him any grudge. He has invented some silly phantom thing, a sort of matinée idol in fancy dress, that does silly things and is dubbed "romantic." Boy scouts and servants love it: and it's so far off the truth that I can go peacefully in its shadow, without being seen.'[3]

Private collection

1. Alder Anderson in the *Daily Telegraph*, 2.10.1919.
Note the mistaken use of 'Thomas' – Lawrence used his second forename, Edward.
2. *Friends*, p. 215.
3. T. E. Lawrence to ? Greenhill, 20.3.1920.

Folded sheet, 25.5 × 19.2

133

192

'WITH GENERAL ALLENBY AT COVENT
GARDEN THEATRE'
Facsimile of an article in *The Sphere*,
23 August 1919

The original Lowell Thomas lecture was
called 'With Allenby in Palestine, including
the Capture of Jerusalem, and the Liberation
of Holy Arabia'. However, public attention
focused more and more on Lawrence, as this
article shows. Shortly afterwards, the title of
the show was changed to 'With Allenby in
Palestine and Lawrence in Arabia'.

WITH GENERAL ALLENBY at Covent Garden Theatre.

*A Remarkable Film Lecture Telling the Strange
Story of Colonel Thomas Lawrence, the Leader of
the Arab Army*

Colonel Thomas Lawrence (on Left) with Mr. Lowell Thomas

Colonel Lawrence is here seen at the entrance to his tent with Mr. Lowell Thomas, the American
journalist, who at Covent Garden is telling the story of the Arab campaign

Colonel Thomas Lawrence

When war broke out Thomas Lawrence was a young archæological
student engaged in work on ancient Mesopotamian cities. His knowledge of Arabia was first made use of in the map department at Cairo,
and finally we find him as leader of the whole Arab Army in its fight
from Mecca to Damascus. He wore this Arab style of dress throughout
the campaign, and gained the confidence of chiefs and followers alike.
A price was set upon his head but Colonel Lawrence won through to
Damascus at the head of a devoted army

Copyrighted in the U.S.A.   *Drawn by D. Macpherson*
The Palestine Film Lecture at Covent Garden

A large number of well-known personalities gathered on the opening night last week to hear
Mr. Lowell Thomas's film lecture on the Palestine campaign. The lecturer showed pictures of Arab
and other cavalry columns in motion which were quite unfamiliar to the man in the street

Mr. Lowell Thomas's wonderful pictures of the operations in
Palestine, at Covent Garden, have revealed to many what
a really big cavalry " show " means, and what it entails in the way
of general organisation and detail, writes a military correspondent. Few laymen, at any rate in England, ever get the chance
of seeing large bodies of cavalry massed for operations of war
or of peace. In India, where there is elbow room and space,
and where cavalry both on manœuvres and in the almost unending
warfare on the N.-W. Frontier get more practice than any other
cavalry in the world, we have, upon occasion, seen something of
it. Ever since the times of what were called the " Kitchener
tests," those of us who have served in India have had a taste
of what the handling of large masses of Horse means.   But
even in India, when we perhaps had the equivalent of a cavalry
division on manœuvres, it was a ceremonial parade compared to
what this tremendous cavalry operation which Field-Marshal
Lord Allenby conducted in Palestine connoted. These pictures,
perhaps, brought home to the layman what it meant; they
perhaps made him think of what it meant in terms of fodder, in
terms of sore backs, and in terms of horse-shoes, quite apart from
the little matter of the feeding and watering of both the horse
and the man on his back. Good cavalry are supposed to be
able to exist on the smell of an oil-rag; they are supposed to
be able to fend for themselves if put to it.

Sometimes this thing is politely called " foraging," but people
have also another name for it. Fending for yourself is possible
when only a comparatively small body is involved; it is a different
pair of shoes, however, when something very like a whole cavalry
corps is on the warpath, as was the case in Palestine. Allenby
started his service with the Inniskillings; he has been a cavalry
soldier all his days, and the cavalry spirit has been breathed
into him since the time when he first learnt how to " carry
swords."

No one but a cavalry leader of such brilliance would have
dared to conceive an operation of this magnitude over such
country. Allenby, however, knew the quality of the cavalry he
had under him—hunting yeomen from the " shires " and the
" provinces," Anzacs who were bred in the saddle, Sikhs,
Punjabis, Pathans, Gukkars from the Salt Range, natural horse-
men, and, above all, horse-masters, every man Jack of them, and
he took it on and knew that his Horse would not fail him. The
most astounding fact to the cavalry soldier, who happens to know
what it all meant, was the low percentage of casualties in horse-
flesh—on an all-round reckoning, less than 25 per cent. If the
percentage had been 50 per cent, it would still have been a magnificent performance. As Mr. Lowell Thomas rightly adjudged,
it is the most astonishing cavalry achievement in the whole history
of war, ancient or modern.

193

'"THE UNCROWNED KING OF ARABIA", COLONEL T. E. LAWRENCE: THE MOST ROMANTIC CAREER OF MODERN TIMES'

Facsimile of an article by Lowell Thomas in *The Strand Magazine*, January 1920

Thomas's show was enormously successful in London, and he was soon planning a popular biography of Lawrence. He published three articles in the American journal *Asia* in 1919 which Lawrence found greatly distressing (he said that they were 'red-hot lying'[1]). When he learned that there was to be a series of similar articles in *The Strand Magazine* he worked with Lowell Thomas to tone them down.

At this time publicity was extremely valuable to Lawrence, who was campaigning in the press to win public support for his views about the Middle East settlement.

City of Westminster Libraries

1. T. E. Lawrence to E. M. Forster, 17.6.1925.

194

'MESOPOTAMIA – THE TRUTH ABOUT THE CAMPAIGN'

Facsimile of an article by T. E. Lawrence in the *Sunday Times*, 22 August 1920

Lawrence took advantage of the fame provided by Lowell Thomas's lectures. He wrote letters to the press exposing the bankruptcy of British policy in the Middle East and demanding the redress of Arab grievances.

Lawrence excelled as a polemicist: 'The people of England have been led in Mesopotamia into a trap from which it will be hard to escape with dignity and honour. They have been tricked into it by a steady withholding of information. The Bagdad communiqués are belated, insincere, incomplete. Things have been far worse than we have been told, our administration more bloody and inefficient than the public knows. It is a disgrace to our imperial record, and may soon be too inflamed for an ordinary cure . . . The Cabinet cannot disclaim all responsibility . . . Our government is worse than the old Turkish system.'

(not illustrated)

195

TRAVELS IN ARABIA DESERTA
By C. M. Doughty, London, 1921

Doughty's *Travels in Arabia Deserta* is one of the undisputed classics of travel literature. It describes how Doughty spent two years among the Arabs between November 1876 and August 1878. Lawrence first read it in 1909, when he was planning his own trek through Syria to examine crusader castles.

He did not, as has sometimes been claimed, carry *Arabia Deserta* with him during the Arab Revolt. It was, however, used during the war. The Arab Bureau in Cairo assembled a very fine collection of works on Middle Eastern travel, which provided a basis for maps, geographical handbooks and route guides. According to D. G. Hogarth, *Travels in Arabia Deserta* was in almost daily use: 'When Sherif Husein's messages about adherence of fresh tribes or occupation of new districts or villages came in, one turned for light first to *Arabia Deserta*, and often found there the only light!'[1]

The book was originally published in 1888, the year of Lawrence's birth. By the end of the war copies were virtually unobtainable, and despite his immense reputation Doughty was living in very reduced circumstances. Lawrence was determined to get *Arabia Deserta* reprinted, and eventually in 1920 he persuaded Jonathan Cape to undertake a new edition. At that time Cape was working for the Medici Society, but was planning to set up in business on his own. This two-volume edition was published in January 1921 jointly by Jonathan Cape Ltd. and the Medici Society. It was Cape's first book, and since the market was likely to be quite small it represented a very large financial risk. Five hundred sets were produced, and offered for sale at nine guineas, then a very high price. Lawrence was asked to contribute an introduction to help it sell, and an extract from this was printed on the dust-jacket to ensure that it attracted attention.

The edition was widely reviewed and sold out quickly. It was followed by cheaper reprints, and the work has remained almost continuously in print up to the present day. Following the success of the January 1921 printing Lawrence withdrew his introduction. It was restored, however, after Doughty's death in 1926.

J. M. Wilson

1. D. G. Hogarth, *Life of C. M. Doughty*, 1928, p. 184.

Printed book, (vol. I of two), 624 pp. 22.8
(not illustrated)

196
SIR WINSTON CHURCHILL
By Walter Sickert, c.1927

In December 1920 Lloyd George's Coalition
Government set up a Middle Eastern
Department under Winston Churchill (1874-
1965), who had been appointed Colonial
Secretary. His task was to resolve the
political confrontations in the Middle East
resulting from the Versailles Treaty and from
the lack of co-ordination between several
British government departments which had
been active in the area. Churchill appointed
Lawrence as political adviser on Middle
Eastern affairs.

This informal portrait of Churchill was
painted by Walter Sickert, who was a friend
of Clementine Churchill's mother, Lady
Blanche Hosier. In September 1927 Sickert
went to stay at Chartwell Manor, Churchill's
country home, and instructed Churchill in
different painting techniques. At the time,
Churchill was Chancellor of the Exchequer.
Sickert's portrait of Churchill was based
partly on photographs. A preliminary
drawing is in a British private collection.

National Portrait Gallery (NPG 4438)

Oil on canvas, 45.7 × 30.5
Unsigned
Provenance: The Hon. Baillie Hamilton, (presumably
purchased from the Savile Gallery, 1928); the Hon.
Michael Berry, 1936; sold Christies, 12 July 1950
(138), purchased by the National Art Collections Fund;
presented by the NACF, 1965.
Literature: W. Baron, Sickert, 1973, pp. 171, 174, 380,
ill. fig. 281.
Exhibitions: London, Savile Gallery, Sickert Exhibition,
1928 (10); Agnews, Sickert Retrospective, 1933 (13);
National Gallery, Sickert Exhibition, 1941 (98); Arts
Council (Hull, Glasgow, Plymouth), Walter Sickert, 1978
(55); Arts Council (Hayward Gallery, Norwich,
Wolverhampton), Late Sickert, 1982 (9).

197

AGENDA NOTES FOR THE CAIRO
CONFERENCE
By T.E. Lawrence (1921)
Facsimile of autograph manuscript

A minute prepared for the Colonial Office by
Lawrence and his assistant Hubert Young in
late February 1921. It outlines the
Department's general policy towards the
Middle East, with specific comments on
Mesopotamia, Kurdistan, Palestine and
Transjordan.

Lawrence had agreed the terms for
settling the Middle East with Churchill at
least two months before the Cairo
Conference met. Thus he wrote to
Churchill's private secretary, Edward Marsh,
in January 1921: 'Concerning Feisal this is
how it stands: he has agreed to make no
reference to the French-occupied area of
Syria in his talks with HMG. He has agreed
to abandon all claims of his father to
Palestine.' After listing Feisal's own
demands, Lawrence notes: 'I think all he asks
. . . can be made useful to ourselves. They
tend towards cheapness and speed of
settlement.'[1]

The documentary evidence suggests that
Lawrence's own account of the Cairo
settlement (as noted down by Liddell Hart)
is substantially correct: 'Everything staged
before they went out for Cairo Conference.
T.E. had settled not only questions the
Conference would consider, but decisions
they would reach . . . Before going out
T.E. arranged things with Feisal . . . Then
Winston and Feisal met at lunch and W.S.C.
(primed by T.E.) explained decisions to
Feisal.'[2]

Public Record Office, London (CO 732/4)

1. T. E. Lawrence to E. Marsh, 17.1.1921, in Martin
Gilbert, *Winston S. Churchill*, 1977, companion vol. IV
part 2, p. 1314.
2. *Biographers* (Liddell Hart), pp. 143-4.

(not illustrated)

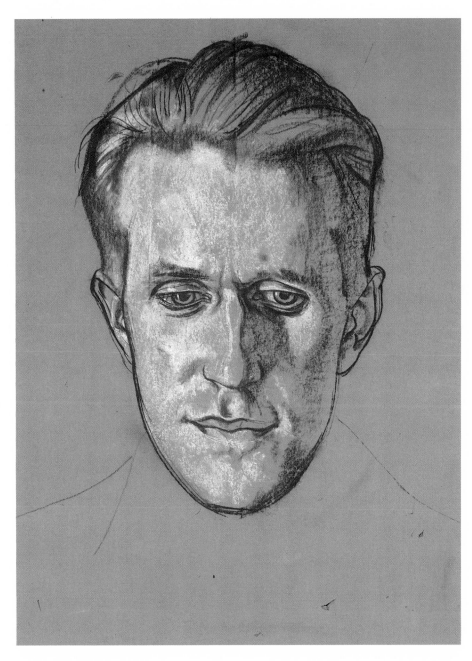

198

T. E. LAWRENCE
By Eric Kennington, 1921

Both Lawrence and Eric Kennington went to
Egypt shortly before the official opening of
the Cairo Conference on 12 March 1921.
They had arranged to meet in Cairo where
Kennington drew this portrait. Lawrence
dubbed it the 'Cheshire Cat', because, as he
explained, 'if one had tickled it, it would
have grinned'.[1]

He was clearly delighted with the drawing, but found its insight into his character
almost unnerving. Kennington recalled: 'He
would not use this for the *Seven Pillars* though

he liked it best. Reason: it was too obviously
the spider in the web of its own spinning'.[2]
A decade later Lawrence gave 'the Cheshire
cat mask of myself'[3] to his biographer Basil
Liddell Hart.

Adrian Liddell Hart

1. T. E. Lawrence to E. H. Kennington, 16.4.1927.
2. *Friends*, p. 266.
3. T. E. Lawrence to E. H. Kennington, October 1926.

Pastel, 44.7 × 32.8
Provenance: T. E. Lawrence; given to Basil Liddell
Hart, 1933; by descent.
Literature: *Home Letters*, p. 352; *Letters*, p. 253; *Friends*,
p. 233; *The Golden Reign*, p. 166; *Grosvenor*, no. 19.
Exhibitions: London, Picture Hire Limited, *Eric
Kennington Exhibition*, 1936 (12).

199

A GROUP AT THE CAIRO CONFERENCE
By an unknown photographer (1921)

Winston Churchill (front row centre) with his advisers, nicknamed the 'forty thieves'. These included: Sir Herbert Samuel, Sir Percy Cox (on Churchill's right and left respectively); and (in the second row): Sir A.T. Wilson, Gertrude Bell, Jaafar Pasha (fifth left), Lawrence (fourth right) and Hubert Young (extreme right).

The Conference agreed that Feisal should be offered the throne of Iraq, subject to approval by plebiscite. A similar offer, of Transjordan to Abdullah, was postponed for further negotiation.

British troops were subsequently withdrawn from Iraq, and replaced by the RAF, which policed the country very effectively from the air. The outcome was a triumph for both Churchill and Lawrence. Churchill secured a large reduction in expenditure, while Lawrence obtained a throne for Feisal.

BBC Hulton Picture Library

200

T. E. LAWRENCE WITH GERTRUDE BELL, EGYPT
Photograph by Maxwell H. Coote (1921)

Lawrence had known Gertrude Bell (1868-1926) for ten years when they attended the Cairo Conference. They had first met at Carchemish in July 1911, when both were practising archaeologists. They had also met in Cairo and Basra during the war, and at the Paris Peace negotiations. Gertrude Bell considered Lawrence the 'most picturesque'[1] figure at the Cairo Conference. Maxwell Coote was temporary ADC to Winston Churchill during the Cairo Conference.

Bodleian Library, Oxford (MS.Res.c.54)

1. The Letters of Gertrude Bell, ed. Lady Bell, II, 1927, p. 468.

Literature: Friends, ill. fp. 234.

201
DELEGATES FROM THE CAIRO
CONFERENCE ON A VISIT TO THE
PYRAMIDS
Photograph by G. M. Georgoulas (20 March
1921)

The Cairo Conference lasted for ten days,
during which a trip was organised to visit the
Pyramids and the Sphinx. This group was
taken by a local professional photographer.
Those present included (left to right):
Clementine Churchill, Winston Churchill,
Gertrude Bell, Lawrence, and Churchill's
detective.

Churchill was thrown by his camel and
hurt his hand, but rode back to Cairo with
Lawrence.

Department of Archaeology, University of
Newcastle Upon Tyne

202
DELEGATES FROM THE CAIRO
CONFERENCE AT AMMAN
By an unknown photographer (1921)

Included in the front row: Gertrude Bell,
Sir Herbert Samuel, Lawrence, and
Abdullah. As another member of the British
delegation recalled, Lawrence was 'quiet to
a degree of dullness in his dress [and] was
taken by me on first sight to be a junior
secretary to some lesser light at the Cairo
Conference'.[1]

Abdullah made it particularly difficult to
implement the terms agreed at the Cairo
Conference. At his father's instigation he
raised an army in Transjordan and threatened
to march on Syria to expel the French.
Lawrence was sent to discuss the position
with both Abdullah and Feisal, and diverted
Abdullah's ambition by offering him
constitutional authority in Transjordan,
where he later became king.

IWM Q60171

1. *Friends*, p. 233.

203
JIDDA
Photographs by T. E. Lawrence, 1921

After Lawrence had persuaded Feisal and
Abdullah to accept the decisions of the Cairo
Conference, his next task was to reach a
similar agreement with King Hussein. He
therefore travelled to Jidda in July 1921, his
first visit for three years. The ageing King
was acutely exasperating, using threats of
abdication and even suicide as a negotiating
technique, and frequently retracting clauses
of the agreement he had previously accepted.
Lawrence found: 'His ambitions are as large
as his conceit, and he showed unpleasant
jealousy of his sons . . . Reason is entirely
wasted on him since he believes himself all-
wise and all-competent, and is flattered by
his entourage in every idiotic thing he does.'[1]

Jidda was the first place that Lawrence
had visited in the Hejaz, during the early
months of the Revolt. He described it as 'a
remarkable town. The streets were alleys,
wood roofed in the main bazaar, but
elsewhere open to the sky in the little gap
between the tops of the lofty white-walled
houses. These were built four or five stories
high, of coral rag tied with square beams and
decorated by wide bow-windows running
from ground to roof in grey wooden panels.
There was no glass in Jidda, but a profusion
of good lattices, and some very delicate
shallow chiselling on the panels of wood
casings . . . There was much moulded or cut
plastering, and on the older houses fine stone
heads and jambs to the windows looking on
the inner courts.'[2]

There was little there to appeal to a
European: 'The atmosphere was oppressive,
deadly. There seemed no life in it. It was not
burning hot, but held a moisture and a sense

of great age and exhaustion such as seemed
to belong to no other place: not a passion of
smells like Smyrna, Naples or Marseilles, but
a feeling of long use, of the exhalations of
many people, of continued bath-heat and
sweat. One would say that for years Jidda had
not been swept through by a firm breeze:
that its streets kept their air from year's end
to year's end, from the day they were built
for so long as the houses should endure.'[3]

Courtauld Institute of Art, University of
London

1. T. E. Lawrence to the Foreign Office, telegram L.6,
4.8.1921, FO686/93.
2. SPW 1935, ch. 9, p. 72.
3. SPW 1935, ch. 9, p. 73.

Literature: SPW 1926, ill.; SPW 1935, ill. fp. 72.

204
CARVED WOODEN DOORS FROM JIDDA

Lawrence brought this pair of wooden doors from Jidda in 1921, and kept them in store in England. Ever since his first visit to Jidda in October 1916 he had admired the carved doors there, describing them in *Seven Pillars* as 'heavy two-leaved slabs of teak-wood, deeply carved, often with wickets in them; and they had rich hinges and ring-knockers of hammered iron.'[1]

In the early 1930s, when he was planning to settle at Clouds Hill, he had a large water reservoir built as a fire precaution near the cottage. The pool was later roofed over with glass, with room for a private study at one end. The doors were incorporated into this building, as he explained to his mother: 'Next week the floors of my little study at its N. end and of the entrance-porch at the S. end will be laid. Then the Jeddah gates go in, to form the N. wall. They are just the right width, though unnecessarily high. However we cannot cut them down, so we have made the study *too* high, instead.'[2] (See no. 330.)

The Visitors of the Ashmolean Museum, Oxford

1. *SPW 1935*, ch. 9, p. 72.
2. T. E. Lawrence to his mother, 6.4.1934, *Home Letters*, p. 389.

Wood, iron fittings, copper straps, 244 × 79 each
Provenance: Purchased by T. E. Lawrence in Jidda; presented by A. W. Lawrence.

SEVEN PILLARS OF WISDOM

T. E. Lawrence, Egypt
Photograph by Maxwell H. Coote, 1921
(detail, no. 200)

Lawrence's ambition to write a major work of some kind is clear even in his pre-war letters. At Carchemish he had contemplated several projects, including a book on seven cities of the East to be called *Seven Pillars of Wisdom*. None of these had been completed by the outbreak of war. Two years later, however, he realised that chance had given him the kind of subject he had been hoping for: the Arab Revolt, and his own part within it.

Lawrence's intention of writing a book about the campaign is referred to in correspondence as early as September 1917, and for some months before this he had been making notes on the army message pads he carried with him. These were descriptive rather than military, since there was a risk that they might fall into enemy hands. They contained vivid word-pictures of people and places.

At the end of the war, Lawrence made no secret of his plans for a book. But, as he told Doughty: 'I'm afraid it is not likely to be written for publication, since some of it would give offence to people alive (including myself!), but I hope to get it put on paper soon.'[1]

Most of the first draft of *Seven Pillars* was written in France during the spring of 1919, while Lawrence was attending the Paris Peace Conference. That autumn, on leaving government service, he began to seek factual and literary criticisms. In November, however, he lost almost the whole manuscript while changing trains at Reading Station. This was a tremendous blow, and but for persuasion from friends, particularly Hogarth, the book might have been abandoned. As it was, he began hurriedly to write it down again while the old draft was still fresh in his memory. He worked almost continuously on the reconstruction of his text for three months at 14 Barton Street, Westminster. When finished the draft was some 200,000 words long but 'hopelessly bad'.[2] During 1920 he slowly corrected it against his surviving notes.

At this time the scheme to get a private press under way was high among his priorities. As he could not bring himself to release the full text of *Seven Pillars* for general circulation, he hoped to print a small edition himself. But first he needed money to build premises for the press on land he had bought at Chingford in Essex.

With this in mind, he decided to offer the American publisher F.N. Doubleday a popular abridgement: 'Unless I am starving (involuntarily) there will be no London publisher. My whole object is to make money in U.S.A. and so avoid the notoriety of being on sale in England.'[3] By July 1920, he had begun to consider the physical production of the abridgement, and wrote to Doubleday seeking agreement on matters such as maps and illustrations. By August 1920 about 40,000 words (eight chapters) of the abridgement were in draft. Then, abruptly, Lawrence abandoned it.

By the end of 1920 Lawrence had spent a considerable amount of time on *Seven Pillars*, but much of his effort had been wasted because of the lost manuscript and the cancelled abridgement. He was also increasingly self-conscious about defects in his literary technique: 'What is the perversity which makes me, capable of many things in the world, wish only to do one thing, book-writing: and gives me no skill at it?'[4] Yet his ambitions for the book were higher than ever: he now hoped to make it a 'titanic' work comparable in stature to *The Brothers Karamazov* or *Moby Dick*. He began a third draft of *Seven Pillars*, rewriting the text with great care.

It is clear that by this time he intended, in the long term, to produce a finely-printed private edition. While revising the text, he had begun to collect illustrations. He had been painted and sketched by Augustus John during the Peace Conference, and had since acquired not only one of those portraits, but also one of John's two oils of Feisal (also present at Versailles). During 1920 Lawrence went round London art

1. T. E. Lawrence to C. M. Doughty, 25.12.1918,
Letters, p. 271.
2. *SPW 1935*, p. 22.
3. T. E. Lawrence to F. N. Doubleday, 29.3.1920.
4. *Biographers* (Graves), p. 20.

shows to see the work of other contemporary painters. Finally he approached one of them, Eric Kennington, seeking advice about illustrations. Kennington was very enthusiastic and in March travelled to Arabia to do portraits of the Arabs involved in the Revolt. He returned in June with a collection of vivid pastel drawings.

From this time on, the 'Kennington Arabs' were to dominate all Lawrence's plans for an edition of *Seven Pillars*. As a first step, he saw the need to balance the Arabs by commissioning portraits of British participants in the Revolt. During the next five years he organised artists and sitters, until he could put twenty Europeans alongside the twenty best Arabian portraits. The additional portraits included work by Frank Dobson, Colin Gill, John, Kennington, Henry Lamb, William Nicholson, William Roberts, William Rothenstein, John Singer Sargent, and Gilbert Spencer. Lawrence sent four of the Kennington Arabs to Whittingham & Griggs in 1921, for reproduction by chromo-lithography.

Meanwhile work on the new text of *Seven Pillars* was only progressing slowly. He had started the new draft in London, but had to continue it while travelling on diplomatic missions to Jidda and Amman. In September 1921 he cabled Whittingham & Griggs asking them to stop work on the plates. He was now short of money, and had increasing doubts about the text.

In February 1922 Lawrence took three months' leave from the Colonial Office and determined to sit in Barton Street until *Seven Pillars* was finished. He was soon very depressed about the book's shortcomings: 'The real trouble is about my book, which is not good: not good enough to come out. It has grown too long and shapeless, and I haven't enough strength to see it all in one piece, or the energy to tackle it properly. After I've got out of the Colonial Office and have been fallow for a time my interest in it will probably come back and then I'll have another go at it: but not for the present.'[5] By the time he wrote this letter he was already planning to enlist in the ranks of the RAF.

He wanted to circulate *Seven Pillars* for criticism, but had no wish to risk losing the unique copy again. When he found that the *Oxford Times* could set the text and print eight copies for £175, he arranged to have this done. Lawrence sent the first sections to the newspaper in late January 1922, and the printing was finished in the third week of July. As a precaution against unauthorised circulation of the complete book, the draft chapters went for typesetting unnumbered and out of order. He kept the potentially sensational chapters (like the account of his experience at Deraa) until the last batch.

In August, while the 'Oxford' copies were still at the binder, he wrote to Edward Garnett and George Bernard Shaw, asking whether they would read and criticise the book. Both agreed to do so. Other copies were to be read by Alan Dawnay, D.G. Hogarth, Eric Kennington and Vyvyan Richards. While waiting for their reactions Lawrence presented himself at a recruiting office in London.

Garnett, a professional publisher's editor, was quick to comment. He was very enthusiastic about the book and offered to make a popular abridgement, as he had earlier done for Doughty's *Arabia Deserta*. Lawrence accepted the idea and sent a corrected set of the 'Oxford' sheets to Garnett, who drafted his abridgement on them during October. Although Lawrence spent several weeks working over this draft, his enthusiasm for the project was already waning. He knew, however, that it represented his best hope of escaping from Air Force life, which he was finding unexpectedly distressing. He wrote: 'if the abridgment is approved by a publisher I'll find myself rich – according to my standard. Whether I'll continue in the R.A.F. then, or return to London life, I don't know.'[6]

On 1 December 1922 Lawrence told Garnett that he could mention the abridgement to Jonathan Cape. That same day Shaw sent his first considered reaction. He had barely sampled the book, but his wife Charlotte had read it from cover to cover and was very impressed. Shaw suggested that since parts of the book could not possibly be published an abridgement should be made for general circulation. Meanwhile, the whole text should be placed in the British Museum under a hundred-year embargo. Lawrence, warmed by this apparent approval of his plans, replied to Shaw on 7 December telling him about Garnett's abridgement. If it were published 'I shall become

T. E. Lawrence
By Colin Gill, 1920
Private Collection
(not exhibited)

5. T. E. Lawrence to E. Kennington, 16.2.1922.
6. T. E. Lawrence to R. D. Blumenfeld, 24.11.1922.

Camel March
By William Roberts, 1923
(no. 231)

a civilian again. You have no idea how repulsive a barrack room is as a permanent home'.[7] Significantly, in a letter to Garnett written the same day, Lawrence said: 'The private press has been a life-dream of mine – and has been twice . . . on the point of coming true. It will come, and will, I hope, be as good as my expectations.'[8]

At this stage, however, Lawrence's advisers began to contradict one another. Cape, supported by his reader Garnett, moved swiftly towards a contract which would have given Lawrence some £7,000. Shaw, on the other hand, viewed Cape as a 'modern ruffian', and recommended Constable instead. On 28 December Shaw let fly in a spectacular volte-face: 'I cannot wait to finish the book before giving you my opinion, and giving it strong. *It must be published in its entirety, unabridged* . . . you must not for a moment entertain the notion of publishing an abridgment first, as no publisher would touch the whole work afterwards'. He continued in the same vein, concluding 'I had ten years on the managing committee of the Society of Authors, and learnt that there is no bottom to the folly and business incompetence of authors or the unscrupulousness of publishers, who, being in a gambling business where one live book has to pay for ten duds, cannot afford to lose a single opportunity.

'You must not mind my shoving into your affairs like this. How else could I be of any service?'[9]

Lawrence was uncertain what to do, and this indecision was reinforced by sudden press exposure of his secret presence in the RAF. After a few days of this unwelcome attention he decided to cancel publication of the abridgement. The reminder of his personal publicity value made the life of an airman suddenly seem very attractive again; a popular account of his wartime experiences would only excite press interest and alarm the RAF authorities. He immediately told his literary agent, Raymond Savage, that the abridgement was 'off' and wrote personally to Cape: 'The cash (my only motive for doing the mean thing which a censored version is) would have been most grateful: and the bother will have upset you. However there it is.'[10]

Needless to say, Cape did not accept this decision easily, and during the weeks of uncertainty that followed while Lawrence strove to keep his place in the Air Force, several ideas were mooted. Lawrence wrote to Shaw at the end of January 1923: 'I cancelled (or rather I refused to complete and sign) the contract with Cape for

7. T. E. Lawrence to G. B. Shaw, 7.12.1922, *Letters*, p. 388.
8. T. E. Lawrence to E. Garnett, 7.12.1922, *Letters*, p. 386.
9. G. B. Shaw to T. E. Lawrence, 28.12.1922, *Letters to T. E. Lawrence*, ed. A. W. Lawrence, 1962, pp. 167-8.
10. T. E. Lawrence to H. J. Cape, 1.1.1923.

publishing an abridgment. Cape was furious . . . a while later I was sorry to have cancelled it, and I began to think of publishing, not an abridgment, but the whole story, as you have advised. So I sketched to Cape the possibility of a limited, privately-printed, subscription edition of 2,000 copies, illustrated with all the drawings made for me by some twenty of the younger artists. Cape was staggered for the first moment, but then rose to it – suggesting half-profits, and a serial issue of a quarter of it in the *Observer* and American copyrights, and all the necessary decorations. It took the form of a beautiful contract, sent me to sign: and that very day I got my dismissal from the Air Ministry: and so I've cancelled it too.'[11]

Once again, moves to publish *Seven Pillars* had ended in total débâcle – but Lawrence did not for one moment abandon his long-term ambition to print the book. Within a week, he was writing to C.E. Wilson, one of the British officers involved in the Revolt, arranging for Kennington to paint still another portrait; and then to William Roberts and Paul Nash, seeking further illustrations.

In March 1923 Lawrence joined the Tank Corps as a private. The 'Oxford' *Seven Pillars* continued to circulate: that year it was criticised by literary figures such as Sydney Cockerell, J. L. Garvin, Thomas Hardy and Rudyard Kipling. It was also sent, with appeals for factual correction, to wartime colleagues: General Bartholomew from Allenby's staff, Robin Buxton of the Imperial Camel Corps, D.G. Hogarth from the Arab Bureau, and so on. In May, Lawrence told Wavell, the latest reader: 'though . . . I can see and say no good of my book, yet I'm glad when others praise it. I hate it and like it by turns, and know that it's a good bit of writing, and often wish it wasn't. If I'd aimed less high I'd have hit my mark squarer . . . Apart from literature, how does it strike you as history?' He continued: 'To publish the whole book might cause a new clamour, for I don't hide from myself that it might be a successful book, as sales went. To censor it would mean practical re-writing, and I'm weary of the work put into it already: also it feels a little dishonest to hide parts of the truth . . . Against these instincts you have to set the vanity of an amateur who's tried to write, and would like to be in print as an author: and my need of money to live quietly upon.'[12]

During May 1923, Lawrence's friends put him under increasing pressure to publish. Lawrence wanted the smallest possible edition, and joked about finding a millionaire who would underwrite it. Shaw, on the other hand, was pushing for wide circulation at a reasonable price. That year Lawrence drew his money from All Souls for the last time and spent it on more illustrations.

In August he toyed briefly once again with the idea of issuing Garnett's abridgement; but by now his friends had decided to force him to a decision by offering to back a viable project. During the autumn, the basis for a subscribers' edition was established. First estimates for printing text and illustrations were a little less than £3,000.

Lawrence, who intended to re-edit the text from an unbound copy of the 'Oxford' printing, rented a cottage to work in: Clouds Hill, near Bovington Camp in Dorset. 'There I can revise my text in about a twelve-month, allowing say 2 hrs average per day . . . the whole project may be complete within 18 months'.[13]

Final decisions about the subscribers' edition were taken at a meeting in Oxford on 9 December 1923. Those present were Lawrence, D. G. Hogarth, Lionel Curtis and Alan Dawnay. Given the £3,000 estimate of costs, they had to decide between selling 300 copies at £10, or 100 copies at £30. Lawrence had already put his own views on this point to Hogarth: 'I'm aiming at a public that will pay but not read . . . If as many as 300 copies were sent out, the book would have to be severely cut down, and that means another edition some day . . . The fewer the copies, the less the cuts.'[14]

The meeting decided to back this scheme. About one hundred subscribers would now have to be found, each paying thirty guineas; in addition a smaller number of copies would be bound up with an incomplete set of colour plates as gifts for people who had fought in the Arab campaign.

Lawrence would be responsible for revising *Seven Pillars*, and for seeing to its production and distribution. His role as both author and publisher would also ensure,

11. T. E. Lawrence to G. B. Shaw, 30.1.1923, *Letters*, p. 397.
12. T. E. Lawrence to A. P. Wavell, 11.5.1923.
13. T. E. Lawrence to D. G. Hogarth, 14.11.1923, *Letters*, p. 440.
14. T. E. Lawrence to D. G. Hogarth, 6.12.1923.

as he put it, 'that the law of libel, civil or criminal, may fall blunted on my penniless status as a private soldier.'[15] The Bank of Liverpool and Martins would provide him with a working overdraft against the security of the Chingford land and Garnett's unused 1922 abridgement which was in Hogarth's safe-keeping.

By this time Kennington had found a potential printer. This was Manning Pike, an American born in Minnesota. Pike was not really a trained printer, but had spent time in his home town working in a small commercial printing shop. He had, however, a strong artistic sense and was attending a course at the London School of Printing, where he studied typographical composition.

During the winter of 1923-4 the scheme for the edition continued to take shape. Revisions of the 'Oxford' text would be 'literary' only. Subscribers were promised that there would be no library copies, no reviews, and no republication of the complete text during Lawrence's lifetime. The first twelve subscriptions were in by mid-January 1924, and Lawrence instructed Whittingham & Griggs to proceed with the plates. By the end of March Pike had submitted estimates, and more subscribers came in during the spring and summer.

Meanwhile Lawrence made detailed revisions to his text, many of them for typographical rather than literary reasons. By the end of September 1924 the first eight chapters were in proof, and he had several copies bound up as pamphlets. He sent one of these to St. John Hornby and another to Sydney Cockerell for criticism of typography, and a further copy to the Shaws. Shaw tackled the proof as though it were his own, repunctuating it from beginning to end. He also advised the suppression of the first chapter and a few passages which might be libellous. It is often claimed that he 'edited' the whole of *Seven Pillars*; but his much-cited criticisms were based on the first forty-four pages, and there is no evidence that he paid any attention to the later proofs Lawrence sent to Charlotte.

As work on the edition progressed, it became clear that the original estimates were optimistic as regards both cost and the time needed to complete the edition. The first text section was not finally run until February 1925, more than a year after the project began. Lawrence ordered 300 copies of this Introductory Book: 100 of these were to be bound up with a colour plate and sent to subscribers as a sample.

By this time the project was in serious trouble. Although half the text was in various stages of proof, little had been run. Pike, who was mainly interested in typesetting, was suffering from fits of depression and unable to cope with the volume of press work.

Matters were little better financially. The bank could not finance the increasing costs. Lawrence agreed to put up his land at Chingford for sale, and to auction his private press books. In mid-March, however, he took the only realistic course open to him, and offered Cape yet another abridgement: 125,000 words from the new text. Hearing of this, Shaw offered to guarantee the *Seven Pillars* overdraft, but Lawrence could not accept. By now there were nearly 100 subscribers, and although the total had been raised to 120, the income from subscriptions would fall at least £1,000 short of costs.

A crucial clause in the new Cape contract, signed at the beginning of May 1925, would allow Lawrence to stop English publication of the abridgement once the *Seven Pillars* overdraft had been repaid. Shaw objected to this idea, proposing instead a licence for Cape to publish during seven years. Lawrence believed, however, that the abridgement would sell well, and pay off the bank overdraft within months of publication, which was scheduled for March 1927.

Once the Cape contract was secure, Lawrence cancelled the sale of his Chingford land and withdrew his press books from auction, telling his bank: 'I'd rather keep them than anything I've ever had.'[16]

During 1925 the projected revenue from the abridgement grew, with sales of serial rights and an American edition. Lawrence now abandoned his original budget completely, spending freely on new tailpieces. The first of these had been conceived in 1922 when Eric Kennington read the 'Oxford' *Seven Pillars*; during 1925 and 1926 Lawrence commissioned many more from William Roberts, Blair Hughes-Stanton and Paul Nash.

15. T. E. Lawrence to E. Kennington, 13.12.1923.
16. T. E. Lawrence to R. V. Buxton, 26.3.1925, *Letters*, p. 472.

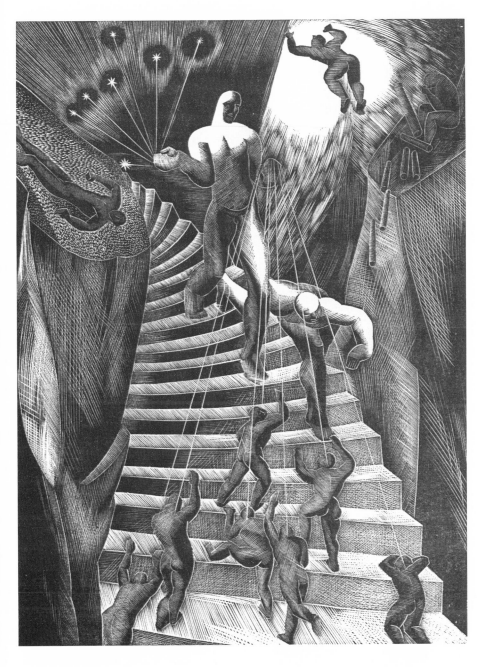

The Poem to S.A.
By Blair Hughes-Stanton, 1926
(no. 237)

By the autumn of 1925 it seemed that the book might be ready for issue in the following March, and Lawrence wrote happily to Charlotte Shaw: 'Isn't it wonderful? The job is nearly over.'[17] The galleys of Books IX and X were almost checked; Books VI-VIII were in page proof, and the whole first part printed. As the chapters went into page proof, he commissioned more and more tailpieces. By the end of the year the cost of the work had already reached £4,500 (not counting the £3,000 spent on illustrations before the edition began).

Lawrence had made it clear from the start that he would not personally take any money from the subscription edition. In later statements he suggested that this was because he did not want to benefit in any way from the fraudulent role he had played during the war. This cannot have been his original reason since as late as December 1922 he had been perfectly ready to accept income from Garnett's abridgement. In all probability Lawrence refused to profit from the subscribers' *Seven Pillars* because he did not want critics to suggest that the high asking price (for a book then unseen) was due to personal greed.

The same condition applied to the proceeds of Cape's abridgement, *Revolt in the Desert*. He would have preferred not to publish this at all, and it was something of

17. T. E. Lawrence to C. F. Shaw, 19.11.1925.

an embarrassment to him with regard to the *Seven Pillars* subscribers, most of whom had committed themselves to buying the book before there was any talk of publishing part of its text. It is probably for this reason that Lawrence took such pains to denigrate the abridgement, claiming for instance that he had made it 'in seven hours . . . on March 26 and 27 1926'.[18] This statement was true in a way but highly misleading; Lawrence actually made the abridgement over several weeks, working in pencil on a set of proofs of the subscribers' *Seven Pillars*. What was produced in a day was a second set of marked-up pages, copied from the first, which was sent to the publishers.

When he first looked for subscribers, Lawrence had hoped that *Seven Pillars* would be ready by the summer of 1925. It was now a year late, and there were still further delays during 1926 owing first to production complications and then to the General Strike.

In November 1926 Lawrence took a month's leave, meaning to see his friends before sailing for a new service posting in India. However, the delays over *Seven Pillars* frustrated his plans, and he had to spend most of the month assembling the copies with their plates to make them ready for the binders. At last, however, the long and involved saga of the production of *Seven Pillars* was at an end. It had cost Lawrence over £13,000, leaving his patient bank with a £7,300 overdraft. The first copy finished went to King George V as a gift (Lawrence had discreetly returned the Royal Library's subscription cheque). He wrote special inscriptions in several copies, including those for Churchill and the long-suffering Trenchard: 'From a contented admirer and, where possible, obedient servant.'[19] An edition of twenty-two copies had been printed in America to copyright the text, preventing piracy. To achieve this, the book had to remain in print: it did so, because copies were priced at $20,000.

On 1 December Lawrence devolved all his possessions on to his banker and lawyer as trustees. They would act for him in the clearing of his bank overdraft. Although *Seven Pillars* remained exclusively his own copyright, they were free to sell the pictures he had commissioned and were empowered to negotiate publishing and other rights in the Cape abridgement.

When *Revolt in the Desert* was published in March 1927 Charlotte Shaw sent the reviews to India. The book's reception was, on the whole, excellent. Lawrence amused himself comparing what different critics said about his style, but there can be no doubt that he found their comments tremendously encouraging. The only sour notes were struck by old political opponents such as Sir Arnold Wilson, who had disagreed with Lawrence's policies towards the Arabs. The book sold so well that the *Seven Pillars* overdraft was repaid within weeks. Since he refused to profit from *Revolt* the trustees he had appointed were able to make large donations to the Royal Air Force Benevolent Fund. In May he asked them to invoke the clause in Cape's contract which halted further publication in Britain during his lifetime. *Revolt* continued to sell in America; and it has been translated into Arabic, Czech, Danish, Dutch, Finnish, French, German, Hebrew, Hungarian, Italian, Polish, Rumanian, Spanish and Swedish.

The success of *Revolt* served to fuel public interest in *Seven Pillars*, and the thirty guinea subscribers proved to have been well rewarded for their patience. The price rose rapidly, and peaked in November 1927 when a copy was sold at an auction room in London for £570. This premium shocked Lawrence, but the price soon slid back, as he had expected, to around £200.

Whatever the book's investment value, his correspondents left him in no doubt that *Seven Pillars* was a masterpiece. The old *Oxford Times* version had been read by numerous people, and almost all of them thought the subscribers' revision better. Churchill told him that it was a 'grand and permanent contribution' to English literature.[20] *Seven Pillars of Wisdom* has proved to be one of the most successful non-fiction works to come out of the First World War.

Lawrence, Kennington, Pike and H. J. Hodgson, a skilled technician who helped with the printing, must share the accolade for the 1926 subscribers' edition. It is now catalogued by rare book dealers at £20,000 and more.

18. T. E. Lawrence to H. J. Cape, 25.5.1927, *Letters*, p. 518.
19. H. Montgomery-Hyde, *Solitary in the Ranks*, 1977, p. 127.
20. Winston Churchill to T. E. Lawrence, *Letters to T. E. Lawrence*, ed. A. W. Lawrence, 1962, p. 24

205
AUGUSTUS JOHN
Photograph by John Hope-Johnstone
(*c*.1922)

Augustus John and Lawrence first met during
the Paris Peace Conference in 1919, when
John painted his most famous portrait of
Lawrence (see no. 115). They remained in
contact after Lawrence enlisted in the RAF
in 1922, and during the years that followed
John painted three more oil studies of
Lawrence and made several further drawings.

Later John recalled that 'Lawrence
actually enjoyed being painted, and always
seemed vastly tickled by the results.'[1]
Lawrence had a high professional regard for
John, describing him as 'the only painter of
today with greatness'.[2] They seem not,
however, to have become close friends, and
towards the end of his life John spoke with
some enthusiasm of Richard Aldington's
debunking biography of Lawrence.

This photograph was taken in Spain when
John was staying with the travel writer,
Gerald Brenan, and is copied from an album
formerly belonging to Brenan.

National Portrait Gallery (NPG P134/25)

1. A. John, *Chiaroscuro*, 1952, p. 238.
2. *Biographers* (Liddell Hart), p. 35.

Literature: G. Brenan, *Personal Record 1920-72*, 1974,
p. 40; M. Holroyd, *Augustus John*, II, 1974-5, p. 113.

206
SIR HERBERT BAKER
By Sir William Rothenstein, 1925

Sir Herbert Baker (1862-1946), a noted
architect who later designed the Bank of
England, was introduced to Lawrence by
Lionel Curtis in Oxford shortly after the
war. When Lawrence began re-writing *Seven
Pillars* in December 1919 having lost the first
draft, he found it difficult to work in the
atmosphere of All Souls. Baker offered a
room above his offices in Barton Street,
Westminster, where Lawrence could
worked undisturbed (see no. 207).

Baker became a close friend and later,
while Lawrence was serving in the RAF in
India, he and Lionel Curtis tried to arrange
civilian employment for Lawrence as a
security official at the Bank of England.

National Portrait Gallery (NPG 4763)

Red chalk, 32.4 × 35.2
Signed r.: *W. R. 1925*
Provenance: The artist's family; purchased from Deval
and Muir, 1970.
Literature: J. Rothenstein, *The Portrait Drawings of
William Rothenstein*, 1926, no. 698, ill. pl. XCIX.

207
14 BARTON STREET, WESTMINSTER
By an unknown photographer

It was here that Lawrence wrote successive
drafts of *Seven Pillars of Wisdom* between 1919
and 1922, and the house served for many
years as his London postal address. In 1929
he went to Barton Street again during his
annual leave from the RAF, to work on his
translation of the *Odyssey*.

The staff in the architect's offices below
were instructed to protect Lawrence from
visitors, and became adept at turning people
away. Baker recalled Lawrence saying that
the attic room was 'the best-and-freest place
I have ever lived in, nobody has found me
. . . despite efforts by callers and
telephones'.[1]

J. M. Wilson

1. *Friends*, p. 249.

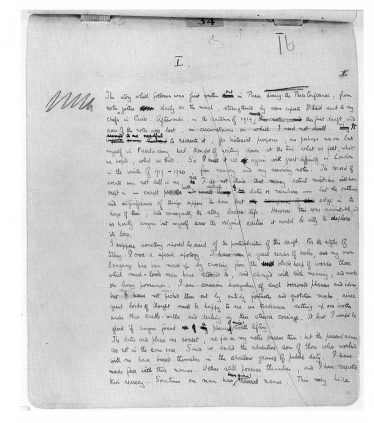

Col. T. E. LAWRENCE.

208

'COL. LAWRENCE'S LOST MS'

Evening Standard, 12 January 1920

Lawrence began writing *Seven Pillars of
Wisdom* early in 1919, and by the end of that
year almost all of it was in draft. The book
would, if completed, have run to about
250,000 words, 50,000 words shorter than
the final version. During the autumn of 1919
he lent this draft for criticism to Alan
Dawnay who lived in Oxford. Afterwards
Lawrence collected it and returned to
London by train, carrying the manuscript in
an official attaché case. He left the case
unattended for a few minutes at Reading
station, and it was stolen.

Despite press coverage the manuscript
was never recovered. Lawrence's initial
reaction was to abandon the book entirely,
but he was persuaded by friends to take it up
again. Only the 'Introduction' remained of
the first draft, and he spent three months
writing down what he could remember of
the old text, 'doing many thousand words at
a time, in long sittings. Thus Book VI was
written entire between sunrise and sunrise.'[1]
Lawrence said the hurriedly rewritten draft
was over 400,000 words in length. He spent
the rest of 1920 correcting it.

J. M. Wilson

1. *SPW* 1935, p. 21.

Newspaper cutting
Literature : T. E. Lawrence, *Some Notes on the Writing of
Seven Pillars of Wisdom and Revolt in the Desert by
T. E. Shaw*, 1927 ; Sir Douglas Brownrigg, *Unexpected*, no
date, p. 58.

209

THIRD DRAFT OF *SEVEN PILLARS OF
WISDOM*

Autograph manuscript by T.E. Lawrence,
1922

As soon as the second, hurriedly re-written,
draft of *Seven Pillars* was finished Lawrence
began to revise and correct it. He spent most
of his time in the spring of 1922 at 14 Barton
Street laboriously completing a new draft in
handwriting that was sufficiently legible for
a typesetter.

He did the work in long sessions,
incorporating further revisions as he wrote.
The manuscript is written in mapping ink on
single sheets punched for a Kalamazoo
binder. As originally written, the chapters
were not numbered. This enabled him to
rearrange them in random order before
sending them to the *Oxford Times* for printing
– a precaution taken to prevent anyone but
himself from assembling the complete text.
The printing order is shown by numbers
written in pencil at the top of each sheet, and
these reveal that he submitted the most
sensational chapters in the final batch.

In March 1923, having no further use for
the manuscript, Lawrence visited Dr Cowley,
the Librarian at the Bodleian, and presented
Seven Pillars of Wisdom to the Library. He
wrote afterwards : 'In giving my M.S. to the
Bodleian I acted perhaps unhumorously,

taking myself a little too seriously as a classic.
Cowley was equal to the occasion, and never
smiled at all throughout the transaction.
Whether he has a treasure or not the next
century can tell . . . There is of course no
restriction in its use : the man who could
read so much of my handwriting would
deserve what he found.'[1]

In addition to the text, which is the
earliest full draft of *Seven Pillars* extant, there
is a brief note in Lawrence's hand giving the
history of the preceding manuscripts. The
note reveals that he burnt the whole of the
second draft except for a single page, which
is bound-in at the rear of this volume. The
sample page is so heavily worked over that
it is barely comprehensible.

Lawrence sent the manuscript page
carrying the dedicatory poem to his friend
Robert Graves, asking whether it was prose
or verse. Graves replied that it was,
potentially, a poem although part seemed to
be prose. In order to illustrate his point he
wrote a paraphrase stanza on the back of
Lawrence's dedication (this was subsequently
published as 'A Crusader').

The Curators of the Bodleian Library,
Oxford (MS.Res.d.33)

1. T. E. Lawrence to S. C. Cockerell, 22.10.1923.

Loose-leaf sheets contained in a leather-bound
Kalamazoo binder, 24.3
Provenance : given by T. E. Lawrence, 1923.

210
THE *SEVEN PILLARS* PEN

Lawrence, who usually wrote in a very small, neat hand, probably first used mapping pens and ink when working in the Geographical Section of the General Staff in the autumn of 1914. Subsequently he spent nearly two years compiling and correcting maps in the Intelligence Department in Cairo, and for some years after the war he continued to use mapping pens for most of his writing and correspondence.

This pen is accompanied by a note on Herbert Baker's 14 Barton Street letterhead which reads: 'Dec. 2 1926. T.E.L. (or S) told me this morning that with this nib – and for some time the holder – he wrote the whole of the *Seven Pillars of Wisdom* in this house. H.B.'

The Warden and Fellows of All Souls College, Oxford

'Eagle Pencil' brand wooden pen with metal nib, 15.8 long
Provenance: Given by Sir Herbert Baker to Lionel Curtis; and by him to All Souls College, 1938.

211
ERIC HENRI KENNINGTON
Self portrait, 1918

Eric Kennington (1888–1960) fought in France during 1914 and 1915, but was then invalided out, and served as official war artist from 1916 to 1919. Lawrence went to see an exhibition of his war pictures at the Alpine Club in 1920, and bought two of them. At the same time he left a message that he would like to meet the artist.

Lawrence arranged that Kennington should go to the Middle East and draw a series of Arab portraits. Kennington returned with a collection of pastel drawings which were to become the most striking illustrations in the subscribers' *Seven Pillars*. They were exhibited at the Leicester

Galleries in 1921. Afterwards, Kennington advised Lawrence on every aspect of the book's illustration. He contributed a range of work to *Seven Pillars* in addition to portraits: watercolour landscapes, tailpieces, and even some cartoons.[1] He also put Lawrence in touch with several other artists who would be interested in some part of the work. Lawrence once described Kennington as 'a great man, an exceedingly fine draughtsman, and a good psychologist'.[2]

In 1926 Kennington executed a portrait bust of Lawrence (see no. 275), one cast of which is now in St. Paul's Cathedral. Lawrence had a great admiration for Kennington's sculpture, and in 1929 warmly recommended him for the Thomas Hardy memorial in Dorchester.

The Visitors of the Ashmolean Museum, Oxford

1. See nos. 223–230.
2. T. E. Lawrence to Liddell Hart, 14.12.1933.

Black chalk, 50 × 36.7
Signed and dated br.: *E. H. K. 1918*
Provenance: W. Rothenstein; J. Borthwick; sold Sotheby's, 9 February 1972 (58); purchased, 1972.
Literature: Ashmolean Museum, *Report of the Visitors 1971-2*, Oxford, p. 36.

212

THE 'OXFORD' EDITION OF *SEVEN PILLARS OF WISDOM*, 1922

Between January and July 1922 *Seven Pillars of Wisdom* was set up in Linotype by newspaper compositors at the *Oxford Times*. Eight sets of the unnumbered chapters were printed on a proofing press. Afterwards, Lawrence assembled the chapters in their correct order and numbered them by hand, adding typescripts of the title page and other preliminaries as well as appropriate maps.

During August 1922 he corrected misprints and punctuation in five copies, and

gave them for binding to the London firm C. & C. McLeish. Athough he often talked of destroying them, all five survive. Three are in England (two in the British Library, one in the Bodleian Library) and two in private collections in the USA. One further copy, used by Lawrence and Edward Garnett to make a draft abridgement in the autumn of 1922, is now in the Houghton Library at Harvard. The two remaining sets of pages were used and largely discarded during production of the 1926 subscribers' edition.

The British Library Board (C108 K 7)

Printed book with typescript preliminaries, bound in full morocco with snakeskin endpapers, 28.7
Autograph inscription on final page : *This copy has been lent in turn to :* /G. B. Shaw./S. C. Cockerell./*Siegfried Sassoon.*/E. M. Forster./C. M. Doughty./Frank Stirling./H. G. Wells, [a humorist has added 'Ella Wheeler Wilcox' ; she died in 1919 before the book was printed].
Provenance : Loaned by T. E. Lawrence to G. B. Shaw ; given by him to the British Museum.

213

RECEIPTED INVOICE FROM THE *OXFORD TIMES* FOR PRINTING EIGHT COPIES OF *SEVEN PILLARS OF WISDOM* 1 August 1922

See no. 212.

The Curators of the Bodleian Library, Oxford (MS.Res.c.52/1)

Printed leaf with MS additions and stamps, 20.4 × 16.9
Provenance : Given by A. W. Lawrence.

214

EDWARD GARNETT
Photograph by Lucia Moholy, 1936
Vintage print

Edward Garnett (1868-1937) was a novelist, playwright, and critic, but he is best remembered for his work as editorial adviser to Jonathan Cape Ltd. He is credited with the discovery of Joseph Conrad, and gave much encouragement to D. H. Lawrence, E. M. Forster, and many other authors.

Lawrence approached Garnett in 1921 and asked him to read the 'Oxford' draft of *Seven Pillars*. Garnett was impressed with the work, and wanted to help with its publication : 'The ''SP'' is the thing above all you've got to get perfected . . . You've gone very far in that direction, but I can help you go further.'[1] During the autumn of 1922 Garnett prepared an abridgement of the 'Oxford' text, hoping that it would give Lawrence financial independence, but it was never published.

In gratitude for Garnett's encouragement Lawrence later gave him the manuscript of *The Mint*, which is dedicated 'To Edward Garnett – You dreamed I came one night with this book crying, ''Here's a masterpiece. Burn it.'' Well – as you please'.

National Portrait Gallery (NPG P132)

1. E. Garnett to T. E. Lawrence, 9.9.1922, *Letters to T. E. Lawrence*, ed. A. W. Lawrence, 1962, p. 88.

40 × 31
Provenance : Purchased from the photographer, 1979.
Exhibitions : National Portrait Gallery, *Lucia Moholy, 14 English Portraits*, 1979.

215
EDWARD MORGAN FORSTER
By Dora Carrington, *c.*1925

Dora Carrington's portrait of E.M. Forster (1879-1970) was painted some time between 1925 and 1932 at Ham Spray House, Lytton Strachey's home. Forster never saw the painting.

Forster was first introduced to Lawrence in 1921, and sought a reintroduction to him in 1923 after reading Siegfried Sassoon's copy of the 'Oxford' *Seven Pillars*. Lawrence was extremely grateful for Forster's detailed criticisms of *Seven Pillars*, and during 1924 Forster visited Clouds Hill on at least two occasions to help Lawrence with revisions of the text. By the time it was completed the two had become firm friends.

Later, while Lawrence was serving at Cranwell in 1925-6, he visited Cambridge regularly and met literary friends, notably Forster and F. L. Lucas. Both writers later dedicated books to him. Forster's *The Eternal Moment and other Stories* (1928) is dedicated 'To T. E. Lawrence in the absence of anything else'. Lucas dedicated his novel *Cécile* (1930) 'To T.E. Lawrence of Arabia and All Souls'. It won the coveted Hawthornden prize.

They corresponded, mainly on literary matters, for the rest of Lawrence's life, and more than seventy letters from Lawrence to Forster survive. Lawrence was one of the few people to be shown Forster's homosexual short stories and his unpublished novel *Maurice*, but while he offered constructive criticism, Lawrence's letters made it clear that he was not himself homosexual.

When Forster read *The Mint*, he concluded that it was 'not as great a work as *The Seven Pillars*, either in colour or form; but it is more new, more startling and more heartening than either *The S.P.* or anything else I've read'.[1]

Lawrence had a high regard for Forster: 'Do you know, he is the most civilised person I've ever met? I dally continually with my memory of him and of his books, trying to find out for myself something of their secrets. There was never anything so elusive, so subtle, so delicate, so robust . . . as his way of thinking.[2]

National Portrait Gallery (NPG 4698)

1. E. M. Forster to T. E. Lawrence, 5.7.1928, *Letters to T. E. Lawrence*, ed. A. W. Lawrence, 1962, p. 67.
2. T. E. Lawrence to E. Palmer, 15.3.1927.

Oil on canvas, 50.8 × 40.6
Unsigned
Provenance: By descent from the artist through Ralph Partridge; given by Mrs. Frances Partridge 1969.
Literature: M. Hill, short note in the *Burlington Magazine*, November 1970, p. 776; N. Carrington, *Carrington: Paintings, Drawings and Decorations*, Oxford, 1978, p. 59, ill. pl. 11.
Exhibitions: London, Upper Grosvenor Galleries, *Carrington: A Retrospective Exhibition*, 1970, (ex cat.); Fredericton, Beaverbrook Art Gallery, *Bloomsbury Painters and their Circle*, 1976 (20).

CHAPTER I

HE story which follows was first written out in Paris **Design of** during the Peace Conference, from notes jotted daily **the Story** on the march, strengthened by some reports sent to my chiefs in Cairo. Afterwards, in the autumn of 1919, this first draft and some of the notes were lost. It seemed to me historically needful to reproduce the tale, as perhaps no one but myself in Feisal's army had thought of writing down at the time what we felt, what we hoped, what we tried. So it was built again with heavy repugnance in London in the winter of 1919-20 from memory and my surviving notes. The record of events was not dulled in me and perhaps few actual mistakes crept in—except in details of dates or numbers—but the outlines and significance of things had lost edge in the haze of new interests.

Dates and places are correct, so far as my notes preserved them : but the personal names are not. Since the adventure some of those who worked with me have buried themselves in the shallow grave of public duty. Free use has been made of their names. Others still possess themselves, and here keep their secrecy. Sometimes one man carries various names. This may hide individuality and make the book a scatter of featureless puppets, rather than a group of living people : but once good is told of a man, and again evil, and some would not thank me for either blame or praise.

This isolated picture throwing the main light upon myself is unfair to my British colleagues. Especially I am most sorry that I have not told what the non-commissioned of us did. They were inarticulate, but wonderful, especially when it is taken into account that they had not the motive, the imaginative vision of the end, which sustained the officers. Unfortunately my concern was limited to this end, and the book is just a designed procession of Arab freedom from Mecca to Damascus. It is intended to rationalise the campaign, that everyone may see how natural the success was and

3

216

SAMPLE PAGE PROOF OF THE 'INTRODUCTION' TO *SEVEN PILLARS OF WISDOM* (CHAPTERS I – VIII), 1924

In order to produce the subscription edition of *Seven Pillars* Lawrence set up a printing company in which he became a nominal partner. He then employed a trainee printer, Manning Pike, who had been introduced to him by Eric Kennington.

As a first step, Pike set up a number of specimen pages in alternative type-sizes. After one of these had been chosen work began on typesetting the revised text.

At the end of September 1924 a small number of proofs of the 'Introductory' book (chapters I – VIII) were circulated for comment. Seeking technical criticism of the typography and press-work, Lawrence sent copies to St John Hornby and Sydney Cockerell. Other copies went to friends who

had backed the projected subscription edition, such as D.G. Hogarth and Lawrence's banker R.V. Buxton. For literary judgment he sent a copy to Bernard Shaw, whose reply is exhibited (see no. 220).

Few copies of this proof survive. It has a particular literary interest because it shows the text as it stood prior to Bernard Shaw's criticisms. In particular, it is the only source for Lawrence's revised text of the first chapter, suppressed at this stage on Shaw's advice. The proof also contains libellous paragraphs for which Shaw produced alternative drafts, identical in length so as to minimise the cost of re-setting.

Private Collection

Unbound printed page proof, 40 pp., 29 × 23
Provenance : R. V. Buxton.
Literature : J. M. Wilson, 'T. E. Lawrence and the Printing of *Seven Pillars of Wisdom*' in *Matrix* 5, Andoversford, 1985, pp. 62-4.

217
SIR SYDNEY COCKERELL
Photograph by Walter Stoneman (1917)

Sir Sydney Cockerell (1867-1962) was Director of the Fitzwilliam Museum in Cambridge from 1908 until 1937. He and Lawrence first met in March 1922, when they collaborated to help relieve C.M. Doughty's financial difficulties (see no. 195). Through their intervention, a notebook by Doughty relating to his Arabian journeys was bought by the Fitzwilliam, and a group of anonymous benefactors purchased one of his manuscripts for the British Museum. It is thought that Lawrence himself contributed a large part of the money raised for this latter purpose.

Cockerell, who had worked with William Morris at the Kelmscott Press, was one of the people Lawrence consulted in 1924 about the typography of *Seven Pillars*. More than forty letters from Lawrence to Cockerell survive.

National Portrait Gallery (NPR 94076B)

218
ST JOHN HORNBY
By F.H.S. Shepherd, *c.* 1925

St John Hornby (1867-1946) was a Director
of W. H. Smith and a noted authority on
printing. As a hobby he ran the Ashendene
Press, one of the finest of all English private
presses.

In September 1924 Lawrence sent Hornby
a proof of the first eight chapters of *Seven
Pillars*, asking for criticism of the typography
and press work. Later he asked Hornby to
recommend an experienced press operator to
assist in the production of the subscribers'
edition. Hornby introduced him to H. J.
Hodgson, a skilled technician who worked on
Seven Pillars and later at the Gregynog Press
in Wales.

Lawrence thought printing 'one of the
richest things any man can do', and greatly
admired Hornby's publications: '[St John
Hornby] lives in Chelsea, in a huge and
terrible house; but in the bottom of his
garden is an ex-stable, where he and two
printers turn out the Ashendene books. I do
not like his type (Caslon is my ideal) but his
press-work is the finest ever, and his vellum
copies the most sumptuous books in the
modern world.'[1]

Sir Simon Hornby

1. T. E. Lawrence to R. Isham, 22.11.1927.

Oil on board, 43.7 × 33.4
Signed br.: *F.H.S.*
Provenance: By descent.

219
GEORGE BERNARD SHAW
By Dame Laura Knight, 1932

Lawrence once remarked that Shaw's face was too well-known for any artist to see it without preconceptions: 'His best chance is to find some foreign artist who did not know his face'.[1]

Bernard Shaw (1856-1950) was introduced to Lawrence by Sydney Cockerell in March 1922. Six months later Lawrence sent Shaw a copy of *Seven Pillars*, hoping for useful criticisms. Shaw did not read it, however, for many months. Instead he passed the book to his wife Charlotte. The first serious criticism he offered was in 1924, when Lawrence sent him a proof of the first eight chapters of the subscribers' text (see no. 216).

Shaw never accepted Lawrence's reasons for enlisting in the ranks, and on several occasions tried to persuade the Government to provide Lawrence with a pension. Lawrence did not welcome the intrusion: 'You suggest that I'm not genuine in the ranks: but I am: just as good, now, as the others.'[2]

Writing to an RAF friend, Lawrence once said: 'G.B.S. is not a vast electric discharge. He is more like a cocktail. Very beneficent and plain to read. Slightly hard of hearing and short of sight – by which I mean, prone to imagine the whole from an incomplete part.'[3] On another occasion Lawrence wrote that Shaw was 'a great adventure.'[4]

Laura Knight met Shaw at the Malvern Festival, where Barry Jackson regularly staged productions of Shaw's plays. At the time of this portrait (1932), *Too True to be Good*, in which a character is based on Lawrence (see no. 306) was being performed. Lawrence visited the Festival and was also introduced to her.

Hereford City Museums and Art Gallery

1. T.E. Lawrence to W. Rothenstein, 14.4.1928, *Letters*, p. 583.
2. T.E. Lawrence to G. B. Shaw, 20.12.1923, *Letters*, p. 447.
3. T.E. Lawrence to G. W. Dunn, 9.11.1932, *Letters*, p. 752.
4. T.E. Lawrence to E. Elgar, *Letters*, p. 745.

Oil on canvas, 61 × 50.8
Signed br.: *Laura Knight*
Provenance: Given by Friends of the Art Gallery, 1942.
Literature: L. Knight, *Oil Paint and Grease Paint* 1926, pp. 375-81; L. Knight, *The Magic of a Line*, 1965, pp. 265-71.; J. Dunbar, *Laura Knight*, 1975, pp. 149-51; C. Fox, *Dame Laura Knight*, Oxford, 1988, pp. 89-90, ill. p. 82.
Exhibitions: RA, 1933 (145); London, Upper Grosvenor Galleries, *Laura Knight – 75 years of painting*, 1969 (21); Nottingham Castle, *Dame Laura Knight*, 1970 (80).

220
LETTER FROM G. B. SHAW TO
T. E. LAWRENCE
7 October 1924

In September 1924 Lawrence sent Bernard Shaw a proof of the first eight chapters of *Seven Pillars* in the revised text he was preparing for subscribers. Shaw worked through the proof very carefully, and sent Lawrence the letter printed below. It has often been suggested that Shaw corrected the remainder of *Seven Pillars* with similar care, but the evidence suggests that he saw very little of it. Lawrence sent the proofs to Charlotte Shaw, who worked through them herself making marginal suggestions. She only occasionally consulted her husband, who was preoccupied with work of his own.

'10 Adelphi Terrace WC2
7 October 1924

My dear Luruns

Confound you and your book: you are no more to be trusted with a pen than a child with a torpedo.

I have gone through the proof; and as it would be quite impossible to discuss it point by point in a letter, I have just corrected it exactly as I should correct a proof of my own, and made notes where the corrections were on non-technical points. Charlotte has also made some corrections.★

You will ink-in what you approve of on another proof, I suppose. You may discard plenty of my corrections: they may be interesting in shewing my system of punctuation and my way of doing it; but of course they are in no way binding on you, though when it is a case of words and not of stops you had better scrutinize them carefully to see whether they do not remove some ambiguity. I make these corrections mechanically: it would delay me too long to wait to consider whether they were interferences with your rights; so I just go ahead with them and leave you to weed them out.

I invented my own system of punctuation, and then compared it with the punctuation of the Bible, and found that the authors of the revised version had been driven to the same usage, though their practice is not quite consistent all through. The Bible bars the dash, which is the great refuge of those who are too lazy to punctuate: R.B. Sheridan used dashes and nothing else. I never use it when I can possibly substitute a colon; and I save up the colon jealously for certain effects that no other stop produces. As you have no rules, and sometimes throw colons about with an unhinged mind, here are some rough rules for you.

When a sentence contains more than one statement, with different nominatives, or even with the same nominative repeated for the sake of emphasizing some discontinuity between the statements, the statements should be separated with a semicolon *when the relation between them is expressed by a conjunction.* When there is no conjunction, or other modifying word, and the two statements are placed baldly in dramatic apposition, use a colon. Thus, Luruns said nothing; but he thought the more. Luruns could not speak: he was drunk. Luruns, like Napoleon, was out of place and a failure as a subaltern; yet when he could exasperate his officers by being a faultless private he could behave himself as such. Luruns, like Napoleon, could see a hostile city not only as a military objective but as a stage for a *coup de théâtre*: he was a born actor.

To put it another way, when the second statement is a reaffirmation or illustration of the first, use a colon. When it is a modification of it, or a contradiction, or a condition, or a mere correlation, the outward and visible sign being a conjunction, use a semicolon.

Colons are needed for abrupt pull-ups: thus, Luruns was congenitally literary: that is, a liar. Luruns was a man of many aliases: namely, Private Shaw, Colonel Lawrence, Prince of Damascus &c &c &c.

You will see that your colons before buts and the like are contra-indicated in my scheme, and leave you without anything in reserve for the dramatic occasions mentioned above. You practically do not use semicolons at all. This is a symptom of mental defectiveness, probably induced by camp life.

But by far the most urgent of my corrections – so important that you had better swallow them literally with what wry faces you cannot control – are those which concern your libels. I spent fifteen years of my life writing criticisms of sensitive living people, and thereby acquired a very cultivated sense of what I might say and what I might not say. All criticisms are technically libels; but there is the blow below the belt, the impertinence, the indulgence of dislike, the expression of personal contempt, and of course the imputation of dishonesty or unchastity which are not and should not be privileged, as well as the genuine criticism, the amusing goodhumored banter, and (curiously) the obvious ''vulgar abuse'' which *are* privileged. I have weeded out your reckless sallies as carefully as I can.

Then there is the more general criticism about that first chapter. That it should come out and leave the book to begin with chapter two, which is the real thing and very fine at that, I have no doubt whatever. You will see my note on the subject.

I must close up now, as Charlotte wants to make up her packet to you.

ever
G. Bernard Shaw
★ [marginal note in Charlotte Shaw's hand:]
O Mercy! *Suggestions* not corrections. C.F.S.'

While Lawrence adopted Shaw's advice about libels, he disregarded that on semi-colons, continuing to use colons extensively. In the acknowledgements for *Seven Pillars* he thanked the Shaws for their help and the few semi-colons that were left.

Private Collection

Typewritten letter, 2 pp., 17.7 × 22.6.
Annotated and signed *G. Bernard Shaw*.
Literature: Bernard Shaw, *Collected Letters 1911-1925*, ed. Dan H. Laurence, 1985, pp. 884-6.
(not illustrated)

221
REVISIONS TO BOOK VIII OF *SEVEN PILLARS OF WISDOM*, 1925

The subscribers' edition of *Seven Pillars* was set in Monotype galleys by a trade typesetting company in London. Lawrence did not prepare a new manuscript; instead he marked up the changes on one of the unused sets of 'Oxford' *Seven Pillars* pages.

After the galleys had been corrected, the revised 'Oxford' chapters were discarded. These pages of the typesetting draft, however, were sent by Lawrence to D.G. Hogarth early in 1926. Lawrence wrote: 'It's an example of the more drastic revision which some of my sections have had, especially Books VIII and IX. The whole text is in type now, but Books VII-X are still in stages of revision. A slow job. I do not know when it will be finished . . . Burn the enclosed, after having looked at them.'[1]

As Lawrence's letter indicates, the pages are particularly interesting because this was one of the most heavily abridged sections of

the book. Lawrence felt that the original text contained too long a 'flat' section in Books VIII and IX, before the drama of the final advance on Damascus.

Hogarth was one of the small group of friends who had backed the subscription project, and he had been named by Lawrence as literary executor in the event of Lawrence's death before the subscribers' revisions were completed.

Dr Caroline Barron

1. T. E. Lawrence to D. G. Hogarth, undated (c.February 1926).

Unbound printed sheets of the 1922 'Oxford' edition with numerous MS amendments and annotations by T. E. Lawrence and others, 20 pp., 28.8 × 22
Provenance: By descent from D. G. Hogarth.

222
PROOF COPY OF *SEVEN PILLARS OF WISDOM*, 1926

The working reference copy of the subscribers' edition assembled by Lawrence as the sections were printed. It was widely read by officers and fellow aircraftmen at Cranwell, where he served from August 1925 until November 1926.

The proof was originally bound-up roughly by Lawrence himself, and titled mischievously 'The complete aircrafthand'. Before leaving Cranwell he presented it to the College Library, which commissioned the present binding.

It was inscribed by Lawrence: 'Copy placed at disposal of Air Commodore Borton.

'This is a spoiled set of proofs of the complete text of my book *Seven Pillars of Wisdom*. It includes two pages in their original form – pages which have been modified for the edition as distributed.

'This copy lacks title page and fly-leaves, table of contents, table of illustrations, nine ''arguments'' prefaced to sections, many woodcuts and line blocks, all the plates, and two appendices; these, being trimmings of the text, are supplied only to subscribers / 18.x.26 T.E.S.'

Royal Air Force College

Bound volume, lacking prelims, flyleaves and illustrations, 25.4
Provenance: Given by T. E. Lawrence, 1926.
Literature: R. de la Bère, 'Aircraftman T. E. Shaw' in *Journal of the Royal Air Force College*, vol. XV, no. 2, Autumn 1935.
(not illustrated)

223
STRATA
By Eric Kennington, 1922

Below the clouds, Kennington portrays an incident from chapter 89 in *Seven Pillars* in which Lawrence was riding his camel, Wodheiha, through a blizzard: 'she rose to her feet whimpering and stood still, in a tremble. When he-camels so baulked, they would die on the spot, after days; and I feared that now I had found the limit of effort in she-camels.'[1]

Lawrence's head appears above the clouds watching the scene: 'As my war was overthought, because I was not a soldier, so my activity was overwrought, because I was not a man of action. They were intensely conscious efforts, with my detached self always eyeing the performance from the wings in criticism.'[2]

The Houghton Library, Harvard University, Gift of Bayard L. Kilgour Jr.

1. *SPW 1935*, ch. 89, p. 497.
2. *SPW 1935*, ch. 105, p. 562.

Pencil, 40.4 × 28
Unsigned
Provenance: Bequeathed by Bayard L. Kilgour Jr., 1958-66.
Literature: *SPW 1926*, ill.; *Letters*, p. 508; *Grosvenor*, no. 28.
Exhibitions: Leicester Galleries 1927 (11).

224
NIGHTMARE
By Eric Kennington, 1922

In chapter 31 of *Seven Pillars* Lawrence
describes how, in March 1917, he took upon
himself the task of executing a murderer,
Hamed the Moor, in order to avoid starting
a tribal feud. He was already ill with fever,
and after a camel march through the lava-
field of Wadi Gara he camped for the night.
'The illness, however, had stimulated my
ordinarily sluggish fancy, which ran riot this
night with dreams of wandering naked for a
dark eternity over interminable lava (like
scrambled egg gone iron-blue, and very
wrong), sharp as insect-bites underfoot; and
with some horror, perhaps a dead moor,
always climbing after us.'[1] Hamed the Moor
is at the top, and Lawrence fleeing bottom
right.
    In 1922, Lawrence wrote to Kennington:
'Your drawings are wonderful . . . the
nightmare, the snow-storm [see no. 223]: I
never imagined my chance of getting such
pictures.'[2]

The Houghton Library, Harvard University,
Gift of Bayard L. Kilgour Jr.

1. *SPW 1935*, ch. 32, pp. 185-6.
2. T. E. Lawrence to E. Kennington, 27.10.1922.

Watercolour, 38.5 × 26.7
Unsigned
Provenance: Bequeathed by Bayard L. Kilgour Jr.,
1985.
Literature: *SPW 1926*, ill.; *Grosvenor*, no. 29.
Exhibitions: Leicester Galleries 1927 (15).

225
FALSE QUIET
By Eric Kennington, 1922

Kennington's watercolour is printed at the end of the list of illustrations in the subscribers' *Seven Pillars*. The picture may have been inspired by a passage which reads: 'It was a noble evening, yellow, mild and indescribably peaceful; a foil to our incessant cannonade. The declining light shone down the angle of the ridges, its soft rays modelling them and their least contour in a delicate complexity of planes. Then the sun sank another second, and the surface became shadow, out of which for a moment there

rose, starkly, the innumerable flints strewing it; each western (reflecting) facet tipped like a black diamond with flame.'[1]

The Family of the Artist

1. *SPW 1935*, ch. 112, p. 607.

Watercolour, 14.5 × 33.5
Signed and dated bl.: *E. H. Kennington. 22*
Provenance: By descent.
Literature: *SPW 1926*, ill. p. xviii; *The T. E. Lawrence Puzzle*, p. 163.
Exhibitions: Leicester Galleries, *Sculpture and other works by Eric Kennington*, 1924, (?17 – *Storm Cloud*).

226
GOOD INTENTIONS
By Eric Kennington, 1926

One of the cartoons by Kennington printed in the subscriber's *Seven Pillars*. It has not been reproduced in subsequent editions of the book. It symbolises Lawrence's attempts to control the flames of Arabian blood feuds.

The Family of the Artist

Pen and ink, 12.7 × 16.4 (sight)
Signed and dated, bl.: *EHK. 1926*
Provenance: By descent.
Literature: *SPW 1926*, p. 521; *Grosvenor*, no. 26.

227
INTROSPECTION
By Eric Kennington, 1926-7

In the subscribers' *Seven Pillars*, this drawing appeared after chapter 104 (chapter 103 in subsequent editions), where Lawrence wrote: 'I began to dissect my beliefs and motifs, groping about in my own pithy darkness'. He concluded, 'the truth was, I did not like the "myself" I could see and hear'.[1]

The Family of the Artist

1. *SPW 1935*, ch. 104, pp. 563, 566.

Pen and black and red ink, collage, 23.2 × 25.5 (sight)
Signed and dated br.: *E.H.K. 1927*
Provenance: By descent.
Literature: *SPW 1926*, p. 544.
Exhibitions: Leicester Galleries 1927 (25).

228
WIND
By Eric Kennington, 1926

Kennington started reading *Seven Pillars of Wisdom* in August 1922, and Lawrence was a little bemused to learn that he was 'chuckling over it'.[1] The outcome was even more surprising: a series of funny drawings. Far from taking offence, Lawrence was delighted. He subsequently wrote to Sydney Cockerell: 'Kennington was moved to incongruous mirth reading my book, and a dozen Bateman-quality drawings came of it. To my mind they are as rare, surprising and refreshing as plums in a cake . . . It's good that someone is decent enough to find laughter in a stodgy mess of mock-heroic egotism . . . It's Kennington pricking the vast bladder of my conceit.'[2]

The incident depicted here occurred in July 1917 on the station platform at Ismailia. Lawrence, in Arab dress, had just crossed the Sinai peninsula in order to bring news to Cairo of the capture of Akaba. Four officers, including General Allenby, and Admiral Wemyss, descended from a train and began to walk up and down a busy platform: 'A terrible tension grew along the platform as

the party marched up and down it in weighty talk. Officers saluted once: twice: still they marched up and down. Three times was too much. Some withdrew to the fence and stood permanently to attention: these were the mean souls. Some fled: these were the contemptibles. Some turned to the bookstall and studied book-backs avidly: these were the shy. Only one was blatant.'[3] In this way Lawrence managed to catch the eye of one of the officers and break the good news.

On the reverse of the cartoon is a preparatory sketch of Lawrence (see right).

Private Collection

1. T. E. Lawrence to E. Garnett, 26.8.1922, *Letters*, p. 360.
2. T. E. Lawrence to S. C. Cockerell, 15.10.1924, *Letters*, pp. 468-9.
3. *SPW 1935*, ch. 56, p. 319.

Pen and ink, 27.9 × 36.8
Signed and dated br.: *E. H. K. 1926*; inscribed tl.: *Chap 60. para 8.* and on reverse with unfinished drawing of T.E. Lawrence: *The General*
Provenance: Maggs Bros. Ltd
Literature: *SPW 1926*, ill. p. 301; *SPW 1935*, p. 320; *Grosvenor*, no. 23.
Exhibitions: Leicester Galleries 1927 (9).

229

THINKING

By Eric Kennington, 1926

This watercolour was probably inspired by a
passage in chapter 99 of *Seven Pillars*: 'This
sunset was fierce, stimulant, barbaric;
reviving the colours of the desert like a
draught – as indeed it did each evening, in
a new miracle of strength and heat – while
my longings were for weakness, chills, and
grey mistiness, that the world might not be
so crystalline clear, so definitely right and
wrong.'[1]

Harry Ransom Humanities Research Center,
the University of Texas at Austin

1. *SPW 1935*, ch. 99, p. 544.

Casein and tempera, 35 × 24.2
Unsigned
Provenance: Gift of Mr and Mrs T. E. Hanley, 1966.
Literature: *SPW 1926*, ill.
Exhibitions: Leicester Galleries 1927 (19).

230

ENDPAPERS FOR *SEVEN PILLARS OF WISDOM*
By Eric Kennington, 1926

The two wood-cuts which constitute *The Eternal Itch* served as the front endpapers for the subscribers' edition of *Seven Pillars*. In the bottom right hand corner a figure is being flogged, perhaps an allusion to Lawrence's experiences at Deraa. The other pair of wood-cuts, *The World, the Flesh and the Devil*, were used as the rear endpaper. Lawrence was delighted with the designs. As he told Kennington: 'The new tail pieces are lovely.

The devil is the brightest bit of woodcutting which has yet passed my eyes. I also like the flesh very much . . . Nobody else could have done me things like these.'[1]

The extreme difficulty of printing such a large area of black on a small press made it impossible to print the endpapers on single sheets; they were therefore printed in two halves.

The Family of the Artist

1. T. E. Lawrence to E. Kennington, October 1926.

4 woodcuts, artist's proofs printed in black, 25.3 × 19.1 each
Unsigned
Provenance: By descent.
Literature: *SPW 1926*, endpapers; *The T. E. Lawrence Puzzle*, p. 163, ill. pl. 1.
Exhibitions: Leicester Galleries 1927 (2); London, Picture Hire Limited, *Eric Kennington Exhibition*, 1936 (20, 21).

The Eternal Itch

The World, the Flesh and The Devil

231
CAMEL MARCH
By William Roberts, 1923

When Lawrence gave William Roberts the photograph on which this pen and wash is based, he commented: 'There's a big subject hidden in it: I hope not too deep hidden for you to see it, second-hand. If only you had been out with me!'[1]

Two months later the painting was finished, and Lawrence wrote to Roberts: 'I saw the camels yesterday. The colour first delighted me: it's the most beautiful thing to look at: then I saw how excellent was the design: and the landscape is just what one would have wished (but hardly imagined anything so quiet as that lawn of uncrinkled sand): the whole thing is nearly marvellous: better than anything I thought possible.

'It's a trifle . . . but the technique of dress, shapes of camels, seats of riders etc. are as right as if you had worked them up on the spot. I'm afraid that means that you have exhausted yourself in continual study of those photographs. However I'm enormously grateful.'[2]

Robert's Camel March was reproduced in Seven Pillars as a double-page plate, tipped in at the centre. Its tone was difficult to reproduce, as Lawrence wrote to

Kennington: 'The Roberts camel march is clean and sharp . . . but wasn't its ground-yellow more brilliant? By artificial light it looks heavy – brownish. A very fine plate this.'[3] He was delighted, however, with the final result, which 'came out as much the best reproduction'.[4]

Spink & Son Ltd

1. T. E. Lawrence to W. Roberts, 21.10.1922.
2. T. E. Lawrence to W. Roberts, 11.12.1922.
3. T. E. Lawrence to E. Kennington, 20.6.1925.
4. T. E. Lawrence to S. Cockerell, 15.3.1927.

Pen, ink and watercolour, 33 × 57
Signed br.: *William Roberts*.
Provenance: Sir Edward Marsh; Michael Ayrton; sold Sotheby's, 13 May 1987 (103).
Literature: *SPW 1926*, ill. pp. 294-5 (double page spread); *SPW 1935*, ill. fp. 308; *Studio*, vol CXXXIV, 1947, p. 131; *The T. E. Lawrence Puzzle*, pp. 163, 175.
Exhibitions: London, Chenil Galleries, *Paintings and Drawings by William Roberts*, 1923 (30); Edinburgh, Royal Scottish Academy, 1924 (655); Leicester Galleries 1927 (56); Newcastle, Laing Art Gallery, *Modern Paintings and Drawings lent by Edward Marsh Esq*, 1931 (76); Johannesburg, British Council, *British Empire Exhibition*, 1936; National Gallery, London, *British Paintings since Whistler*, 1940 (275); London, Grosvenor Gallery, *Cubism and its Influence*, 1965 (ex cat.); Tate Gallery, *William Roberts Retrospective Exhibition*, 1965 (145a).
(illustrated in colour p. 144)

232
TAILPIECE DRAWINGS FOR *SEVEN PILLARS OF WISDOM*
By William Roberts c.1925-6

William Roberts had been closely associated with Vorticism before the First World War, and it seems likely that the highly stylised work he produced under the War Artists Scheme made a considerable impression on both Lawrence and Kennington. Vorticism explored the violent energy of the machine and was expressed by sharply delineated geometrical abstractions. Wyndham Lewis, Jacob Epstein and David Bomberg (see nos. 75 and 259), were among its other principal exponents, as was Edward Wadsworth who was also recruited for work in *Seven Pillars* (see no. 240). Lawrence, despite having made an advance payment, failed to persuade Wyndham Lewis to contribute any illustrations.

In January 1926 Lawrence received three commissioned tailpieces from William Roberts, all still very much influenced by Vorticism. Lawrence was delighted with the designs, and John Rothenstein recalled that Lawrence had a 'clearly marked preference'[1] for the Vorticist style. Lawrence encouraged Roberts to continue with the work: 'Those three tail-pieces were A.1. . . . quite wonderful in my opinion. Do carry on, and draw millions of the sort. They are still almost too good value for tail-pieces: but what a joy to have!'[2] Twenty-nine of Roberts's tailpieces were printed in *Seven Pillars*, mainly in the earlier chapters, the later tailpieces being designed by Kennington, Hughes-Stanton and Nash. According to Vyvyan Richards 'the tail-pieces . . . by William Roberts . . . Lawrence himself liked best of all.'[3]

The stages of Roberts's work are shown here. He began with a preliminary sketch, then progressed to a full-scale study in chalk or pencil. He then copied these sketches into a pen and ink line version, giving them a greater clarity for final reproduction in *Seven Pillars*.

The last two of these drawings, *Revolt*
(no. x) and *Torture* (no. xi), were not used
in the 1926 *Seven Pillars*. It is possible that
Revolt was excluded because it was replaced
by Gertrude Hermes's woodcut on a similar
subject (see no. 235). *Torture* was not
included probably because illustration of the
subject may have seemed inappropriate to
Lawrence (but see no. 230). The chapter
about Deraa, therefore, ends dramatically
with the largest area of blank space in the
book.

1. J. Rothenstein, *Summer's Lease*, 1965, p. 65.
2. T. E. Lawrence to W. Roberts, 15.1.1926.
3. V. Richards, *Portrait of T. E. Lawrence*, 1936, p. 190.

**The Houghton Library, Harvard University,
Gift of Bayard L. Kilgour Jr.**

Provenance : Given by Bayard L. Kilgour Jr., 1958-66.
Literature : *The T. E. Lawrence Puzzle*, pp. 160, 162, 170
ill., 172, 173 ill., 174, 175, 176 ill., 177.
Exhibitions : Leicester Galleries 1927 i (50); v (48); vi
(21).

(iii) *Object lesson*

Ink, 30.6 × 24.6
Signed br. : *William Roberts*.
Literature : *SPW 1926*, ill. p. 29.

(i) *Flashing sword*

Ink, 28.4 × 19.7
Signed br. : *William Roberts*; inscribed tl. : *Flashing
Sword*.
Literature : *SPW 1926*, ill. p. 6.

(ii) *Dignity*
There is also a preliminary drawing in the
Houghton Library.

Ink, 37 × 28.6
Signed bc. : *William Roberts*.
Literature : *SPW 1926*, ill. p. 23.

(iv) *Ibrahim Pasha*

Ink, 30.6 × 24.7
Signed tl. : *William Roberts*.; inscribed bc. : *Ibrahim
Pasha*.
Literature : *SPW 1926*, ill. p. 59.

(vii) *The dogs of Harith*

Ink, 36.5 × 28.3
Signed br. : *William Roberts.* ; inscribed bc. with the title
by T. E. Lawrence
Literature : *SPW 1926*, ill. p. 192.

(v) *Male and female*

There is also a preliminary charcoal drawing
in the Houghton Library.

Ink, 28.4 × 19.7
Signed br. : *Roberts.*
SPW 1926, ill. p. 119.

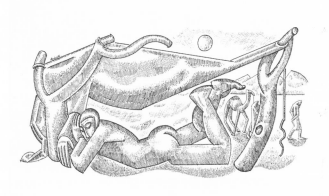

(vi) *Luxury*

There is also a preliminary charcoal drawing
in the Houghton Library.

Ink, 28.5 × 19.5
Signed tl. : *Roberts.*
Literature : *SPW 1926*, ill. p. 161.

(viii) Study for *The dogs of Harith*

There are substantial differences from (vii).

Red chalk, squared up, 28.2 × 23.5
Signed bl. : *Roberts*

(x) *Revolt*

Not used in the subscriber's *Seven Pillars*;
possibly abandoned in favour of G. Hermes's
High Explosive (see no. 235).

Ink and pencil, 30.7 × 24.8
Signed tl.: *William Roberts*; inscribed above: *Page 47* and
br: *Revolt*

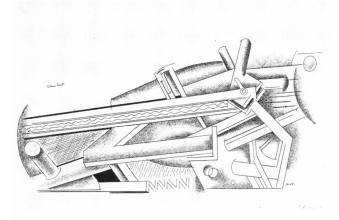

(ix) Study for *Dhaif Allah*

There is also another preparatory drawing in
the Houghton Library for this untraced
tailpiece.

Pencil, 38.1 × 28
Signed bl.: *William Roberts*.
Literature: *SPW 1926*, ill. p. 509.

(xi) *Torture*

Not used in the subscribers' *Seven Pillars*. A
pencil drawing and a preliminary study are in
the Houghton Library.

Ink, 28.4 × 19.7
Signed tr.: *William Roberts*; inscribed above: *Page 416*.

233
STOKES GUN CLASS
By John Cosmo Clark, 1925

Cosmo Clark's painting of a British gunner
teaching Arabs how to use a Stokes gun at
Akaba is based on a photograph from
Lawrence's collection (no. 234). Lawrence
explained to Paul Nash, to whom he had

234
STOKES MORTAR CLASS, AKABA
By an unknown photographer (1917)

This photograph was taken at Akaba in
September 1917, and shows: Corporal Brook
(called 'Stokes' in *Seven Pillars*), Derwish
(Auda's slave), Lawrence, a Somali crew
member from HMS *Humber*, and Mushagraf
the Sherari.

IWM Q60176

235
HIGH EXPLOSIVE
By Gertrude Hermes, c.1926

Gertrude Hermes, a noted sculptress, was
married to Blair Hughes-Stanton who also
contributed illustrations to *Seven Pillars* (see
no. 236). Her woodcut shows a Turkish train
being blown up on a bridge: 'There followed
a terrific roar, and the line vanished from
sight behind a spouting column of black dust
and smoke a hundred feet high and wide. Out
of the darkness came shattering crashes and
long, loud metallic clangings of ripped steel,
with many lumps of iron and plate; while one
entire wheel of a locomotive whirled up
suddenly black out of the cloud against the
sky, and sailed musically over our heads to
fall slowly and heavily into the desert
behind.'[1]

Judith Russell

1. *SPW 1935*, ch. 66, p. 367.

Wood engraving, 10 × 13.3
Signed and dated br.: *Gertrude Hermes/1928*; inscribed in
pencil bc.: *'Explosion'*
Provenance: By descent from the artist.
Literature: *SPW 1926*, ill. p. 599.
Exhibitions: Leicester Galleries 1927 (76); Brighton,
Forum Gallery, *Gertrude Hermes*, 1972.

previously sent the photograph: 'I've found
an ex-Stokes gunner called Clark, who draws
rather in the Kennington manner. He'll do
that group on the Akaba beach, of us learning
Stokes' gunning, better than anybody.'[1]

Lawrence liked the result, telling
Kennington: 'Clark's figures would be the
perfect caption for a Burne-Jones church
window. Title "The sons of Zebedee". Jolly
good it is, too. I think we should try and
tempt Clark to draw us some more.'[2] Clark
later contributed two further drawings to the
book. Both Paul Nash and William Roberts
also based illustrations for *Seven Pillars* on
photographs.

Eric Clark

1. T. E. Lawrence to Paul Nash, 17.8.1922.
2. T. E. Lawrence to Kennington, 20.6.1925.

Oil and gouache (monochrome) on canvas, 45.5 × 34.7
Signed in pencil br.: *COSMO CLARK*
Provenance: Purchased from Bankside Gallery, 1983.
Literature: *SPW 1926*, ill.; *Revolt*, ill. fp. 180.
Exhibitions: Leicester Galleries 1927 (35); London,
Bankside Gallery, *Cosmo Clark, Jean Clark*, 1983.

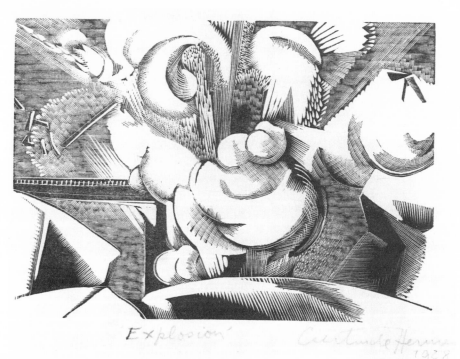

Explosion

236
WOOD ENGRAVINGS AND DRAWINGS
FOR *SEVEN PILLARS OF WISDOM*
By Blair Hughes-Stanton, 1926

Seven Pillars was the first book illustrated by Blair Hughes-Stanton, a trained wood engraver. He contributed a number of tailpieces. In April 1926 Lawrence asked him to ensure that they had 'the balance of print about one black to eight white in area.'[1] Lawrence was impressed with the result: Blair H-S is very subtle. People will go around goggling to know who it is.'[2]

Not all the tailpieces were easy to understand. According to Herbert Baker: 'of some of the stranger wood-cuts at the end of chapters he would say, ''I don't know what they mean; they're mad; the war was mad.'''[3]

1. T. E. Lawrence to Kennington, 1.4.1926.
2. T. E. Lawrence to M. Pike, 18.10.1926.
3. *Friends*, p. 250.

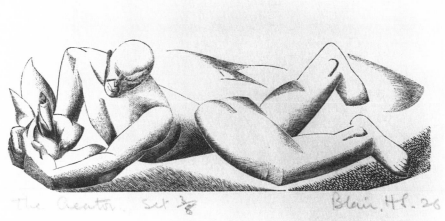

(i) *The Creator*

This illustrates a passage from *Seven Pillars*: 'Some men, there might be, uncreative; whose leisure was barren; but the activity of these would have been material only. To bring forth immaterial things, things creative, partaking of spirit, not of flesh, we must be jealous of spending time or trouble upon physical demands, since in most men the soul grew aged long before the body. Mankind has been no gainer by its drudges.'[1]

1. *SPW 1935*, ch. 74, p. 412.

Wood engraving, 4.5 × 12.6
Signed br.: *Blair.HS.26*; inscribed with title and numbered 3/8.
Literature: *SPW 1926*, ill. p. 47.

(ii) Drawing for *The Creator*

Pencil, 4.5 × 12.5

(iii) *Why not run away?*

Wood engraving, 6 × 12.5
Signed br.: *Blair HS 26*; inscribed with title and numbered 3/8.
Literature: *SPW 1926*, ill. p. 321.

(iv) Drawing for *Why not run away?*

Pencil, 6 × 12.5
Inscribed br. with title

(v) *The last prophet*

Wood engraving, 13 × 12.6
Signed br. : *Blair HS 26* ; inscribed with title and
numbered *3/8*
Literature : *SPW 1926*, ill. p. 339.

(vii) *Beyond the end*

'We made the Arabs strain on tip-toe to
reach our creed, for it led to works, a
dangerous country where men might take the
deed for the will. My fault, my blindness of
leadership (eager to find a quick means to
conversion) allowed them this finite image of
our end, which properly existed only in
unending effort towards unattainable
imagined light.'[1]

1. *SPW 1935*, ch. 99, pp. 548-9.

Wood engraving, 10.4 × 12.4
Signed br. : *Blair HS 26* ; inscribed with title and
numbered *3/8*
Literature : *SPW 1926*, ill. p. 515

(vi) *Standards of value*

Wood engraving, 4.7 × 12.7
Signed br. : *Blair HS 26* ; inscribed with title and
numbered *3/8*
Literature : *SPW 1926*, ill. p. 400.

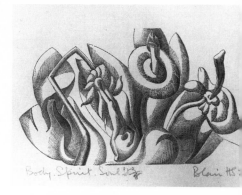

(viii) *Body, spirit, soul*

'Mental and physical were inseparably one :
that our bodies, the universe, our thoughts
and tactilities were conceived in and of the
molecular sludge of matter, the universal
element through which form drifted as clots
and patterns of varying density. It seemed to
me unthinkable that assemblages of atoms
should cogitate except in atomic terms.'[1]

1. *SPW 1935*, ch. 83, p. 468.

Wood engraving, 7 × 12.5
Signed br. : *Blair HS 26* ; inscribed with title and
numbered *3/8*
Literature : *SPW 1926*, ill. p. 489.

(ix) *In his own image*

'Among the Arabs I was the disillusioned, the
sceptic, who envied their cheap belief . . .
But did not the being believed by many make
for a distorted righteousness? The mounting
together of the devoted hopes of years from
near-sighted multitudes, might endow even
an unwilling idol with Godhead, and
strengthen It whenever men prayed silently
to Him . . . it was a theft of souls to make
others die in sincerity for my graven image.'[1]

1. *SPW 1935*, ch. 99, p. 549.

Wood engraving, 13.4 × 10.9
Signed br.: *Blair HS 26*; inscribed with title and
numbered 3/8
Literature: *SPW 1926*, ill. p. 536.

(xii) *Conscience our guide*

Wood engraving, 10.4 × 12.4
Signed br.: *Blair HS 26*; inscribed with title and
numbered 3/8
Literature: *SPW 1926*, ill. p. 569.

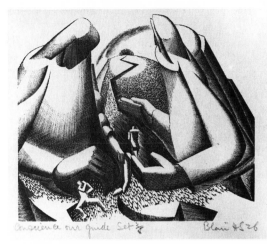

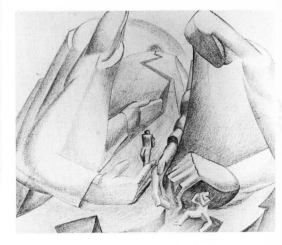

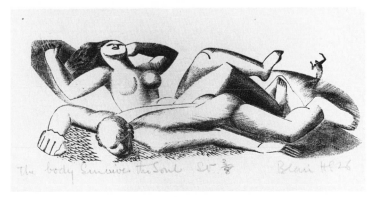

(x) *The sport of kings*

Wood engraving, 8 × 12.3
Signed br.: *Blair HS 26*; inscribed with title and
numbered 3/8
Literature: *SPW 1926*, ill. p. 539.

(xi) *The body survives the soul*

Wood engraving, 4.5 × 12.5
Signed br.: *Blair HS 26*; inscribed with title and
numbered 3/8
Literature: *SPW 1926*, ill. p. 569.

(xiii) Drawing for *Conscience our guide*

Pencil, 10.5 × 12.2

Mrs Anne Hughes-Stanton

Provenance: By descent.
Literature: *The T. E. Lawrence Puzzle*, pp. 160, 166, 167
ill., 168 ill., 177, 182 n. 35.
Exhibitions: Leicester Galleries, 1927 (65-75).

237
THE POEM TO S.A.
By Blair Hughes-Stanton, 1926

This woodcut illustrating the dedicatory poem of *Seven Pillars* was not commissioned by Lawrence, but four special copies of the subscribers' edition are recorded containing original woodcuts (numbered out of 5).

There has been much speculation about the identity of S.A., to whom *Seven Pillars* is dedicated. Lawrence himself clearly intended to obscure the issue. At the end of the book he wrote: 'The strongest motive throughout had been a personal one',[1] and on another occasion he explained that 'the "personal" motive mentioned in the concluding bit was the "SA" of the opening poem.'[2]

Lawrence's statements on the identity of S.A. are apparently inconsistent. On some occasions he seemed to refer to an individual: 'S.A. was a person, now dead, regard for whom lay beneath my labour for the Arabic peoples'.[3] At other times, however, he said that the 'subject of the dedication is rather an idea than a person'[4]; and that 'S. and A. were two different things, "S" a village in Syria, or property in it, and "A" personal'.[5] He also wrote, obscurely, 'S.A. still exists: but out of my reach, because I have changed.'[6]

Despite this deliberate vagueness, there can be little doubt that the central, personal, element in 'S.A.' was Dahoum, his friend at Carchemish before the First World War. Dahoum's real name was Ahmed, and an early note for the dedication is headed 'A(?)'.[7] Linked to this friendship was Lawrence's happiness travelling among the Syrian peoples before the First World War. Thus *Seven Pillars* was dedicated to a composite notion: 'rather an idea than a person'[8]; again, the dedication 'is to an imaginary person of neutral sex.'[9]

Theories have been advanced that both 'S' and 'A' stand for personal names (e.g. 'Sheikh Ahmed', or 'Salim Ahmed'). There is ample evidence, however, to show that only 'A' was personal, and such solutions to the problem must therefore be discounted.

Mrs Anne Hughes-Stanton

1. *SPW 1926*, p. 661.
2. *Biographers* (Liddell Hart), p. 68.
3. T. E. Lawrence to R. V. Buxton, 22.9.1923, *Letters* p. 431.
4. *Biographers* (Graves), p. 55.
5. *Biographers* (Liddell Hart), p. 143.
6. *Biographers* (Graves), p. 17.
7. Manuscript note dating from 1919.
8. T. E. Lawrence to R. Graves, 28.6.1927, *Biographers* (Graves), p. 55.
9. Note on the history of *Seven Pillars of Wisdom*, 1927, facsimile in *Texas Quarterly*, Austin, Autumn 1962.

Wood engraving, 17.8 × 13
Provenance: By descent from the artist.
Literature: *The Woodcut: an Annual*, 1927, appendix, '15 Contemporary Woodcuts', ill.; *The T. E. Lawrence Puzzle*, p. 168 ill.
Exhibitions: Leicester Galleries, 1927 (71).

238
T. E. LAWRENCE
By Augustus John, 1919

This portrait by Augustus John is one of the most famous images of Lawrence. It was drawn at the Versailles Peace Conference, in surprising conditions, as Lawrence explained: 'I was looking out of his flat window, in Paris, into the street, when he caught me in two minutes. It is the first drawing of me he ever made.'[1] Lawrence thought highly of it, and included it in the subscribers' *Seven Pillars*. It was also used as the frontispiece for *Revolt in the Desert*. At different times he said that it was 'a very pretty pencil head of me in Arab dress',[2] and that it showed 'quite a meek creature'.[3]

Two other works by John were reproduced in the subscribers' *Seven Pillars*: his portrait of Feisal (see no. 98) which was used as the frontispiece, and his drawing of D. G. Hogarth (see no. 50).

National Portrait Gallery (NPG 3187)

1. T. E. Lawrence to C. F. Shaw, 16.10.1928.
2. T. E. Lawrence to F. N. Doubleday, 21.7.1920.
3. T. E. Lawrence to C. F. Shaw, 16.10.1928.

Pencil, 35.6 × 25.4
Unsigned
Provenance: Given by T. E. Lawrence to G. B. and C. Shaw; presented by G. B. Shaw, 1944.
Literature: *SPW 1926*, ill.; *SPW 1935*, ill. fp. 610; *Grosvenor*, no. 4; M. Easton and M. Holroyd, *The Art of Augustus John*, 1974, pp. 168-9.
Exhibitions: London, Chenil Galleries, *Augustus John*, 1923 (35); Leicester Galleries 1927 (8); National Gallery, *The Drawings of Augustus John*, 1940 (?610); Colnaghi, *Augustus John: Early Drawings and Etchings*, 1974 (16).
(illustrated in colour, frontispiece)

239
MOUNTAINS
By Paul Nash (1924)
Annotated proof plate for *Seven Pillars of Wisdom*, 1926

In August 1922 Lawrence wrote to Paul Nash asking him to paint landscapes for *Seven Pillars*, and offering photographs to copy from. Kennington had previously refused to do this, saying the result 'would be no good'.[1] Colin Gill and William Roberts were interested in the idea but, as Lawrence told Nash, 'they agreed that it was blasting, humiliating, dishonourable, damnable, to draw from photographs : but said that if I gave them complete freedom . . . it might be done. It was.'[2]

Nash found the exercise intriguing, as he explained in his reply to Lawrence : 'I hold strong opinions but not conventional ones. I see no wrong in it. It is a *problem*, of course, like any other – a second-hand sort of business perhaps – one remove from the best chance since it must be the interpretation of an interpretation but if, in this case, I am permitted to use the photographs purely as data and my imagination may have free play – well, I can only say I quite look forward to the game.'[3]

Nash produced five pen and wash studies from photographs for *Seven Pillars*, of which this is one. It is of Edom and the sandstone hills in the Petra-Rumm area, which Lawrence told Nash were 'gorgeous'.[4] None of Nash's original drawings have been traced.

The Family of Eric Kennington

1. *Friends*, p. 263.
2. T. E. Lawrence to P. Nash, 3.8.1922.
3. P. Nash to T. E. Lawrence, 7.8.1922.
4. T. E. Lawrence to P. Nash, 13.1.1924.

Collotype, 24.9 × 18.6
Inscribed in pencil with comments by Eric Kennington and Paul Nash
Provenance : Given to the present owners by Oliver Brown, c.1965.
Literature : *SPW 1926*, ill.

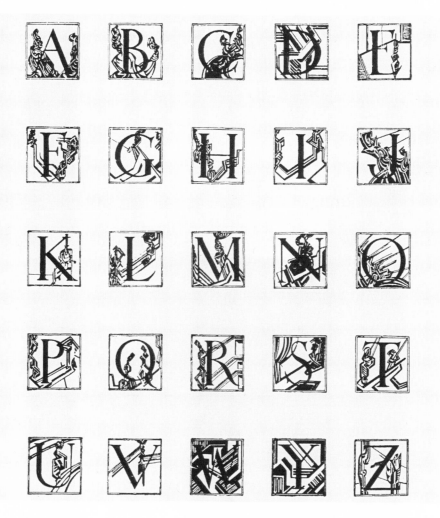

240

SET OF SMALL INITIAL LETTERS USED
IN *SEVEN PILLARS OF WISDOM*, 1926
By Edward Wadsworth, *c.*1919

Lawrence was first shown these Wadsworth
designs by Eric Kennington, and he was
immediately attracted to them. He later
wrote: 'My capital letters were designed by
Edward Wadsworth, a very fine artist, for
John Rodker, who prints in England. He did
not use them, so I bought them off him for
a copy of my book. Wadsworth did A – W
[and Y] I had X . . . and Z done by Hughes-
Stanton to complete the alphabet
(Wadsworth was abroad at the time and
couldn't carry on) and exhausted my
ingenuity to bring in each letter at least once
. . . I thought them uncommonly new and
delightful.'[1] In order to use the 'X' designed
by Blair Hughes-Stanton, Lawrence spelt the
name of the Emir of Salkhad in an entirely new
way: Xury, at the beginning of chapter 81.[2]

Lawrence also wrote: 'They seem to me
not inconsistent with the sobriety of Caslon
[the typeface used in the subscribers' *Seven
Pillars*], and in keeping with the up-to-
dateness of many of my pictures. We reduced
some of them to the three-line scale, and are
using them for the headings of paragraphs,
where these head the page.'[3] The set
exhibited here is the three-line size, and the
letters which were used most frequently in
the book are relatively worn. As no 'X' was
required in this size, the letter may not have
been manufactured. The larger set was used
at the opening of chapters.

The letters are not cast as type, but are
individual zinc line blocks on a lead body,
these may have been based on wood-
engravings. Hughes-Stanton's 'Z' is slightly
different from the others, and must have
been made separately.

Maggs Bros Ltd

1. T. E. Lawrence to Bruce Rogers, 16.4.1928, *Letters*,
p. 589. Lawrence was wrong in thinking that John
Rodker had never used the letters. They appeared in
several books printed by Rodker at the Ovid Press.
Lawrence incorrectly attributes the 'Y' to Hughes-
Stanton in this letter, but Rodker's original proof sheet
survives, showing that only X and Z were missing from
the Wadsworth set.
2. *SPW 1935*, ch. 81, p. 448.
3. T. E. Lawrence to St. J. Hornby, 17.9.1924.

25 zinc blocks, 1.3 square, on lead slugs 2.4 high
(exhibited with a proof impression)
Provenance: John Rodker; T. E. Lawrence.
Literature: *The T. E. Lawrence Puzzle*, p. 162;
V. M. Thompson, *Not a Suitable Hobby for an Airman*,
Long Hanborough, 1986, pp. 73-7; J. M. Wilson,
'T. E. Lawrence and the Printing of *Seven Pillars of
Wisdom*', in *Matrix* 5, 1985, pp. 63,66.

241
JONATHAN CAPE
By an unknown photographer (c.1930)

Jonathan Cape (1879-1960) met Lawrence in the autumn of 1920 in connection with a projected reprint of C. M. Doughty's *Travels in Arabia Deserta* (see no. 195). They became friends, and Cape hoped to publish *Seven Pillars* in some form. During the early 1920s he commissioned two translations from Lawrence: Adrian le Corbeau's *The Forest Giant* (see no. 267), and Pierre Custot's *Sturly*. The former was published in 1924, but Lawrence was dissatisfied with his draft of the latter and burned it. Cape ultimately published Lawrence's abridgement of *Seven Pillars*, *Revolt in the Desert*, in 1927.

Lawrence took considerable interest in Cape's publishing career, often suggesting titles or new authors. During the 1930s he occasionally gave Cape an opinion on manuscripts; he also contributed a foreword to *Arabia Felix* by Bertram Thomas, and edited at least one book for publication.

After Lawrence's death Cape published the first trade edition of *Seven Pillars* as well as editions of his correspondence. *The Mint*, offered to Cape on prohibitive terms in 1928 (£1 million in advance on a 90% royalty), was finally issued in 1955.

Jonathan Cape Ltd

242
GEORGE WREN HOWARD
Photograph by ?Mesdames Moter, 1942
Vintage print

G. Wren Howard (1893-1968) was Jonathan Cape's partner when the firm was founded on New Year's Day 1921. He had no doubt about the important role Lawrence played in the company's history: 'Always, from the very beginning,' he said shortly before his death, 'Lawrence was the key to our success'.[1]

Howard was largely responsible for the high standard of design and production which characterised Cape's early years as a publishing house. Lawrence therefore enjoyed working with him: 'Howard is a good chap. A little bit of an artist. Cape calculates; Howard is genuine.'[2]

Jonathan Cape Ltd

1. M. S. Howard, *Jonathan Cape Publisher*, 1971, p. 82.
2. T. E. Lawrence to G. W. M. Dunn, 4.5.1934.

23.1 × 17.9
Signed in monogram and dated 1942

243
PROOF COPY OF *SEVEN PILLARS OF WISDOM* MARKED UP BY T. E. LAWRENCE FOR *REVOLT IN THE DESERT*

Lawrence had considered publishing an abridgement of *Seven Pillars* in 1920 and again in 1922. On each occasion he had spent a fair amount of time shortening the text (in the latter instance working in collaboration with Edward Garnett). Finally in 1925, when it became clear that the production cost of *Seven Pillars* would greatly exceed the revenue from subscribers, he was obliged to sell rights for a popular abridgement to Jonathan Cape.

Even though he had already worked on two earlier abridgements, he spent several weeks making pencil deletions and additions for the Cape edition, using a proof of the subscribers' *Seven Pillars*. Then, thinking that he might later have to supply a text of the abridgement to the American publisher, he made a duplicate with another set of proofs. This was the copy he submitted to Jonathan Cape.

It was extremely important to him that *Revolt in the Desert* should succeed. The venture involved not only his reputation as a writer but also his financial security. If the royalties failed to repay the debts of *Seven Pillars* he might have to sacrifice his property at Pole Hill and his valuable collection of private press books, both of which were investments he had put aside against future need.

Jonathan Cape Ltd

Bound volume with numerous autograph amendments, 25.5
Provenance: Submitted by T. E. Lawrence for publication, 1926.
(not illustrated)

244

SEVEN PILLARS OF WISDOM,
SUBSCRIBERS' EDITION, 1926
Copy presented by T. E. Lawrence to H.M.
King George V

Once the decision had been taken to produce
Seven Pillars in a private press edition,
Lawrence's friends began to look for
subscribers. At thirty guineas, the price was
more than seventy times as expensive as the
average hardback novel, equivalent therefore
to about £650 today.

During the first few months subscriptions
came in slowly, and Lawrence began to
worry whether his target of 100 copies
would be reached. It was suggested to him
that he should contact J. G. Wilson, manager
of Bumpus, at that time booksellers to the
King. Wilson succeeded in obtaining a
number of subscriptions from Bumpus
clients, including one from the Royal Library
at Windsor. When Lawrence learned of this
he wrote: 'The Windsor copy will be duly
sent: but I'm an old-fashioned person, to
whom it seems improper that Kings should
buy and sell among their subjects'. He
decided to return the advance cheque and ask
the Royal Librarian not to inform the King:
'for I should prefer Him to think He is paying
for it, since that is His notion of propriety.'[1]

*This book was given one by the Author
in February 1927.*

George R.I.

A few copies of the finished book were
received from the binders in December
1926, just before Lawrence left for India. He
told his mother that he had sent the first of
these to the Royal Library. The inscription
by King George V may have been written
some time later since it appears to be mis-
dated. In February 1927 Lawrence was at the
RAF Depot in Karachi.

Lent by gracious permission of Her Majesty
The Queen

1. T. E. Lawrence to J. G. Wilson, 25.5.1926.

Printed book, bound dark blue Morocco with a gold
tooled geometric design, 25.6
Inscribed on flyleaf: *This book was given me by the Author/in
February 1927./George R. I.*
Provenance: Given by T. E. Lawrence, 1926.
Literature: *Home Letters*, p. 364.

245

SEVEN PILLARS OF WISDOM,
SUBSCRIBERS' EDITION, 1926
Winston Churchill's copy

Churchill, under whom Lawrence had served
in the Colonial Office, tried to subscribe to
Seven Pillars but Lawrence refused him,
writing: 'I hope you won't continue to want
a copy of my book. It's very dear (30
guineas): it won't be ready for at least a
year: and it's not at all the sort of thing you
will like: much too hesitant: hysterical
sometimes, long-winded, and quite
unpleasant in parts. It has no political
interest, and does not slang any prominent
people'.[1] Finally, however, Lawrence
decided to give Churchill a copy. Before
sending it to be bound he wrote on the
flyleaf:

*Winston Churchill/ who made a happy/ ending
to this show./1.12.26 TES.*[2]

This was one of a few special copies put
into costly bindings, and it was not
completed until the spring of 1927. After
reading it Churchill wrote to Lawrence:
'Having gone on a three days' visit to Paris,
I never left my apartment except for meals,
and lay all day and most of the night cuddling
your bulky tome. The impression it
produced was overpowering. I marched with
you those endless journeys by camel, with
never a cool drink, a hot bath, or a square
meal except under revolting conditions.

What a tale! . . . The copy which you gave
me, with its inscription, is in every sense one
of my most valuable possessions. I detected
one misprint, but to torture you I will not
tell you where.

'I am always hoping some day to get a
letter from you saying that your long holiday
is finished, and that your appetite for action
has returned'.[3]

In 1932 Lawrence added a further
inscription to the flyleaf:

*And eleven years after we set our hands to
making an honest / settlement, all our work still
stands: the countries having / gone forward, our
interests having been saved, and nobody / killed,
either on our side or the other. To have planned
/ for eleven years is statesmanship. I ought to have
given / you two copies of this work! T.E.S.*[4]

Winston S. Churchill MP

1. T. E. Lawrence to W. S. Churchill, 23.12.1923.
2. W. S. Churchill, *Great Contemporaries*, London, 1937,
p. 163.
3. W. S. Churchill to T. E. Lawrence 16.5.1927, *Letters
to T. E. Lawrence*, p. 24.
4. Winston S. Churchill, *Great Contemporaries*, London,
1937, p. 163.

Printed book, 26
Inscribed by T. E. Lawrence on flyleaf
Provenance: By descent.
Literature: W. S. Churchill, *op. cit.*, pp. 162-4
(facsimile of Lawrence's inscriptions on p. 163).

*Winston Churchill
who made a happy
ending to this show.
1.12.26 TES.*

*W.S.C.
And eleven years after we set our hands to making an honest
settlement, all our work still stands: the countries having
gone forward, our interests having been saved, and nobody
killed, either on our side or the other. To have planned
for eleven years is statesmanship. I ought to have given
you two copies of this work!*

TES.

246
GEORGE DORAN
Photograph by Underwood and Underwood,
Washington (c. 1930)

When Jonathan Cape had finalised the
publishing contract for *Revolt in the Desert* he
arranged for the American edition to be
published by the George H. Doran Company
of New York. As a result Doran was also
asked to produce and copyright a small
edition of *Seven Pillars* (see no. 247).

In 1927 Doran's company merged with
Doubleday, forming Doubleday, Doran, Inc.,
and subsequently George H. Doran left the
firm. After Lawrence's death Doubleday,
Doran published a copyright edition of
The Mint (see no. 284), as well as the first
American trade printing of *Seven Pillars*.

Bantam Doubleday Dell Publishing Group
Inc.

247
THE SEVEN PILLARS OF WISDOM
American copyright edition, New York,
1926
One of 22 copies

Since books printed and published in Great
Britain were not protected under American
copyright law there was a considerable risk
that an American publisher would produce a
pirate edition of *Seven Pillars*. For this reason
an agreement was signed on 26 September
1925 under which the George H. Doran
Company of New York undertook to produce
a small printing of *Seven Pillars* and thus
secure American copyright. Lawrence had
always intended to give this job to his friend
F. N. Doubleday, but it proved impossible to
do so since the American rights to the text
of *Revolt in the Desert*, which was almost
entirely reproduced in *Seven Pillars*, had been
sold to Doran.

Lawrence paid Doran to produce an
edition of not more than twenty-two copies,
each to be strictly numbered. Ten were to
be put on sale at $20,000 each – a price
intended to deter anyone from buying.

In the event Doran found an excellent use
for the edition. The $20,000 copies were
exhibited, with elaborate security
precautions, in leading bookstores across
America as part of the promotion for *Revolt
in the Desert*. As Doran later wrote : 'the
public flocked to purchase the slightly
abridged . . . book for $3.'[1]

The edition was typeset from a proof copy
of the English subscribers' text and for this
reason there are one or two variant passages.
There are no colour plates and few tailpieces.

In later years Lawrence gave away some
copies of this American edition to friends.
Doran too gave copies away. In addition to
the six reserved for the publisher under the
terms of the contract, he had assembled a
small number of extra copies from 'surplus
sheets'. One of these went to Jonathan Cape,
who had originally offered him *Revolt*. When
Lawrence died in 1935 it was used for
typesetting the first English trade edition of
Seven Pillars.

Private Collection

1. G. H. Doran, *Chronicles of Barabbas*, New York, 1935,
pp. 395-7.

Printed book, half-vellum with blue paper boards, 31
(not illustrated)

248
CATALOGUE OF AN EXHIBITION OF
PAINTINGS, PASTELS, DRAWINGS AND
WOODCUTS ILLUSTRATING COL.
T. E. LAWRENCE'S BOOK *SEVEN PILLARS
OF WISDOM*
The Leicester Galleries, 5-21 February 1927

Lawrence had written an introduction to the
catalogue for Kennington's exhibition of
Arab portraits held at the Leicester Galleries
in 1921. In 1927 the Galleries put on a larger
exhibition, of a wide range of the artwork
used in *Seven Pillars*, and reprinted
Lawrence's 1921 introduction in a slightly
shortened form. The 1927 catalogue also
contains a preface by George Bernard Shaw.

Lawrence was unaware of the exhibition
until he read about it in an Indian newspaper.
He had, however, given the illustrations to
the Trustees of *Revolt in the Desert*, and
instructed them to sell any that would help
to repay the overdraft incurred during the
production of *Seven Pillars*.

When he saw Bernard Shaw's preface to
the catalogue he wrote to Charlotte Shaw :
'I crowed with delight over the preface.
There's such a lovely cool overarm sweep
about his writing, like a bath in Lago
Maggiore. I'm glad, too, that he thought my
1921 trifle not too bad. It [Lawrence's 1921
preface] was written one August night at
Aden, after dinner . . . to catch the mail I sat
in a greatcoat till nearly dawn, manoeuvering
a parrafin lamp in the sea-breeze, to give me
writing light. The haste may partly account
for its homespun feeling. It is all nobbly, and
each paragraph (nearly every sentence) tears
off at a tangent into the blue. Whereas
G.B.S. lets in his clutch so smoothly that his
passengers hardly notice their starts and
stops.' Lawrence felt 'astonishment [at]
finding his name and mine together on a title
page. Oh yes, a very small title page,
admittedly, but a title page. "We" are
coming on.'[1]

National Portrait Gallery

1. T. E. Lawrence to C. F. Shaw, 24.2.1927.

Printed pamphlet, 27 pp., 14.4
(not illustrated)

249
REVOLT IN THE DESERT
New York, 1927
First edition

English and American editions of *Revolt in the Desert*, Lawrence's abridgement of *Seven Pillars* were published in March 1927. The English edition was handsomely designed by G. Wren Howard and produced to a very high standard compared to most trade publications. It was priced at thirty shillings, about four times as much as a hardback novel, nevertheless it sold extremely well. By May 1927 there had been four reprints totalling almost 90,000 copies. The brief success of this one title put Jonathan Cape Ltd on a sound financial footing. That year the company returned net profits of £28,000 – an increase of about £26,000 on previous years.

George H. Doran, publisher of the American edition, had considerable doubts about its prospects in the US market, and he was agreeably surprised when the book turned out to be a commercial success. Compared to Cape's elegant edition in England, the production standards of the American *Revolt* were very low. Lawrence told friends that the dust jacket was 'simply revolting'.

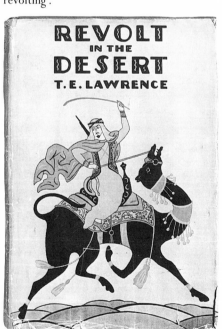

Within weeks of publication the combined royalties from *Revolt* were more than sufficient to pay off the *Seven Pillars* overdraft. Lawrence's Trustees therefore invoked a special clause inserted in the contract with Cape to protect his privacy, and halted publication in England. *Revolt* continued to sell well, however, both in the United States and in translation.

P. C. & B. A. Metcalfe

Printed book, 356 pp., 23.2
Literature: M. S. Howard, *Jonathan Cape, Publisher*, 1971, pp. 82-94.

250
T. E. LAWRENCE WITH MR AND MRS FRANK NELSON DOUBLEDAY
Still photographs from amateur film (*c.* 1930s)

The American publisher F. N. Doubleday was a frequent visitor to England, and at that time owned the British publishers, Heinemann. He had first met Lawrence in London in December 1918, and again in Paris during the Peace Conference. He shared Lawrence's interest in fine printing.

During 1920 Lawrence discussed with Doubleday the possibility of publishing an abridgement of *Seven Pillars* in the United States, but the plan was abandoned. Lawrence nevertheless always hoped that Doubleday would publish his work in America.

In the event Cape offered the American rights of *Revolt in the Desert* to George H. Doran. A few months after *Revolt* was published, however, Doubleday acquired the Doran company in a business merger, and thereby Lawrence's wish was accidentally fulfilled.

During the late 1920s and early 1930s Lawrence met the Doubledays from time to time, and he was taken by them to visit Rudyard Kipling and the Heinemann production works at Kingswood. These stills are taken from an amateur film of a picnic.

After Lawrence's death Doubleday, Doran (later Doubleday & Co.) became the principal publisher of Lawrence's works and letters in the USA.

J. M. Wilson

251
AUTHOR'S NOTE TO *REVOLT IN THE DESERT*

The foreword to *Revolt in the Desert* was signed 'T.E.L.' but was written by Bernard Shaw, who had rejected Lawrence's proposed draft. It was not until Lawrence first saw the book in March 1927 that he realised that there was no equivalent in the *Revolt* text to the footnote that he had inserted in *Seven Pillars*.[1]

Accordingly he wrote to G. Wren Howard on 30 March asking for a paragraph to be added to the foreword:

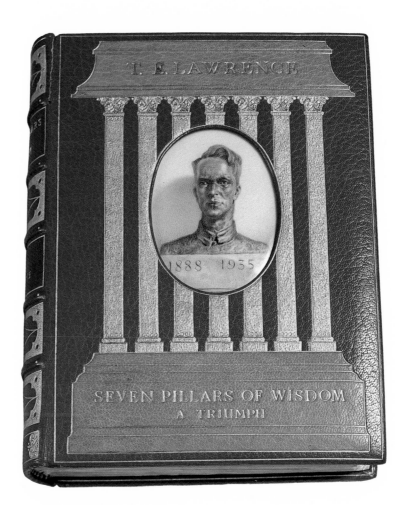

'This text dates from 1919, when the fate of the Arabic-speaking provinces of the former Turkish Empire still hung in the balance, and its tone was affected by the political uncertainty in which the Arabs stood: but two years later Mr. Winston Churchill was entrusted by our harrassed Cabinet with the settlement of the Middle East; and in a few weeks, at his conference in Cairo, he made straight all the tangle, finding solutions fulfilling (I think) our promises in letter and spirit, where humanly possible, without sacrificing any interest of our Empire, or any interest of the peoples concerned. So we are quit of the war-time Eastern adventure, with clean hands, after all.'

This important statement was added in the fifth and last printing of *Revolt in the Desert*, unaltered except for the correction of 'harassed', which Lawrence had misspelt.

Jonathan Cape Ltd

1. *SPW 1935*, p. 276.

Autograph MS, single sheet, 23.3 × 17.2
Literature: T. E. Lawrence, *Revolt in the Desert*, 5th impression, 1927, pp. 9-10; M. Howard, *Jonathan Cape, Publisher*, 1971, p. 92.
(not illustrated)

252
REVOLT IN THE DESERT, PUBLISHER'S ADVERTISEMENT, 1927

This press advertisement was issued by Jonathan Cape Ltd shortly after *Revolt* was published. It quotes favourable comments from reviewers: 'like Byron he has the genius of literature as well as the genius of adventure', 'a masterpiece', '[as] monumental and momentous as Doughty's masterpiece'. The advertisement states that 'The first and second impressions are now exhausted'; they had been taken up by booksellers' advance orders.

Lawrence was delighted by the tone of the reviews, and wrote happily: '*Revolt* is selling like apples. Something like 40,000 copies in the first three weeks, they say!'.[1]

J. M. Wilson

1. T. E. Lawrence to H. H. Banbury, 20.4.1927.

20 × 12
(not illustrated)

253
SEVEN PILLARS OF WISDOM
London, 1935, in 'Cosway' binding with miniature portrait of T. E. Lawrence by Miss Currie

When Lawrence died in May 1935 Jonathan Cape immediately ordered a reprint of *Revolt in the Desert*, and began to arrange publicity. The *Evening Standard* announced a new serialisation even before the funeral. Lawrence's brother and Literary Executor, A. W. Lawrence, protested at this hasty re-issue of *Revolt* and offered Cape publication rights of *Seven Pillars* instead. Before the end of the month, therefore, the Alden Press at Oxford began typesetting the first trade edition. When news of this appeared, owners of the subscribers' edition feared that the value of their copies would be affected, and there was even a letter of protest in *The Times*.

Seven Pillars was published in a handsome edition only ten weeks after Lawrence's death, and the production of this 672-page volume in so short a time was a considerable feat. Demand proved to be enormous: the first printing order had to be doubled to 60,000 copies before publication, and the binding was sub-contracted to three different companies. There were several more reprints before the end of 1935 and at one point, when the Alden Press could no longer keep up with orders, stereos of the type were cast for production by the Cambridge University Press. Few books in history can have been reprinted simultaneously at Oxford and Cambridge within weeks of publication.

Because of its fame and large format, the first trade edition of *Seven Pillars* has often been given special bindings. This copy is in a 'Cosway' binding produced in the 1930s by Sotheran's, the London booksellers. There is another copy in a Cosway binding at the Houghton Library, Harvard.

Mr Clifford H. Irwin

Printed book, leather bound with watercolour miniature on ivory inset on upper cover, 15.9

IN THE RANKS

1922-28

T. E. Lawrence
By an unknown photographer, 1925–6
(detail, no. 274)

Lawrence enlisted in the RAF as an Aircraftman, 2nd Class, on 30 August 1922; he was 34. Months of mental strain and desk work were no preparation for the medical examination, and it took a special chit from a senior officer to get him through. 'I thought I was fitter: but when it came to the point, walked up and down the street in a blue funk, and finally went in with my nerves dithering, and my heart dancing.'[1]

Although there were other men serving in the ranks who had been junior officers during the war, the Air Force was very sensitive about taking such a celebrity. Lawrence was given the name 'John Hume Ross', and attempted to hide his old identity completely. He was pleased to escape from public life, and told very few people of his actions or whereabouts. Instead, he teased them with tales of retirement 'into a kind of community . . . remote and cut off from normal ways.'[2]

The gruelling training course at the Uxbridge depot came as a shock. He was barely able to stand the pace and often found himself 'longing for an empty room, or a solitary bed, or even a moment alone in the open air.'[3] There had been an unusual condition in his enlistment: unlike the other men he would be free to leave at any time. This began to seem a wise precaution.

Edward Garnett, one of the few friends who knew what Lawrence was really doing, was very impressed by *Seven Pillars* and offered him the editorship of a new magazine, *Belles-Lettres*: he refused. Despite the unpleasantness of Uxbridge, there was subject matter there to write about. It was not, however, the kind of material he had expected. After roll call each night he began to make the notes that would one day become *The Mint*, his unsparing account of life at the recruits' training depot.

At the beginning of November 1922 he was transferred to the RAF School of Photography at Farnborough. His pre-war experience as a photographer at Carchemish put him far ahead of the other recruits, and he was impatient to finish the course. Compared with Uxbridge, however, this was a happy station. The recruits' training had seemed to crush individuality, forming the men into disciplined automata; at Farnborough some individuality was restored as they worked to develop the specialist skills they would use when posted to a squadron. Lawrence suddenly began to see the task of the RAF in heroic terms, describing it as 'the conquest of the air'. At Farnborough he began to form the first of his service friendships.

Then on 27 December 1922 the *Daily Express* revealed that 'Lawrence of Arabia', war hero, was serving in the ranks.

Afterwards he claimed that one of the 'beastly officers' had given him away; but he may himself have been to blame since he had told several people about his enlistment, albeit in strictest confidence.

The publicity that followed alarmed the RAF. Crowds of pressmen besieged the camp and made Lawrence's position there untenable. George Bernard Shaw chided him for expecting anything different: 'You have just had a crushing demonstration of the utter impossibility of hiding or disguising the monster you have created . . . Lawrence may be as great a nuisance to you sometimes as G.B.S. is to me, or as Frankenstein found the man he had manufactured: but you created him, and must now put up with him as best you can.'[4]

Within three weeks of the press revelation, Lawrence had been dismissed from the RAF. During the month that followed he made frantic efforts to get himself reinstated, hoping in vain that the authorities would let him go to another camp where he was not known; but his enlistment under a false name had proved an embarrassment, and neither the Air Force nor the Government was prepared to run this risk again.

Finally, with the help of a friend in the War Office, Lawrence managed to enlist in the Army. At the beginning of March 1923 he arrived at Bovington Camp in Dorset,

1. T. E. Lawrence to Sir Oliver Swann, 1.9.1922, *Letters*, p. 364.
2. T. E. Lawrence to J. M. Keynes, 18.9.1922.
3. T. E. Lawrence to E. Garnett, 7.9.1922, *Letters*, p. 366.
4. G. B. Shaw to T. E. Lawrence, 4.1.1923, *Letters to T. E. Lawrence*, ed. A. W. Lawrence, 1962, p. 168-70.

the home of the Tank Corps. He was now Pte. T. E. Shaw, a name chosen at random from a directory. It was later claimed, wrongly, that he had taken the name out of admiration for George Bernard Shaw; and even that he was Shaw's son.

At Bovington, the beauty of the surrounding countryside contrasted almost unbearably with the ugliness of the barrack-room talk and endless square-bashing. He had glorified the ranks of the RAF as a team of skilled individuals dedicated to the conquest of the air. By contrast the traditions of the army set little value on individual excellence: 'the person is at a discount: the combined movement, the body of men, is the ideal.'[5] It seemed in these early weeks that mental ability counted for nothing whatsoever in the Tank Corps; moreover, the drunkenness and lechery of the camp were abhorrent to him.

During 1923 he wrote a deeply revealing series of letters to Lionel Curtis, a friend he had made at All Souls. In them Lawrence explained his unhappiness during these early months in the Tank Corps: 'at Farnborough I grew suddenly on fire with the glory that the air should be, and set to work full steam to make the others vibrate to it like myself . . . The Army seems safe against enthusiasm. It's a horrible life, and the other fellows fit it. I said to one "They're the sort who instinctively fling stones at cats". . . and he said "Why what do you throw?" . . . Seven years of this will make me impossible for anyone to suggest for a responsible position, and that self-degradation is my aim. I haven't the impulse and the conviction to fit what I know to be my power of moulding men and things.'[6]

Off duty, he sought a physical release from this tension in speed, riding a powerful Brough motorcycle through southern England. But his mind still craved intellectual stimulation. Robert Graves gave him an introduction to Thomas Hardy, who lived within easy reach of Bovington, and Lawrence became a regular visitor at Max Gate. He would arrive in uniform to join literary figures such as Edmund Blunden, Siegfried Sassoon and Walter de la Mare at the tea table. On one memorable occasion he accompanied Hardy, Sassoon and E. M. Forster to a production of *Tess*, and then rode around the New Forest afterwards until dawn, because 'bed wasn't any good after an experience like that.'[7]

Although he had stopped working on *Seven Pillars*, and there seemed no future for the RAF book he had once planned, Lawrence still wanted to write. He asked Jonathan Cape for the chance of a translation, and in June 1923 agreed to tackle Adrien Le Corbeau's *Le Gigantesque*, an obscure novel about the life of a sequoia tree. This proved a wearisome task, but was completed in three months and duly published. The translator's name was given as 'J.H. Ross'. Cape commissioned a second work, *Sturly*, but Lawrence felt he could not capture the spirit of the book, and abandoned it. The failure made him reject the offer of Flaubert's *Salammbô*.

At the end of 1923 the decision was taken to print a subscribers' edition of *Seven Pillars*. He rented a cottage near Bovington called Clouds Hill, where he could work on the revision undisturbed. During 1924 he went there whenever possible, adding many hours of concentrated study to his Tank Corps duties as a clerk and a storeman.

By now his identity was well known in the camp, although he continued to use the name Shaw, which he kept for the rest of his life (he adopted it by Deed Poll in 1927). Some of the rougher men taunted and even ill-treated him, but he began to find others who shared his interests in literature and music: Alec Dixon, 'Posh' Palmer and Arthur Russell. A gramophone was installed at Clouds Hill, and this small group of friends would gather there for tea, listening to Elgar and other composers. His attitude towards these young men was paternalistic. He referred to them in letters as 'the children', and delighted in watching their minds open up to music and literature they had not encountered before.

Lawrence had not given up hope of returning to the RAF. After a year in the Tanks he applied for readmittance, but was again refused. In May 1924 Trenchard offered him a commission, with the task of writing an official history of the RAF, but Lawrence declined; his energies were fully committed to *Seven Pillars*, which was not going as quickly as he had hoped. In any case he did not want to be an officer; clerical work in the ranks gave him security without onerous responsibilities. Service life made few demands on his intellect, leaving him much more time and mental

5. T. E. Lawrence to R. Graves, 28.6.1928, *Biographers* (Graves), p. 53.
6. T. E. Lawrence to L. Curtis, 19.3.1923, *Letters*, p. 411.
7. T. E. Lawrence to C. F. Shaw, 29.11.1924.

energy to concentrate on his own projects than he had enjoyed as a civilian working in the diplomatic service.

In February 1925 he pleaded once again with Trenchard to be allowed to rejoin the ranks of the RAF. He quoted the character description given of him by his senior officer in the Tank Corps: 'Exceptionally intelligent, very reliable, and works well.'[8] He admitted to being a misfit but protested that he had never been a trouble-maker.

This time Trenchard accepted, provided that his Secretary of State agreed too; but when Samuel Hoare considered the question he turned Lawrence down. In desperation Lawrence asked Churchill to put pressure on Hoare, but to no avail.

During these difficult months, Lawrence was working hard on *Seven Pillars* and as a result had become utterly depressed: 'It was so incredibly unlike what I'd thought my talents (of which I'd had too good an opinion) would bring forth.'[9] He knew that the book was successful in some ways, but it fell far short of his literary aspirations.

Worse still, the revision brought back stark memories of the war, and reminded him constantly of the deceitful role he had played. He became increasingly over-wrought, and his letters began to show an obsessive self-contempt. This destructive mood attacked the very roots of his personality, and his mind focused more and more on the humiliating incident at Deraa in November 1917: 'think of the offence, and the intensity of my brooding over it for three years. It will hang about me while I live, and afterwards if our personality survives. Consider wandering among the decent ghosts hereafter, crying "Unclean, Unclean!"'[10]

During the two and a half years that he served in the Tank Corps, he struggled without success to overcome the forces that were driving him downwards. Outwardly he maintained a semblance of control, yet within himself he was confused and unstable. The experience at Deraa had left him with an utter loathing of the carnality which was so important to others in the ranks, and he was quite unable to come to terms with these forces in his own nature. In his desire for self-punishment, and perhaps in an unconscious search for equilibrium, he even went so far as to have himself beaten.

By June 1925 his unbalanced mind had focused on a single lifeline: return to the RAF. But that door had been closed. He wrote to Edward Garnett, despairing both of his book and of his imprisonment in the army: 'Trenchard withdrew his objection to my rejoining the Air Force. I got seventh-heaven for two weeks: but then Sam Hoare . . . refused to entertain the idea. That, and the closer acquaintance with *The Seven Pillars* (which I now know better than anyone ever will) have together convinced me that I'm no bloody good on earth. So I'm going to quit: but in my usual comic fashion I'm going to finish the reprint and square up with Cape before I hop it . . . I shall bequeath you my notes on life in the recruits camp of the RAF. They will disappoint you.'[11]

The threat of suicide quickly mobilised his friends. Garnett got in touch with Shaw and John Buchan, who put pressure on the Prime Minister to overrule Hoare. A fortnight later Lawrence was summoned to meet Trenchard, and told that he could return to the RAF. His presence in the ranks was an embarrassment to the Government, but this was preferable to the scandal that would follow his suicide. Lawrence could scarcely contain his delight. On the ride back to Bovington he did 108 mph. Doubtless the politicians were surprised that Lawrence should so value service in the Air Force compared to the Tank Corps. In itself, the difference between the two cannot possibly have explained the strength of his feelings.

In August 1925 he was posted to the RAF Cadet College at Cranwell in Lincolnshire. This meant parting from his friends and from Clouds Hill, though he had grown so attached to the cottage that he now planned to keep it as his permanent home. The flat landscape and cold winds of Lincolnshire had little appeal for him, yet the move was a turning point in his life.

He now joined the ground crew of 'B' flight at Cranwell, whose main duties were to look after the training aircraft used by cadets during term time. He made no attempt to conceal his past, and was to begin with the subject of some curiosity; but after a while things settled down. Cranwell was an unusual station, and for the first time

Facing page
T. E. Lawrence
By William Roberts, 1922–3
(no. 257)

8. T. E. Lawrence to Sir Hugh Trenchard, 6.2.1925.
9. T. E. Lawrence to H. Williamson, 2.4.1928.
10. T. E. Lawrence to C. F. Shaw, 26.3.1924.
11. T. E. Lawrence to E. Garnett, 13.6.1925, *Letters*, pp. 476-7.

Advertisement for Brough Motorcycles,
c.1929
(no. 305)

he mixed freely with some officers, notably Rupert de la Bère who edited the Cadet College magazine.

As Lawrence's involvement in the production of *Seven Pillars* tailed off, he had much more time to write letters and to visit friends. In September 1926 he told George Brough that he had ridden 100,000 miles on the five Brough Superior motor cycles he had owned since 1922. When off duty he would ride to Cambridge to see E. M. Forster and F. L. Lucas, or to Ayot St. Lawrence to visit the Shaws. If the opportunity arose, he would go down to Dorset where Pte. Palmer was looking after Clouds Hill. He now greatly enjoyed the different attractions of the two societies he associated with, recognising in himself the need for both. To confine oneself to the company of writers and intellectuals such as the Shaws would 'soon become a vice – like dram-drinking.'[12]

After all his efforts on *Seven Pillars*, he had at last the leisure to consider other literary work, though he showed little immediate interest in committing himself to a new project. C. M. Doughty had died early in 1926 and Lawrence was asked to write a study of him. He declined, but allowed Cape to reinstate the introduction he had written to *Arabia Deserta*. For the time being he also turned down an offer to contribute to the *Spectator*, but a year later was persuaded to change his mind. More attractive was Florence Hardy's invitation to help edit her husband's diary; but for various reasons this came to nothing.

Lawrence was reluctant to commit himself to such schemes because he intended to leave England. He remained fearful of publicity, and realised that publication of *Revolt in the Desert*, the title of the abridged version of *Seven Pillars*, would again make him newsworthy. While *Seven Pillars* had not been available to reviewers, the publication of *Revolt* would be covered everywhere, and he wanted to be away from England when this happened. His time at Cranwell had been very happy, and the thought of going abroad again was not one he relished; it was a painful but necessary decision.

His application for posting overseas was accepted, and on 7 December 1926 he left England on the SS *Derbyshire* to a posting at Karachi in India. The journey by crowded troopship was not enjoyable, and Lawrence was very pleased to reach Karachi, in January 1927. He was posted to the RAF station at Drigh Road, seven miles outside the town. It was a dull, lifeless place set in a desert landscape uncomfortably reminiscent of Arabia. Yet it was large enough for him to remain fairly inconspicuous. Unlike the other airmen, he would never go outside the bounds of the camp. To have done so would have invited speculation that he was involved in some kind of clandestine activity.

His duties were to log the progress of each aircraft engine that passed through the engine repair shop. The task was not demanding, and the hours were much shorter than in England. Work stopped at 1 pm, with every Thursday and Sunday free. For the first time in many years he was confronted with boredom.

When Lawrence had first enlisted in August 1922 it had been in the hope of resolving a personal crisis. His reasons for staying in the ranks were no longer the same. For the past four years, service had given him security and companionship in exchange for an undemanding workload. This had enabled him to give thousands of hours to the revision and production of *Seven Pillars*: a project whose scale can perhaps be judged by the fact that its cost in today's terms was something over a quarter of a million pounds. Now that the book was finished he needed a project to replace it; service life in itself had little appeal for him.

Within days he was writing despondently: 'Karachi feels inordinately far away from every interest I ever had'.[13] He decided that he would fill his time with challenging literature, and asked friends to send him books, not only in English, but in Greek and other languages.

In this way he began to accumulate a respectable library of books and gramophone records. He received many serious contemporary novels as presents from publishers, authors and other friends, and lent books freely around the camp. At first he was amused to see the books his fellow airmen preferred, but later he found their choice very interesting. They condemned his own book, *Revolt*, as a 'binder'. As a result

12. T. E. Lawrence to C. F. Shaw, 8.6.1926.
13. T. E. Lawrence to Mrs Hardy, 11.1.1927, *Letters*, p. 503.

186

his writing underwent a radical change, leaving behind the contrived language of *Seven Pillars* in favour of a much simpler style.

During the past two years he had exchanged many letters with Charlotte Shaw, who had helped him proof-read *Seven Pillars*. Now it was she who took the initiative, sending regular parcels of books and gramophone records, and occasional hampers from Fortnums. She was a wealthy woman in her own right and could well afford such extravagances. Her frequent letters and gifts brought replies from Lawrence almost every week. During the next two years he wrote her many thousands of words, and she became his most regular correspondent, though neither his closest friend nor, in his eyes, the most important.

In June 1927 came a peculiar distraction. Jonathan Cape, who was making a great deal of money from *Revolt in the Desert*, was not at all pleased when Lawrence's trustees decided to halt British publication. In collaboration with the American publisher of *Revolt*, George H. Doran, Cape decided to commission a popular biography which would capitalise on the thriving Lawrence market. The commission went to Robert Graves, who was already an established writer and had known Lawrence personally in Oxford. Graves, therefore, wrote that he would take on the project if Lawrence agreed. As it happened Graves was also Lawrence's choice for such a book : the Graves family needed money, and Lawrence knew that such a biography would earn quite a lot for its author.

There was probably another reason why Lawrence wanted Graves to write the book. An industrious biographer might quite easily have come upon the truth about Lawrence's illegitimacy. Graves was indebted to Lawrence for numerous acts of generosity in the past, and could be relied upon to be discreet. Privately, however, Lawrence did not welcome the Graves project. It revived precisely the sort of public interest he had hoped to quell by withdrawing *Revolt*. Its one advantage in his eyes was to reduce the influence of the even more romantic study, *With Lawrence in Arabia*, which Lowell Thomas had now published.

Another threat at this time was the possibility that *Revolt* would be turned into a film. Lawrence had not thought to forbid his agent to sell the book for this purpose. He told Newcombe : 'some fatuous idiot has bought the film-rights . . . and is talking publicly about making an accurate film of it, in the *actual places* . . . Poor benighted wretches. It's like painting a peacock, and for historical accuracy, glueing feathers on its tail.'[14]

The scheme for a *Revolt* film would linger for several years, causing Lawrence considerable worry whenever it seemed on the point of fruition. Once Graves' book was out of the way, Lawrence began to work seriously on the notes he had made during the recruits' training course at Uxbridge in 1922. In August 1927 he was moved from the engine repair shop to the station office, where in his free time he practised typing by producing a draft from the notes on the office typewriter. As counterbalance to the grim Uxbridge material he added a section describing the happiness of his life at Cranwell.

In November he received a telegram to say that D. G. Hogarth had died. The news shook him deeply, and he was unable to concentrate on his writing work for some weeks. Since the death of his father in 1919, he had often sought Hogarth's level-headed advice : 'He was really to me the parent I could trust, without qualification, to understand what bothered me. And I had grown to lean on his knowledge of my motives not a little.'[15] In particular, it was Hogarth who had persuaded Lawrence to rewrite *Seven Pillars* in 1920, and who had afterwards taken a leading hand in the scheme for a subscription edition. Hogarth and Doughty were now both gone. Thomas Hardy, the greatest writer Lawrence had known, died a few weeks later.

At the time of his death, Hogarth had been working on a biography of Doughty. Lawrence was offered the task of completing the book, and considered the idea seriously. It turned out, however, that Hogarth's draft was well advanced, and the biography was finished by his son.

Lawrence was continually receiving interesting or highly lucrative offers. In December 1927, he turned down a seven-week lecture tour of America which would

14. T. E. Lawrence to S. F. Newcombe, 24.2.1927.
15. T. E. Lawrence to E. Garnett, 1.12.1927, *Letters*, p. 551.

have paid $100,000, and refused to sell one of his five copies of the 'Oxford' *Seven Pillars* for £5,000. His penury, living on twenty-four shillings a week in the Air Force, was entirely voluntary.

While he was still working on the Uxbridge book, Lawrence was offered another writing project. A proof copy of the subscribers' *Seven Pillars* had come into the possession of Bruce Rogers, one of America's leading typographers and book designers. At that time Rogers was contemplating an edition of the *Odyssey*, and wanted to commission a new 'free' translation. Having read the epic prose of *Seven Pillars* he came to think that Lawrence might produce a magnificent English version. He had therefore set about finding someone who could put him in touch with Lawrence.

At the end of 1927 Lawrence received a letter from Ralph Isham, a wealthy American who had bought James Boswell's papers from Malahide Castle. Isham had met Lawrence at the Peace Conference, and only recently had offered him the job of editing Boswell's papers for publication. Lawrence had declined this, but was intrigued when Isham wrote on Rogers' behalf, especially since Isham stressed that it was Lawrence's writing, rather than his name, which Rogers wanted: in fact the translator could remain anonymous. Lawrence, who read Greek for pleasure, and by coincidence had been intending to reread the *Odyssey*, replied at once. While stressing the difficulties of the proposed task, he was willing to attempt it. 'Bruce Rogers' dressing of the book will make it glorious, so that even an inferior version would pass muster. You are fortunate to be able to dine with him. I have for years admired him from ground level . . . he's the ideal of all those who have tried to produce books. Or perhaps I should say, of all who have gone far enough in the direction of producing books, to know what a job it is.'[16]

During April 1928 Lawrence began to feel that his position was threatened by one of the officers at Karachi, and he wrote privately to Air Vice-Marshal Sir Geoffrey Salmond, head of the RAF in India, asking to be transferred to another station. He was sent to Miranshah, a lonely outpost on the North West Frontier which was manned by minimal RAF and army units. In normal times it was the smallest Air Force station in India, though there were facilities for a much larger garrison. The squadrons serving at Miranshah changed regularly but Lawrence, serving as station clerk, was to be one of only three or four permanent RAF personnel.

The Miranshah fort, with its backdrop of mountains, provided exactly the calm Lawrence needed to make a start on the *Odyssey*. 'It's the station of a dream: as though one had fallen right over the world, and had lost one's memory of its troubles. And

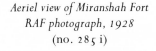

Aeriel view of Miranshah Fort
RAF photograph, 1928
(no. 285 i)

16. T. E. Lawrence to R. Isham, 2.1.1928.

the quietness is so intense that I rub my ears, wondering if I am going deaf.'[17] He now spent an hour or two each day on the specimen passage given him by Isham: 'It has not dashed my pleasure in Homer. I like doing it. Translating is an ingenious game, very exciting for a man who has no originalities of his own to express.'[18]

He sent the draft section (the whole of Book I of the *Odyssey*) to Isham on 30 June 1928. When Rogers received it he was delighted; Lawrence's rendering was precisely what he had hoped for, and a formal contract was drawn up under which Lawrence would be paid £800 for the complete translation. There is no doubt, however, that Lawrence would have found something else if he had not accepted the *Odyssey*. Indeed his friends in London were now showering him with ideas, *The Mint* having shown that his talent was not confined to descriptions of Arabia. Jonathan Cape proposed a translation of Rousseau's *Confessions*, E. M. Forster suggested writing a study of women, and David Garnett even wanted Lawrence to try his hand at a fairy tale!

By Christmas 1928 Lawrence had completed the first three of the twenty-four Books that make up the *Odyssey*. Life at Miranshah suited him so much that he arranged to extend his period of active service from seven to the full twelve years, which would run until March 1935. Only months earlier he had been planning to find a night-watchman's job in London when he left the Air Force in 1930.

Once again, however, his contentment was to be interrupted by press speculation. There were internal disturbances in Afghanistan during 1928, and on 16 December a totally fabricated story appeared in the *Empire News*, declaring that Lawrence had disguised himself as a holy man and was exciting the Afghan insurgents. By the time the fiction was exposed it had been published in India, and a genuine holy man, mistaken for Lawrence, was beaten up in Lahore. At home, socialist politicians and anti-Imperialists were outraged, believing that Lawrence was a British agent paid by the Conservative Government to stir up reactionary elements in Afghanistan against the reforming, pro-Soviet King Amanullah. Ironically, Lawrence had refused a clerical post at the Kabul embassy only months before.

It would have been futile to deny the press rumours, and in any case the truth – that Lawrence of Arabia was translating Homer in his off-duty hours at Miranshah – would have seemed just as implausible as the stories that were now appearing. The British Minister in Afghanistan demanded that Lawrence be moved away from the frontier.

Lawrence was ordered to leave Miranshah in January 1929. He was hurriedly flown to Lahore, and was only told what had happened when a letter from Salmond reached him there. Given the choice of coming home or accepting another overseas posting, Lawrence decided to face whatever publicity awaited him in England. He sailed from Bombay on board the SS *Rajputana*, a passenger liner, on 12 January, travelling back to England in conditions of unexpected comfort. During the voyage he translated another three books of the *Odyssey*.

17. T. E. Lawrence to H. S. Ede, 30.6.1982,
Letters, p. 615.
18. T. E. Lawrence to C. F. Shaw, 15.6.1928.

254

HUGH MONTAGUE, 1st VISCOUNT
TRENCHARD
By Sir William Orpen, 1917

Lawrence first met Sir Hugh Trenchard
(1873-1956) Chief of Air Staff, at the Cairo
Conference in 1921. Trenchard was grateful
for Lawrence's support in finding a useful
role for the RAF in the Middle East.
Afterwards, when Lawrence asked to be
allowed to enlist in the ranks of the RAF, it
was Trenchard who arranged it.

Lawrence had a great admiration for
Trenchard's work as Chief of Air Staff. He
wrote in 1928: 'the R.A.F. is your single
work . . . [and] it's thanks to your being head
and shoulders greater in character than
ordinary men that your force even in its
childhood surpasses the immemorial army
and navy. No man in the three or four
continents I know could have done what
you've done.'[1] This was no mere flattery: a
few months later, anticipating Trenchard's
retirement from the RAF, Lawrence told
John Buchan 'I feel Trenchard's going,

almost as a personal loss. There was a breadth
and honesty, and devotion, about him that
made one accept his headship as according to
the course of nature. I do not think that any
other man in the three kingdoms has had his
job – and privilege – of making, from the
first man upward, a whole new arm. His
work has been very good.'[2]

Trustees of the Imperial War Museum
(IWM 325)

1. T. E. Lawrence to Lord Trenchard, 1.5.1928.
2. T. E. Lawrence to John Buchan, 26.12.1928,
Letters, pp. 626-7.

Oil on canvas, 76.2 × 63.5
Signed and dated tl.: *HEADQUARTERS RFC 13th MAY
1917 ORPEN*
Provenance: Given by the artist, 1918.
Literature: Sir W. Orpen, *An Onlooker in France 1917-
1919*, 1924, p. 29, ill. pl. ix; B. Arnold, *Orpen, Mirror
to an Age*, 1981, p. 340, ill. p. 312.
Exhibitions: Agnews, *WAR, Paintings and Drawings. . .
by William Orpen ARA*, 1918 (44).

255
RAF DEPOT, UXBRIDGE
RAF photograph (c. 1920-5)

Lawrence wrote about the recruits' training
course at Uxbridge in *The Mint*. The aim, he
said, was to produce, 'by drill and instant
obedience, an airman', and he hated the
regime: 'I find myself longing for an empty
room, or a solitary bed, or even a moment
alone in the open air.'[1] He was totally
unprepared for the experience, and admitted
that 'Uxbridge . . . never had a recruit less
adaptable than myself.'[2] Nevertheless he
endured the training for ten weeks.

After he had been posted for specialist
training to the RAF School of Photography at
Farnborough he wrote: 'Uxbridge is pretty
miserable in its way: miserable and splendid
at once, since the fellows rise to it so well.
I'm awfully glad I went there and stayed a
couple of months: and awfully glad to have
got away.'[3]

Royal Air Force, Uxbridge

1. *The Mint*, 1955, p. 40.
2. *ibid*
3. T.E. Lawrence to Sir O. Swann, 9.11.1922,
Letters, p. 377.

256
HUT 4, RAF TRAINING DEPOT, UXBRIDGE
By an unknown photographer, 1922

'Our hut is a microcosm of unemployed England: not of unemployable England, for the strict R.A.F. standards refuse the last levels of the social structure. Yet a man's enlisting is acknowledgement of defeat by life. Amongst a hundred serving men you will not find one whole and happy. Each of us has a lesion, a hurt open or concealed, in his late history.'[1]

Lawrence was anxious not to be photographed, knowing that his anonymity would vanish if someone recognised him from a print (one of his first acts at Uxbridge had been to remove a photograph of himself, as Colonel Lawrence, from the camp's 'dry-bar').

He refused to join the group outside in this photograph, but can be seen looking from the window on the left of the hut.

The group also includes fellow-aircraftmen memorable from *The Mint*: Corporal Parker and Drill-Sergeant 'Taffy' Davies (centre); 'China' (extreme right) and 'Sailor' (front row, second from left).

R. Benson-Gyles

1. *The Mint*, part I, ch. 6, p. 30.

Provenance: Given to present owner by T. B. Jones.

257
T. E. LAWRENCE
By William Roberts, 1922-3

William Roberts was introduced to Lawrence by Colin Gill, and first met him in September 1922, one month after Lawrence's enlistment in the ranks of the RAF. Three months later Lawrence sat for this portrait, the only one from the Uxbridge period. He later said that Roberts had 'painted with astonishing certainty: not like John who put a new expression in his eyes and mouth on each sitting: but as though there was a fixity in my appearance and mood.'[1] Lawrence wrote also that the Roberts portrait was 'heroic in size . . . It flatters me, I think'[2], and elsewhere that he was shown 'looking very bad tempered'.[3]

This is scarcely surprising, if the portrait is considered in the context of Lawrence's service life as described in parts I and II of *The Mint*.

The Visitors of the Ashmolean Museum, Oxford (A727)

1. T.E. Lawrence to E. Kennington, 27.6.1923.
2. T.E. Lawrence to E. Kennington, 30.3.1923, *Letters*, p. 406.
3. T.E. Lawrence to R. de la Bère, 26.11.1933, *Letters*, p. 781.

Oil on canvas, 92 × 61
Signed tl.: *Roberts*.
Provenance: Given by A.W. Lawrence, 1946.
Literature: *Letters*, p. 406; *Grosvenor*, no. 46.
(illustrated in colour p. 185)

258
'UNCROWNED KING AS PRIVATE SOLDIER'
Facsimile of an article in the *Daily Express*, 27 December 1922

During the autumn of 1922 Lawrence told friends that he had enlisted, and inevitably this intriguing news began to circulate. By mid-December *Daily Mail* and *Daily Express* reporters were on to the story.

When the news broke Lawrence claimed that the 'beastly officers' had given him away, but it seems much more likely that the fault was his own. The *Daily Express* exposed his enlistment on 27 December: 'he is a private soldier, unknown and unrecognised, performing humdrum barrack routine, in a dull garrison town.' Within days he had been traced to Farnborough.

Sir Samuel Hoare, then Secretary of State for Air, was 'horrified at the disclosure . . . The position, which had been extremely delicate even when it was shrouded in secrecy, became untenable when it was exposed. The only possible course was to discharge Airman Ross'.[1] He was therefore dismissed in January 1923.

1. Viscount Templewood [Sir Samuel Hoare], *Empire of the Air*, 1957, p. 255.

259

OUTSIDE DAMASCUS GATE,
JERUSALEM
By David Bomberg, 1923

When Lawrence was expelled from the RAF
in January 1923, Sir Hugh Trenchard
suggested that he should take a short service
commission as an Armoured Car officer in
Palestine. Lawrence turned the idea down,
writing to one friend: 'I feel somehow that
I don't want any more commissions.'[1]. To
another, he wrote: 'No-one will offer me a
job poor enough for my acceptance! It has
cost me great pains to get admitted to low
life again, and my wish is to progress
downward, rather than up the ladder once
more.'[2]

By an odd coincidence his observation of
life in the armoured car units during the
Arab Revolt had been one of the factors that
had led him into the ranks: 'these friendly
outings with the armoured car and Air Force
fellows were what persuaded me that my best
future, if I survived the war, was to enlist'.[3]

In March 1923 he joined the Tank Corps,
but as a private rather than an officer. He
objected to service in the Middle East, and
although there was some question of sending
him with an armoured car unit to India, he
remained in England throughout the two
years he spent with the regiment.

When Lawrence entered Jerusalem with
the Allied forces in 1917 there were few
armoured cars in evidence. Bomberg's
painting was produced in 1923 when he went
to Palestine under the aegis of the Zionist
Organisation (see also no. 75). The armoured
cars shown lined up beside the northern gate
of the city were those of the British
occupying forces.

Manchester City Art Galleries (MAG
1928.29)

1. T.E. Lawrence to H. W. Bailey, 4.2.1923.
2. T.E. Lawrence to W. Rothenstein, 5.2.1923.
3. T.E. Lawrence to R. Graves, *Biographers* (Graves),
p. 95.

Oil on canvas, 41 × 51
Signed and dated bl.: *Bomberg 23*
Provenance: Purchased, 1928.
Exhibitions: Leicester Galleries, 1928; Arts Council,
David Bomberg, 1958 (10); Jerusalem, The Israel
Museum, *David Bomberg in Palestine 1923-1927*,
1983 (21).

260
BOVINGTON CAMP
By an unknown photographer (c. 1920s)

In March 1923 Lawrence enlisted in the Tank Corps and was sent to Bovington Camp, near Dorchester, where recruits were trained for eighteen weeks. The setting was beautiful (Lawrence often described it as Hardy's Egdon Heath), but he found the Camp abhorrent: 'I've really struck bed-rock – or base material – this time. The army is unspeakable: more solidly animal than I believed Englishmen could be. I hate them, and the life here: and am sure that it's good medicine for me.'[1] Although he made several close friends in the Tank Corps he drifted into a period of deep depression and insta-bility. He continually spoke of returning to the RAF, and eventually, after more than two years, he overcame official resistance to this move by threatening to commit suicide.

The Tank Museum, Bovington Camp, Dorset

1. T. E. Lawrence to Edward Garnett, 12.4.1923.

261
T. E. LAWRENCE AT BOVINGTON CAMP
Photograph by Arthur Russell (c. 1924)

Arthur Russell was one of Lawrence's closest friends at Bovington. In this photograph Lawrence is seen, somewhat incongruously, reading a copy of *The Times*. Although he found the camp hateful he tried very hard to come to terms with it: 'It's a horrible life, and the other fellows fit it . . . I'm not yet in the picture: but I will be in time.'[1]

From an album in the possession of the family of Wing Commander R. G. Sims

1. T. E. Lawrence to Curtis, 19.3.1923.

262
LETTER FROM T. E. LAWRENCE TO LIONEL CURTIS
Bovington Camp, 19 March 1923

Lawrence arrived at Bovington in March 1923 deeply depressed, both at his expulsion from the RAF and with life in general. Between March and June he wrote a series of five profoundly introspective letters to Lionel Curtis, exploring his outlook on the world in the most pessimistic terms. He later described these letters as 'essays in misery, for I felt like Lucifer just after his forced landing, at that time.'[1]

This, the first letter, was written only a week after arriving in Bovington:

'. . . the only rational conclusion to human argument is pessimism such as Hardy's, a pessimism which is very much like the wintry heath, of bog and withered plants and stripped trees, about us. Our camp on its swelling in this desolation feels pustular, and we (all brown-bodied, with yellow spots down our front belly-line), must seem like the swarming germs of its fermentation. That's feeling, exterior-bred feeling, with reason harmonising it into a picture: but there's a deeper sense which remembers other landscapes, and the changes which summer will bring to this one: and to that sense nothing can be changeless: whereas the rational preference or advantage of pessimism is its finality, the eternity in which it ends: and if there isn't an eternity there cannot be a pessimism pure. 'Lorde what a fog of words! What I would say is that reason proves there is no hope, and we therefore hope on, so to speak, on one leg of our minds . . . *Quelle vie.*'

The Warden and Fellows of All Souls College, Oxford

1. T. E. Lawrence to C. F. Shaw, 18.12.1927.

15.2 × 11.4
Provenance: Given by Lionel Curtis.
Literature: *Letters*, no. 205.
(not illustrated)

263

THOMAS AND FLORENCE HARDY AT MAX GATE
Photograph by Emil Otto Hoppé (*c.*1920)

When Lawrence arrived at Bovington in 1923 he wrote to Robert Graves asking for an introduction to the Hardys, and in April that year he first visited them at Max Gate, their home near Dorchester.

He liked the Hardys greatly, and went to tea with them frequently. After some months he wrote to Graves: 'The truth seems to be that Max Gate is very difficult to seize upon. I go there as often as I decently can, and hope to go on going there so long as it is within reach . . . Hardy is so pale, so quiet, so refined into an essence: and camp is such a hurly-burly. When I come back I feel as if I'd woken up from a sleep: not an exciting sleep, but a restful one. There is an unbelievable dignity and ripeness about Hardy: he is waiting so tranquilly for death, without a desire or ambition left in his spirit, as far as I can feel it: and yet he entertains so many illusions, and hopes for the world. . . . He takes me as soberly as he would take John Milton (how sober that name is), considers me as carefully, is as interested in me: for to him every person starts scratch in the life-race, and Hardy has no preferences: and I think no dislikes . . . T.H. is an experience that a man must keep to himself.'[1]

Lawrence was serving in India when Hardy died in January 1928. He wrote to Mrs Hardy: 'He had finished and was so full a man. Each time I left Max Gate, having seen that, I used to blame myself for intruding upon a presence which had done with things like me and mine. I would half-determine not to trouble his peace again. But as you know I always came back the next chance I had.'[2]

The Trustees of the Thomas Hardy Memorial Collection in the Dorset County Museum, Dorchester, Dorset

1. T.E. Lawrence to R. Graves 8.9.1923, *Biographers* (Graves), p. 26.
2. T.E. Lawrence to Mrs T. Hardy, 15.1.1928, *Letters*, p. 564.

264
THOMAS HARDY
By Augustus John, 1923

It was Lawrence who suggested that Augustus John should paint this portrait of Thomas Hardy. When Hardy saw it, he commented: 'I don't know whether that is how I look or not, but that is how I *feel*'.[1]

Lawrence too was pleased. He wrote to Hardy's wife: 'I saw the John portrait, and liked it. John, when he feels respect, paints simply, honestly, and with great clearness and dignity. I thought it charming, so lively in colour and gay in feeling: and am very glad you liked it.'[2]

The portrait was presented to the Fitzwilliam Museum, Cambridge in 1923. Mrs Hardy wrote that her husband 'was genuinely delighted . . . He said he would *far* rather have had that happen than receive the Nobel prize – and he meant it.'[3]

The Syndics of the Fitzwilliam Museum, Cambridge (1116)

1. M. Holroyd, *Augustus John*, II, 1974-5, p. 95.
2. T.E. Lawrence to Mrs Hardy, 14.11.1923.
3. *Friends of a Lifetime, Letters to Sydney Carlyle Cockerell*, ed. V. Meynell, 1940, p. 310.

Oil on canvas, 61.3 × 51.1
Signed and dated tr.: *John/1923*
Provenance: Given by Thomas Henry Riches, 1923.
Literature: Fitzwilliam Museum Syndicate, 27 November 1923, minute 6; Mrs T. Hardy in *Friends of a Lifetime, Letters to Sydney Carlyle Cockerell*, ed. V. Meynell, 1940, p. 310; A. John, *Chiaroscuro*, 1952, p. 134; J. W. Goodison, *Catalogue of Cambridge Portraits*, Cambridge, 1955, pp. 124-5, ill. pl. xxxi; M. Holroyd, *Augustus John*, II, 1974-5, p. 95; J. W. Goodison, *Catalogue of Paintings, British School*, III, Fitzwilliam Museum, Cambridge, 1955, pp. 135-6, ill. pl. 58.
Exhibitions: Cambridge, Fitzwilliam Museum, *Augustus Edwin John 1878-1961*, 1978 (18).

265

T. E. LAWRENCE'S COPY OF *THE DYNASTS*

By Thomas Hardy, volume II, London 1923

The volume is inscribed by Hardy to Lawrence and by Lawrence to himself as T. E. Shaw.

Four months after first meeting the Hardys, Lawrence asked Mrs Hardy : '*If* Mr. Hardy does such things, would he inscribe me copies of his thin-paper *Poems* and *Dynasts*. I have them and could bring them across. I know it's a vulgar desire ; but I live in vulgar company : and they would be very precious possessions.'[1]

There was no inscribed copy of Hardy's poems in Lawrence's library when he died.

The Warden and Fellows of All Souls College, Oxford

1. T. E. Lawrence to Mrs Hardy, 15.8.1923.

Printed book, 18.5
Inscribed by Thomas Hardy ; *Colonel Lawrence : |from| Thomas Hardy.* and by T. E. Lawrence : *To T. E. Shaw|for his comfort in camp|from|Lawrence.*
Provenance : T. E. Lawrence ; T. L. Guthrie, 1952 ; Mrs W. Porter ; given 1967.

267

THE FOREST GIANT

By Adrien le Corbeau, translated from the
French by J.H. Ross, London, 1924

In May 1923 Jonathan Cape asked Lawrence
to translate *Le Gigantesque*, a novel by Adrien
le Corbeau about the life of a giant sequoia
tree. Lawrence read the book, and concluded
that it was 'banal in style, and ordinary in
thought, and very interesting in topic.'[1]

By the time he had finished the translation
his views on the French original were
outspoken. He wrote: 'Damn Adrien le
Courbeau and his rhetoric. The book is a
magnificent idea, ruined by jejeune bombast.
My version is better than his: but dishonest
here and there'.[2]

J. M. Wilson

1. T.E. Lawrence to H.J. Cape, 8.7.1923.
2. T.E. Lawrence to H.J. Cape, 13.9.1923.

Printed book, 160 pp., 19.4

266

T. E. LAWRENCE

By Augustus John, 1923

This is one of a series of sketches drawn by
John in March 1923, when Lawrence was in
the Tank Corps stationed at Bovington Camp
in Dorset. Lawrence said it 'looked like a
budding sergeant . . . it's a pity Trenchard
didn't see it before he sacked me.'[1]

Private Collection

1. T. E. Lawrence to D. G. Hogarth, 1.4.1923, *Letters*,
p. 407.

Charcoal, 44.5 × 33
Signed r.: *John*
Provenance: Mrs D. H. St Leger, sold Christies, 4 June
1971 (108); Robert Payne, sold Sotheby's, New York,
11 December 1984 (265, ill.); Maggs Bros Ltd, 1985.
Literature: *Letters*, pp. 406-7; *Apollo*, May 1971, p. 23,
ill.; R. Payne, 'On the Prose of T. E. Lawrence' in
Prose, no. 4, Spring 1972, ill. fp. 91; *Grosvenor*, no. 11.
Exhibitions: London, Alpine Club Gallery, *Augustus
John*, 1923 (40).

268

THE TWILIGHT OF THE GODS
By Richard Garnett; introduction by T.E.
Lawrence, London, 1924

Richard Garnett (1835-1906) was for many
years Keeper of Printed Books at the British
Museum. He was the father of Edward
Garnett, and grandfather of David Garnett,
both of whom became close friends of
Lawrence.

In December 1923 John Lane was
working on a new illustrated edition of
Richard Garnett's *Twilight of the Gods*, a
collection of short stories first published in
1888. The book was to be an expensive
production, and Edward Garnett asked
Lawrence if he would write an introduction.
Lawrence replied: 'It's mad of Lane to pay
for my profound introduction . . . and I'll
write it if I can, and confess to you if I can't.
There's one good thing about cheques. . .
they are delicate things, quick to disappear
if you feel them unearned.'[1]

Lawrence knew and liked Richard
Garnett's stories, and finished his
introduction in good time. In it, he wrote:
'please, purchasers-of-this-edition, don't
lend your copies too freely. For one thing,
you won't get them back. It's packed with
a delicious callous cruelty, of the playful sort
which thrills bookish men . . . This book will
make you chuckle: nothing vulgar. There
. . . [are] allusions recondite, and yet so
broad and human that I've heard the chuckles
spread from the reader across a barrack full
of troops.' He was paid twenty guineas for
the work – one of the few writing projects
for which he accepted money.

J. M. Wilson

1. T. E. Lawrence to E. Garnett, 16.12.1923.

Printed book, 302 pp., 24.6
(not illustrated)

269
T.E. LAWRENCE
By an unknown photographer (*c.* 1924)

Lawrence is seen in a bombardier's tunic,
which must have been borrowed. One object
of his enlistment had been to refuse all
authority and he never rose above the rank
of Private in the Tank Corps, or its
equivalent, Aircraftman, in the RAF.

Bodleian Library (MS.Res.c.54)

270

WITH LAWRENCE IN ARABIA
By Lowell Thomas, New York, 1924

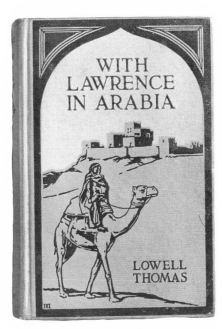

Lowell Thomas lectured on Lawrence for
four years, and afterwards adapted his
material for this popular biography. It was
published in America in 1924 and in Britain
a few months later. Lawrence was disgusted
by its sensationalism and outrageous
inaccuracies, writing to Charlotte Shaw: 'So
glad you felt the vulgarity of Lowell Thomas'
book. It's horrible.'[1]

With Lawrence in Arabia sold extremely
well. During the ten years following
publication more than 100,000 copies were
printed in England, and this total had nearly
doubled by the beginning of the Second
World War. Lawrence hoped fervently that
any future biography would be more
accurate. This was one of the principal
reasons for his help to Robert Graves and
Liddell Hart when they were researching
their books about his life.

P. C. & B. A. Metcalfe

1. T. E. Lawrence to C. F. Shaw, 29.9.1927.

Printed book, 428 pp., 20.5

271
JOHN BUCHAN, 1st BARON
TWEEDSMUIR
By Thomas Clapperton, 1935

Lawrence was first introduced to John
Buchan (1875-1940) in the summer of 1920.
They had many literary interests in common
and thereafter met occasionally whenever
Lawrence was in England. Buchan was one of
the original subscribers to *Seven Pillars of
Wisdom*.

In 1925 Buchan played some part in
Lawrence's efforts to return to the ranks of
the RAF, although it was almost certainly
Lawrence's threat of suicide, in a letter to
Edward Garnett, that finally settled the
matter.

Buchan held Lawrence in high regard, and
is believed to have modelled characters on
Lawrence in his popular novels. In his
autobiography, written some years after
Lawrence's death, he wrote: 'I am not a very
tractable person or much of a hero-
worshipper, but I could have followed
Lawrence over the edge of the world. I loved
him for himself . . . he was the only man of
genius I have ever known.'[1]

National Portrait Gallery (NPG 3636)

1. John Buchan, *Memory-Hold-the-Door*, 1940, p. 229.

Bronze, 35.6 h.
Incised on left side of neck: *T. Clapperton*
Provenance: Purchased from the sculptor, 1948.
Exhibitions: RA, 1937 (1546).

272
ROYAL AIR FORCE COLLEGE,
CRANWELL
RAF photograph (1923)

Just after his thirty-seventh birthday
Lawrence was at last allowed to return to the
RAF. He was posted to the Cadet Training
College at Cranwell, Lincolnshire. His duties
as a member of 'B' Flight were to help look
after training aircraft, and he worked at this
with fifteen other men, under the command
of two officers.

He was extremely happy at Cranwell, and
remained there until November 1926 when
he was posted abroad so as to avoid the
publicity surrounding *Revolt in the Desert*,
which was to be published in March 1927.

Lawrence described his life at Cranwell in
part III of *The Mint*. The hangar in which he
worked is the central one of the three seen
to the right of the photograph. It is described
in *The Mint*: 'Our hangar is a girder frame,
sheathed in iron. The floor is concrete,
without one pillar or obstruction across its
main expanse. The mere space of it is
rewarding, to a daily dweller in low rooms.
Too rewarding, perhaps. An airman alone in
it feels puny and apprehensive. It is as great
as most cathedrals, and echoes like all of
them put together. We have parked fourteen
aeroplanes within its central hall . . . I like
the hangar well in storms. The darkness and
its size conspire to make it formidable,
ominous. The leaves of the closed doors
tremble in the guides, and clap boomingly
against the iron rails. Through their crevices,
and through hundreds of other crevices,
packs of wind hurtle, screaming on every
high note of the scale, to raise devil-dances
across the dusty floor.'[1]

Royal Air Force College, Cranwell (Crown
copyright, reproduced by permission of the
Controller)

1. *The Mint*, part III, ch. 7, p. 180.

273
EDWARD TURNOUR, 6th EARL
WINTERTON
Photograph by Felix Man, 1938 (printed
c.1976)

Winterton first met Lawrence during the
later stages of the Syrian campaign, when he
served for a time as a British liaison officer.
The two became friends, and when Lawrence
returned to England in October 1918,
determined to take up the political struggle
on behalf of the Arabs, Winterton wrote
introducing him to the Under Secretary of
State for Foreign Affairs, Lord Robert Cecil.

After the war both Lawrence and Feisal
were occasionally guests at Shillinglee Park,
Winterton's magnificent country house.
However, a later meeting between them, in
1925, provoked one of the most bitter
introspective letters Lawrence wrote:
'Winterton of course had to talk of old
times, taking me for a companion of his
again, as though we were again advancing on
Damascus. And I had to talk back, keeping
my end up, as though the R.A.F. clothes
were a skin that I could slough off at any
while with a laugh.

'But all the while I knew I couldn't . . .
My reason tells me all the while, dins into
me day and night, a sense of how I've crashed
my life and gone hopelessly wrong: and
hopelessly it is, for I'm never coming back,
and I want to.'[1]

National Portrait Gallery (NPG P372)

1. T. E. Lawrence to C. F. Shaw, 28.9.1925.

29.5 × 19.8
Provenance: Given by the photographer's widow, 1988.
Exhibitions: National Portrait Gallery, *Felix H. Man*,
1976 (72).

274
T. E. LAWRENCE ON HIS BROUGH SUPERIOR MOTORCYCLE, RK 4907
By an unknown photographer (1925-6)

Lawrence wrote on the reverse of this photograph, taken at Cranwell: 'here is a photograph of Boa . . . These were taken for the maker of the machine, to show technical details of its build. The rider is an accident.'

He nicknamed his Brough motorcycles 'Boanerges', meaning 'sons of thunder', and also referred to them as George I to VII, after their maker George Brough. The Brough shown here was Lawrence's fifth, which he bought two months after his posting to Cranwell in August 1925.

Lawrence's joy in motorcycling is described in *The Mint*: 'Boanerges' first glad roar at being alive again jarred the huts of Cadet College into life. "There he goes, the noisy beggar", someone would say in every flight . . . Another bend: and I have the honour of one of England's straightest and fastest roads. The burble of my exhaust unwound like a long cord behind me. Soon my speed snapped it, and I heard only the cry of the wind which my battering head split and fended aside. The cry rose with my speed to a shriek: while the air's coldness streamed like two jets of iced water into my dissolving eyes. I screwed them to slits and focused my sight two hundred yards ahead of me on the empty mosaic of the tar's gravelled undulations . . . A skittish motor-bike with a touch of blood in it is better than all the riding animals on earth'.[1]

In December 1925 Lawrence crashed this Brough on ice: 'knee: ankle; elbow: being repaired . . . Hobble like a cripple now.'[2] A year later, again on a slippery road, he 'got into a trough in the wood paving, and fell heavily, doing in the footrest, kickstart, brake levers, handlebar, and oil pump. Also my experienced knee-cap learned another little trick. Alb Bennett took the wreck for 100. I limp rather picturesquely'.[3]

See also no. 305.

Bodleian Library (MS.Res.c.54)

1. *The Mint*, part III ch. 16, pp. 199-202.
2. T. E. Lawrence to E. Palmer, 10.12.1925, *Letters*, p. 487.
3. T. E. Lawrence to D. Knowles, 3.12.1926, *Letters*, p. 501.

275
T. E. LAWRENCE
By Eric Kennington, 1926

In late 1926 Lawrence sat for the bust from which this bronze cast was taken. Kennington modelled it in five half-hour sittings, just before Lawrence left England on a five-year posting to India at the end of 1926. Afterwards Kennington recalled that Lawrence 'looked much the same [as usual] but was remote, and did not giggle at all. Exceedingly still, he seemed to have done with every barrier, and to sit naked.'[1] The explanation may be given in a letter from Lawrence shortly afterwards, saying: 'I went off into a day-dream whenever we were left alone: and that I was usually dog-tired before I ever came.'[2] He had spent the whole of his last leave in London, collating sets of pages of *Seven Pillars* and adding their plates.

Lawrence saw a photograph of the bust in February 1927, and wrote to Kennington: 'magnificent; there is no other word for it. It represents not me but my top-moments, those few seconds in which I succeed in thinking myself right out of things . . . The face and neck are treated with a dry precision and strength and confidence very unusual in recent sculpture: in any portrait sculpture. I trace a little hesitation in your handling of the lips . . . The balance and proportion of head, neck and supports are apparently exact. I'd have liked more surface difference in treatment of hair, flesh and clothing – especially the last two . . . the structure of the forehead seems to be one of the very best things in the whole . . . It hangs together as a most convincing portrait of a person very sure of himself.'[3]

The cast exhibited here is one of a set made in 1961. There are earlier casts in St Paul's Cathedral (see no. 352) and at Clouds Hill.

National Portrait Gallery (NPG 4298)

1. *Friends*, p. 278.
2. T. E. Lawrence to E. H. Kennington, 15.2.1927, *Letters*, pp. 507-8.
3. *ibid.*

Bronze, 41.3 h., edition of 12, 1961
Inscribed: *T.E.L. – E.H.K. 9*
Provenance: Purchased from Leicester Galleries, 1963.
Literature: *Letters*, pp. 507-8; *Friends*, p. 244; *Biographers* (Graves), p. 131 n.; *Grosvenor*, no. 30.

276
RAF DEPOT, DRIGH ROAD, KARACHI
RAF photograph, 1929
Vintage print

On 7 January 1927 Lawrence arrived at the RAF Depot at Drigh Road, Karachi. He found it hard to settle down in its environment: 'The Depot is dreary, to a degree, and its background makes me shiver. It is a desert, very like Arabia: and all sorts of haunting likenesses (pack-donkeys, the colour and cut of men's clothes, an oleander bush in flower in the valley, camel-saddles, tamarisk) try to remind me of what I've been for eight years desperately fighting out of my mind. Even I began to doubt if the coming out here was wise. However there wasn't much chance, and it must be made to do. It will do, as a matter of fact, easily.'[1]

Working hours at the Depot were very short, and Lawrence began to fill his leisure with reading and writing. In little more than a year he had completed *The Mint*, and begun a translation of Homer's *Odyssey*.

J. W. Easton

1. T. E. Lawrence to C. F. Shaw, 28.1.1927.

15.1 × 20
Provenance: Acquired 1929.

277
T. E. LAWRENCE AT KARACHI
By an unknown photographer, 1927
Vintage print

This is one of the very few photographs which Lawrence signed. Another print of the same photograph, also signed, is in an American private collection.

J. M. Wilson

19 × 12.1
Autographed br.: *T. E. Shaw*

278
ROBERT GRAVES
By Eric Kennington, *c.* 1918

After serving in the First World War, Robert Graves went up to Oxford as an undergraduate. It was there that he met Lawrence in March 1920. Graves was already an accomplished poet, and Lawrence, who was working on *Seven Pillars*, enjoyed discussing the technicalities of writing with him. Through Graves he met other writers such as Siegfried Sassoon.

Lawrence maintained a great interest in Graves' work, and for many years he was the only person Graves trusted for criticism. In 1921, to help Graves out of financial difficulties, Lawrence gave him some fragments of *Seven Pillars* to sell for publication in America. For his part, Graves dedicated several books and poems to Lawrence.

They saw each other fairly often until Lawrence enlisted, and while Lawrence was serving in India in 1927 Graves wrote a popular biography (see no. 279). Shortly after Lawrence's return to England in 1929, Graves moved to Mallorca where he lived for the rest of his life. More than sixty letters from Lawrence to Graves survive. In 1933 Lawrence wrote: 'Recall the hundreds of times we have met and talked. You cannot know how much I have seen in you, and learned of you – but please take it for written. R.G. has been a main current influencing my life for nearly fifteen years.'[1]

By the 1930s, however, their relationship had become slightly strained. Lawrence was distressed by the brutality of *I, Claudius*, telling a friend that he found it 'sickening'.[2] He also offended Laura Riding, Graves' companion, by a casual remark, and she tried to turn Graves against him. After Lawrence's death Graves published *T.E. Lawrence to his Biographers* jointly with B.H. Liddell Hart.

National Museum of Wales, Cardiff

1. T. E. Lawrence to R. Graves, 24.1.1933, *Biographers* (Graves), p. 170.
2. T. E. Lawrence to F. Manning, 25.7.1934.

Pastel, 52.1 × 38.1
Unsigned
Provenance : Given by the sitter, 1919.

279
LAWRENCE AND THE ARABS
By Robert Graves, London, 1927

In June 1927 the interest in Lawrence generated by Lowell Thomas and by *Revolt in the Desert* led George H. Doran, the American publisher of *Revolt*, to commission a biography for younger readers. The idea was taken up in England by Jonathan Cape.

Lawrence soon heard of the scheme, and suggested that such a book might be written by his friend Robert Graves (who badly needed some income at the time). By coincidence Cape had reached the same conclusion, and a contract was quickly agreed to. As it was hoped that the book could be out for Christmas, Graves was asked to deliver his manuscript within a few weeks.

He had barely begun work when it was learned that Lowell Thomas had spotted the same gap in the market, and was about to publish a new book of his own, *The Boys' Life of Colonel Lawrence*. As a result Graves was asked to adapt his study of Lawrence to a more general readership. He was fortunate, however, because Lawrence's Trustees in England had meanwhile arranged to halt British sales of *Revolt in the Desert*, which would have competed directly with any new adult biography.

Although Graves was now expected to write a longer and more demanding book, he still had to deliver it very quickly. By mid-

August Lawrence had seen and corrected the draft, but the work was unimpressive and there was too little time to improve it. Lawrence wrote : 'Every page of R.G.'s own had inaccuracies. I corrected it till I was sick : and let as much more slip. Eighty per cent of the book was what I'd call a bare parody of *Revolt* : I do not think it was quite right to make so free with another's work.'[1] To Graves himself Lawrence wrote : 'The thing that was really important was for you to do yourself really well, and I don't feel it's up to the level of your other prose.'[2] The only recompense, in Lawrence's eyes, was the fact that the book would provide Graves with financial security for several years.

J. M. Wilson

1. T. E. Lawrence to C. F. Shaw, 18.8.1927.
2. T. E. Lawrence to R. Graves, 17.8.1927, *Biographers*, (Graves), p. 133.

Printed book, 454 pp., 20.5
(not illustrated)

280
'D.H. LAWRENCE'S NOVELS'
Facsimile of a review by 'C.D.' in the
Spectator, 6 August 1927

In June 1927 Francis Yeats-Brown, literary editor of the *Spectator*, sent Lawrence a parcel of books to review. These included some volumes of Secker's pocket edition of D.H. Lawrence's novels.

Lawrence finished the review a month later. By agreement it was to be published under the initials 'C.D.' (standing for Colindale, the last London underground station Lawrence had entered before he left England in 1926).

He sent it to Yeats-Brown with a covering note : 'I enclose you a note on D.H.L. Your books . . . came to me on Wednesday . . . I read the three D.H.L's on Thursday, and have written this today. Too quickly, no doubt, but I did not want to keep you longer without a sample : besides I've been reading him since before the war, so that my mind was made up before this week.

'As for the note, of course it's no good. By nature I wasn't meant to write. The job comes very hard to me. I can't do it without

trying my best : and if I've ever in my past written decently it was under the dire command of some mastering need to put on paper a case, or a relation, or an explanation, of something I cared about. I don't see that happening with literature and so I don't expect you to like what I write.

'I've signed it C.D. because it's the first, if you do print it, after all. I'd suggest the first five or six things worth signing be restrained to their initials. If the miracle continues after that (surely either your forebearance or my endeavour will break down) we might climb so far as Colin D., keeping the full truth about the D. till it was certain that the fellow could write and had a character. In my heart of hearts I know he hasn't.'[1]

Two further 'C.D.' reviews were published during August. A few weeks later Lawrence received an unexpected letter from Martin Secker, forwarded by the *Spectator*, 'to say that he had read my review, and would be glad to know if "C.D." would undertake a short critical book on D.H. Lawrence ! Either Secker is badly off for someone to write about D.H.L. . . or ? What is the "or" . . . I give it up.'[2]

Lawrence wrote five reviews for the *Spectator* in all. The last, on H.G. Wells' short stories, was published in February 1928.

1. T. E. Lawrence to F. Yeats-Brown, 5.5.1927.
2. T. E. Lawrence to C. F. Shaw, 15.9.1927.

(not illustrated)

281
CHARLOTTE SHAW
By an unknown photographer (c. 1915)

Lawrence first met Charlotte, the wife of G.B. Shaw, in 1922. She was then sixty-five. When he sent a copy of the 'Oxford' *Seven Pillars* to her husband she was the first to read it, and she heaped praises on it. Afterwards she maintained a constant correspondence with Lawrence until his death.

More than 300 letters from Lawrence to Charlotte Shaw survive, but he destroyed almost all those that she sent to him. As a result it is difficult to assess the true nature of their relationship. Some biographers have suggested that Lawrence looked to Charlotte Shaw as some kind of 'substitute mother', but the evidence shows that it was she, rather than Lawrence, who kept the correspondence going. In addition to frequent letters she sent him countless gifts including books, gramophone records and food hampers. Even though Lawrence knew that she was a wealthy woman in her own right he found this bounty embarrassing. He repaid her amply by giving her an early corrected draft of *The Mint* (see no. 283), the manuscript of his *Odyssey* translation (see no. 312), his surviving war notes and diaries (see no. 119), and his commonplace book *Minorities*. On one occasion he refused her generosity: in 1929 she was the prime mover in a plan to give him a new Brough Superior motorcycle. He refused the gift, insisting on paying for it himself.

Charlotte Shaw remained enthusiastic about *Seven Pillars* throughout its production and helped to correct the proofs. He valued her comments on his writing, and knew that she would occasionally consult her husband. When he went to India it was she who sent him reviews of *Revolt in the Desert*; she subscribed to 'T.E. Lawrence' clippings from a press cuttings agency for several years.

Much of their correspondence was on literary matters, but as their friendship deepened Lawrence showed little reticence in writing to her about his family background and other personal matters. On her side there were equally revealing letters, a few of which have survived. The nature of his feelings towards her was probably summed up when he wrote: 'You are rather like the Semitic God, of whom it is easy to say what isn't, but impossible to say what is . . . As for feeling at home with you: this is not the word. I do not wish to feel at home. You are more completely restful than anyone I know, and that is surely better? Homes are ties, and with you I am quite free.'[1]

British Library of Political and Economic Science, London School of Economics (Shaw Collection, MSS Division)
1. T. E. Lawrence to C. F. Shaw, 10.7.1929.

282
LETTER FROM T. E. LAWRENCE TO CHARLOTTE SHAW
Karachi, 2 January 1928
Facsimile

Lawrence had first mentioned his notes on the RAF recruits training depot at Uxbridge to Charlotte Shaw in November 1927, and she immediately asked to see them. On 2 January 1928 he sent her the first part of his typed working draft, with a covering letter:

'So soon as I found, at the end of your letter, your request for the Uxbridge notes [parts I and II of '*The Mint*'] I unlocked my box, thrust the rough copy of them into an envelope, and took them to the post. It was a matter of minutes only, before I could think it over.

'Please regard yourself (in reading it) as being in an equivocal position, eavesdropping in a men's barrack. Those of us who live publicly together have to depend on each other's common decency to respect our inevitable confidence. We are all in the mire together. The rest relied on me, to keep their custom, and I break it. What is given away is not myself, as in the Seven Pillars, but my fellows. I take you into their confidence, showing only just so much of myself as seems to illuminate their dark

places. I fear you will not like them. Yet I have censored out their secretest things, their best or worst intimacies. So many of them came to confide in my greater age and experience. What I have left is too much: to my informed mind there are things, poignantly unbearable, suggested behind these notes: and a great and lovely cleanness of spirit. So gay.

'I wrote them for myself, and copied them for Garnett: and was going to ask him not to lend them except to two specific people. Now there will be you and G.B.S. (if you wish) added. I do not want others even to know that the notes exist: least of all that they exist in book-form. You see, all the men are living airmen: only their names have been changed twice or thrice, after the S.P. fashion. But we lived together, really, in the huts I mention, and we said and did and suffered these things. There is nothing added – and only the intimacies subtracted. They talked like this to me, because I was one of them. Before you they would have been different: and they would be angry to think that a woman had shared their life. They cannot have the privilege of knowing you: nor could all of them have the largeness to understand you, if they did. It has been bred into them that a woman is different: holy almost, despite the soilings they receive when men handle them.

'I should tell you the history of the notes. Garnett has waited for his promised copy since early 1923, when I looked back on the finished *Seven Pillars*, about the time I had correspondence with G.B.S., and gave up my ambitious hopes of being a writer: a great writer, I should say, for only those deserve the name. I doubt whether you will wish to copy his patience. He may wait years yet, so often have I picked them up, lost heart, laid them down. The original notes were made, mostly in bed, from day to day, after evening roll call at Uxbridge. They were naturally piece-meal. I did each parade or fatigue often, noting its flavour each time with new intensity, and recording it, pages apart from last time. Through this labyrinth nobody but myself could walk. So I told Garnett he must wait for them to be clean-copied.

'The process of clean-copying is to index the stuff, isolate the related items in a flush, and re-arrange them as one chapter. You will see that the chapters are short, and the words close and spare. I have tried to avoid prolixity, this time. Indeed I fancy that the writing is competent, as prose. These skeleton chapters I worked over, arranging their bones, and articulating their joints, till they grew too tangled to read. You know the description of Shelley's M.S. ''like the sketch of a marsh, with wild ducks taking flight from its clumps of reed''? Like that.

'Then I typed them out, my first lessons on the office typewriter. About October last. Upon these typed drafts I made improvements in style, and added a few incidents which had not found place in the first boiling down. What has been sent to you is this typed draft, after copying clean into a notebook (Version IV, you see) which will be Garnett's, if he and I live so long. The copying has reached the end of your pages, which take A/c Ross from his sorry enlistment to the moment when he was on the barrack-square for instruction in drill, etc. That is the initiation of an airman.

'To complete *The Mint* would require about as much again. Some of it is in Stage III : but I have not touched it for a month or two – to be accurate, since D.G.H[ogarth] died. Perhaps I will carry it to the end, some day. I dislike leaving loose bits about me. But then I do not like reading so much as I have done, or what is left for me to re-do. There are so many things which it hurts me to remember. You will realise that I was abruptly turned out of the R.A.F. soon after this time, and that for two years I was heart-bound in the tanks-corps, trying to get back. At last I managed it. . . but very late, and not like the first time, on my naked merit.

'I suppose women in their club-rooms would not like men to overhear them. Please do not believe that I like this dirt. It hurts me, and makes my mind ache night after night : for I know that the only difference between me and the worst of them is that I keep a closer guard on my lips. We are all alike, as animals : and while the exercises and excitement of a puppy are beautiful, the same conduct in an old dog is horrible.

'Will you please hold the sheets as a loan, till I complete the Garnett copy (if I do complete it) and send it you to post on to

him? It will only be a month or two, if I begin on it again : for really the changes I make are formal. But in such a work I must wait for the mood. It would be different if I were writing it for someone, to meet some obligation. Then I could drive myself to it. A very real shrinking and reluctance hedge it round. When you turn over an aged stone, all manner of feeble, pale-coloured things scrabble away in search of cover. I am like that, with *The Mint*.

'Please realise it is in three sections.
Vigil (yours) which is sorry :-
Initiation (on the square) which hurts :-
Service (at Cranwell) when the sun shines :
T.E.S.'

British Library (Add.MS 45916)
(not illustrated)

283
THIRD DRAFT OF *THE MINT*
By T. E. Lawrence, 1928

When Lawrence enlisted in the RAF in August 1922 one of his purposes was to write a book. During the ten weeks he spent at the Uxbridge Training Depot in 1922 he wrote pages of descriptive notes : 'They were photographs, snap-shots rather, of the places we lived in and the people we were, and the things we did'.[1] When he moved to the RAF School of Photography at Farnborough, however, he found the material less interesting. Then came his abrupt dismissal in January 1923, and the RAF notes stopped.

During the ensuing years he was preoccupied with the revision of *Seven Pillars*, but he did not forget about the notes, and soon after arriving in India in January 1927 he asked a friend to send them to him. He began re-writing them that summer, and *The Mint* was completed the following year.

This heavily corrected typescript, given to Charlotte Shaw, is the third draft, and is the earliest full-length version to survive.

The British Library Board (Add.MS 45916)
1. T.E. Lawrence to E. Garnett, 12.11.1922.

Bound volume, typescript with numerous MS revisions, ff. ii + 180 pp., 35
Provenance : Sent in instalments to Charlotte Shaw ; given to the British Museum by G. B. Shaw, 1944.
(not illustrated)

284
THE MINT
By T.E. Lawrence, New York, 1936
Edition of 50 numbered copies

In March 1928 Lawrence completed a manuscript fair copy of *The Mint* and sent it to Edward Garnett, writing to a friend : 'When he asked me for it in 1922, I was nobody : and he didn't think it was as big a thing as this. He will get a shock.'[1] He realised that the book had some merit, but he knew that publication would harm the image of the RAF. In a letter to his brother A. W. Lawrence he wrote : 'I will not publish these notes . . . in my day. And I hope that you will not (without the permission of the Chief of Staff of the R.A.F. for the time being) publish them, if the option is yours, before 1950.'[2]

After Lawrence's death Edward Garnett's son, David, decided to sell his manuscript of *The Mint*. In order to protect copyright in America it was necessary to print a small edition there, and Lawrence's American publishers, Doubleday, Doran, produced this edition of fifty copies. They were put on sale in America at the prohibitive price of $500,000 each.

The binding was designed to match that of the 1926 New York edition of *Seven Pillars* (see no. 247).

A. W. Lawrence

1. T. E. Lawrence to C. F. Shaw, 16.3.1928.
2. T. E. Lawrence to A. W. Lawrence, 2.5.1928, *Letters*, p. 600.

Printed book, 202 pp., 29.3

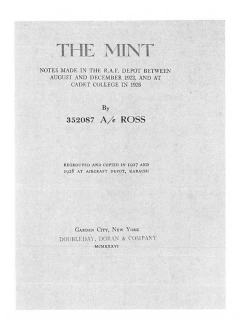

THE MINT

NOTES MADE IN THE R.A.F. DEPOT BETWEEN AUGUST AND DECEMBER 1922, AND AT CADET COLLEGE IN 1925

By
352087 A/c ROSS

REGROUPED AND COPIED IN 1927 AND 1928 AT AIRCRAFT DEPOT, KARACHI

GARDEN CITY, NEW YORK
DOUBLEDAY, DORAN & COMPANY
MCMXXXVI

285
MIRANSHAH FORT
RAF photographs, 1928
Vintage prints

(i) Aerial view (illustrated on p. 188)

(ii) Outside the walls

On 26 May 1926 Lawrence arrived in Miranshah, an outpost in Waziristan near the Afghan border. A month later he sent the following description of the camp to a friend: 'Well, I've moved from Karachi, and come to the most remote R.A.F. station in India: — and the smallest. We are only twenty-six, all told, with five officers, and we sit with 700 India Scouts (half regulars) in a brick and earth fort behind barbed wire complete with search lights and machine guns. Round us, a few miles off, in a ring are low bare porcelain-coloured hills, with chipped edges and a broken bottle skyline. Afghanistan is ten miles off. The quietness of the place is uncanny – ominous, I was nearly saying: for the Scouts and ourselves live in different compartments of the fort, and never meet: and so there's no noise of men: and no birds or beasts — except a jackal concert for five minutes about 10 p.m. each night, when the searchlights start . . .'[1]

1. T. E. Lawrence to H. S. Ede, 30.6.1928.

(iii) The wireless station

Lawrence was employed at Miranshah during office hours as a clerk and had now taught himself to type. In his own time he read, and worked at the *Odyssey*. He spent the day in the wireless station which he shared with the wireless operator, Jack Easton, who became a friend. He described the room in a letter to Charlotte Shaw: '[it] is a fifteen foot square white-washed cube, with cement floor. In the centre is the fan: underneath it the officer's table: against the far wall my table, covered with white American cloth, and carrying the typewriter, which I've taught to produce pages of Homer, as well as Daily Routine Orders! In the corner is a brick arch, leading to a flue: and there we will burn logs all day, if I am lucky, and stay here indefinitely.'[1]

1. T. E. Lawrence to C. F. Shaw, 25.6.1928.

J. W. Easton

(i) 16 × 21.2 (ii) 15.2 × 20.3 (iii) 15.6 × 20
Provenance: Acquired 1928.

286
SIR PHILIP SASSOON'S VISIT TO MIRANSHAH FORT
RAF photograph, 1928
Vintage print

On 21 October 1928 the Under-Secretary of State for Air, Sir Philip Sassoon (1888-1939), was returning from India to England, and broke the journey to inspect the flight at Miranshah. Sassoon wrote the next year: 'The accommodation at this small, advanced station was quite excellent; good, solid brick buildings and hangars and everything as spick and span and in as good order as if under the immediate eye of their Squadron Commander . . . I met here . . . one Aircraftman Shaw, better known as Colonel Lawrence, with whom I had a long talk. He seemed thoroughly happy in his self-chosen exile'.[1]

Sassoon and Lawrence had been acquainted since 1924 when Sassoon ordered a copy of *Seven Pillars*. They became friends after Lawrence returned from India in 1929, and he occasionally visited Sassoon's country home, Port Lympne. Lawrence wrote of Baldwin's defeat in the 1929 General Election: 'My chief regret at the passing of the Government is that Sir Philip Sassoon loses the US of Air!'[2] Later that year, the

Labour Secretary of State for Air, Lord Thomson, allowed Lawrence to remain in the ranks on condition that he refrained from seeing Sassoon, and other 'great men'.[3]

J. W. Easton

1. Philip Sassoon, *The Third Route*, 1929, pp. 205-6.
2. T. E. Lawrence to Lady Astor, 6.6.1929.
3. See *Letters*, p. 673.

15.7 × 20.4
Provenance: Acquired 1928.

287
GROUP OF SERVICEMEN WITH T. E. LAWRENCE AT MIRANSHAH FORT
Photograph by ?Flight Lieutenant Smetham, 10 December 1928
Vintage print

From left to right: Corporal Stone, Private Hayter, Lawrence, and Corporal Easton (the station's wireless operator). Both Hayter and Easton became friends with Lawrence.

J. W. Easton

19.8 × 11.9
Provenance: Acquired 1928.

289

T. E. LAWRENCE IN BARRACKS, ?MIRANSHAH FORT
By an unknown photographer, c.1928
Vintage print

Lawrence wrote on the back: 'This is now my kingdom: my bed. A constitutional kingdom: for I may not change it nor arrange it except after sealed pattern.

'The book is *Ulysses* . . . Joyce's one. I heard the laughing little man preparing to snap me, and changed from the left elbow to the right. The portrait is unrecognisable, I think, but rather fun. The park-paling effect behind my head is a rack of rifles. Under the book is my box of clothes. Over the top of the bed the edge of a mosquito net. Under the bed are boots!

'I hope you'll laugh.'

National Portrait Gallery (NPG X12415)

15.4 × 20.4
Provenance: Sent by T. E. Lawrence to Charlotte Shaw; given by G. B. Shaw, 1944.

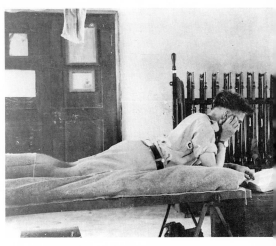

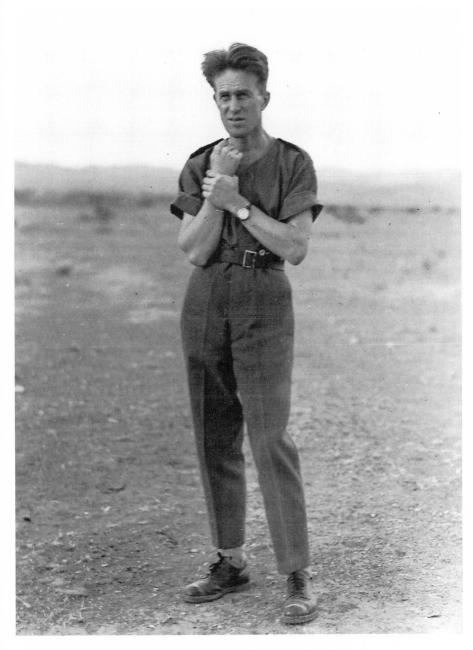

288

T. E. LAWRENCE ON THE AERODROME OF MIRANSHAH
Photograph by Flight Lieutenant Smetham, 10 December 1928
Vintage print

Lawrence sent Charlotte Shaw both this photograph and no. 289. On the back of a similar print now in the British Library he wrote: 'nursing my right wrist which hurt for so long that nursing it became a habit.' He had broken his wrist in the spring of 1926 while at Cranwell.

Flight Lieutenant Smetham was the commanding officer of a flight stationed at Miranshah at the time.

National Portrait Gallery (NPG X12414)

20.3 × 15.2
Inscribed on reverse by G. B. Shaw: *the two are excellent portraits G.B.S.*
Provenance: Sent by T. E. Lawrence to Charlotte Shaw; given by G. B. Shaw, 1944.

290

'LAWRENCE OF ARABIA'S SECRET MISSION'

Facsimile of article in the *Evening News*, 26 September 1928

Lawrence had asked to be stationed overseas in order to avoid publicity in the press, and the posting to Miranshah had seemed ideal. During the autumn of 1928, however, journalists began to link his name with the troubled neighbouring state of Afghanistan.

In September the London *Evening News* claimed that he was 'moving about the Punjab in disguise studying the activities of Bolshevist agents, whose secret headquarters are said to be in Amritsar . . . Lawrence poses as a great Pir (Mohammedan saint or spiritual guide) who has visited many Moslem lands and the tombs of all the great saints. The natives gossip that he is such a religious man that he is always recounting his own deeds'.

Rival newspapers then developed the story. The *Sunday Express* stated, correctly, that Lawrence was near the Afghan border, but suggested that he was working with hillmen against the Afghan leader, King Amanullah. The Foreign Office felt that no denial of such a ridiculous claim was necessary, but the rumours developed still further in November when a minor rebellion began in Afghanistan.

In December the *Empire News*, a scurrilous newspaper based in Manchester, invented someone called 'Dr Francis Havelock', who reported lurid details of Lawrence's activities in Afghanistan. This fiction was repeated by an international press agency and circulated world-wide. On 5 January 1929 it was decided that Lawrence had to be transferred away from India, and three days later he was flown out of Miranshah.

(not illustrated)

291

REQUISITION FOR STEAMER PASSAGE ON THE SS *RAJPUTANA*, BOMBAY, 12 JANUARY 1929

When it became clear that Lawrence had to be moved away from India, in January 1929, he was offered a choice of postings: England, Aden, Singapore, or Somaliland. He chose to return to England, and was flown to Karachi and then Bombay. He sailed for England on board the SS *Rajputana* on 12 January.

During the voyage home he wrote to his friend H.G. Hayter (see no. 287): 'It feels months since I was in Miranshah — and is just a fortnight. Everything is very strange . . . [At] Port Said, last stop, they picketed the quay-side to prevent my going ashore. I'd like to say something with a B in it about the India Government. In London I'll find out what really passed, concerning me, and try to ensure that they do not serve anyone else so . . . I will be quite content and happy if I do not get the sack out of all this. The only blessing has been the dodging a return by trooper. This is a 16,000 ton ship, and we have had a smooth journey. Second-class is comfortable. I have a cabin to myself, as the ship is nearly empty: and pass the whole day in it, working at the Greek book [the *Odyssey* translation]. Since we left Bombay I have done three sections of it — just as much as I did at Miranshah, all the while I was there . . . At Karachi an irk lent me a civvy suit: so I sort of pass muster in the crowd. They stare at me too much for comfort. However, there it is. I shall be stared at, goodness knows, a lot more in England.'[1]

P.C. & B.A. Metcalfe

1. T. E. Lawrence to H. G. Hayter, 22.1.1929, *Letters*, pp. 639-40.

Printed sheet with typewritten and MS additions, 20.6 × 32.8
Signed on reverse: *T. E. Shaw*
(not illustrated)

292

T. E. LAWRENCE AND TWO CREW MEMBERS ? ON BOARD SS *RAJPUTANA*

By an unknown photographer (January 1929)

Lawrence with two unidentified men. The photograph may date from the 1930s and show Lawrence on a private steam yacht, but might equally have been taken on board the SS *Rajputana* during Lawrence's voyage back to England. One fellow passenger commented of Lawrence: 'when we left Bombay not a single soul made any inquiry about the square jawed quiet faced little man wearing a grey lounge suit'.[1]

Bodleian Library (MS.Res.c.54)

1. *Sheffield Telegraph*, 5.2.1929.

THE LAST YEARS
1929-35

When the SS *Rajputana* reached Plymouth early in February 1929 press reporters and even a newsreel team were waiting to question Lawrence about his alleged activities in Afghanistan. The Air Ministry sent out a launch to take him off secretly before the ship docked, but this attempt to avoid publicity only served to increase suspicions that there was something to hide.

Lawrence was escorted to London where he lived as quietly as possible, hoping that the fuss would soon die down; but neither the press nor opposition politicians were easily put off. The *Daily News* demanded that the 'Great Mystery of Colonel Lawrence . . . "The Arch-Spy"' be explained. Questions were asked in Parliament as to why he had been allowed to enlist under an assumed name.

Lawrence was anxious that this publicity should stop, fearing not only the reaction of the RAF, but also that enquiries about his false name could reveal the truth about his ancestry. Taking matters into his own hands, he confronted a group of Labour members at Westminster. This move had the desired effect, and led incidentally to a lasting friendship with the Labour MP Ernest Thurtle, who had put several questions in the House. Lawrence's initiative angered the Air Ministry, however, and earned him a severe reprimand. He was threatened with dismissal if he made any similar approach to the press.

Renewed exposure to publicity and the bitterly cold English weather, which he now felt keenly, made him miserable for the first month after his return. Although he was on leave he saw few of his friends: 'Something's gone wrong with the works, and I find myself breaking every engagement, and avoiding everyone.'[1] He was relieved to go to his new posting at RAF Cattewater.

RAF Cattewater (renamed Mount Batten in October 1929) was a seaplane station located on a promontory in Plymouth Sound. Lawrence found it attractive, especially as he already knew and liked the commanding officer, Sydney Smith. There was no particular stir when he arrived; his clerical duties and friendship with the CO tended to keep him slightly apart from most of the men.

When off duty he continued to translate the *Odyssey*, but this work became a burden now that he was in England and tempted to use his leisure in many other ways. Furthermore, the working day at Cattewater was much longer than in India, and he found it difficult to get into a rhythm for working on the translation. In April he tried to pull out of the project when his part in it was revealed in the magazine *John Bull*. Bruce Rogers wrote back in strong terms, urging him to ignore such irritations and reminding him of his promises: it was much too late to withdraw. In truth, Lawrence himself had told many people about the translation and must have known that there was little hope of keeping it secret now that he was in England.

Though he was untroubled in camp he continued to suffer at the hands of the press, and for a time the Plymouth papers made the most of his presence. He began to think it was his fate: 'I do nothing – and they talk. I do something – and they talk. Now I am trying to accustom myself to the truth that probably I'll be talked over for the rest of my life: and after my life, too . . . They make me retch – and that's neither comfortable nor wholesome.'[2] His news-value leapt still higher when he became friends with Nancy Astor, who was one of the local MPs.

On free weekends he travelled widely on a new Brough motor cycle, visiting London to see the Shaws and Harley Granville-Barker; Sussex to see Kipling with the Doubledays; Dorchester to see Mrs Hardy; and Cambridge to see F.L. Lucas and E.M. Forster. These associations with the great and famous soon led to another clash with the Air Ministry. Sydney Smith was organising the 1929 Schneider Trophy

T. E. Lawrence
Photograph by Wing Commander
Reginald Sims, 1935
(no. 326 i)

1. T. E. Lawrence to A. Dawnay, 28.2.1929.
2. T. E. Lawrence to H. A. Ford, 18.4.1929,
   Letters, p. 650.

air race, and Lawrence acted as his personal clerk. The work was interesting but demanding, and took up a great deal of time during the spring and summer. During the event itself Lawrence was seen in conversation with Churchill, Nancy Astor, Austen Chamberlain, Sir Philip Sassoon (Under-Secretary of State for Air in the previous Conservative administration), Lord Birkenhead, and the leader of the Italian team, Marshal Balbo. The Air Secretary in the new Labour Government, Lord Thomson, was furious: Lawrence, dressed as a simple aircraftman, had even been seen 'giving orders' for the cleaning of the slipway used by the rival Italian team.

Lawrence was summoned to meet Trenchard, and once again came perilously close to dismissal. In future the Government did not want him to take part in prominent RAF activities. Though he had flown as a passenger with various friends he was now officially grounded. He was also forbidden to leave the country or to have any communication with 'great men or women'. Shaw was annoyed to discover that he was not considered by the Labour Government to fall within this category.

The Air Ministry had forbidden him to make public statements as 'T. E. Shaw' but had no control over what he might say as 'Colonel Lawrence'. This proved very useful when he wanted to help Ernest Thurtle's campaign to abolish the death penalty for cowardice in the armed forces. He told Thurtle to quote 'Colonel Lawrence' saying: I have run too far and too fast under fire (though never fast enough to suit me at the time) under fire, to dare throw a stone at the fearfullest creature. You see, I might hit myself in the eye.'[3] The law was finally amended in the summer of 1930.

Lawrence made little progress with the *Odyssey* translation during 1929, and although he aimed to devote forty hours a week to it (in addition to his RAF duties) he had only completed half of the text by February 1930. He grew increasingly impatient with the task but refused to lower his standards.

While his own writing energies were entirely concentrated on the *Odyssey* translation, *The Mint* continued to circulate, earning a mixed reception. F.L. Lucas, who had been impressed with *Seven Pillars*, was saddened 'at following the lion from the desert to the circus and the cage.'[4] On the other hand Noel Coward and many others greatly admired the vivid descriptive quality of the writing. During 1930 Lawrence toyed with the idea of printing a dozen copies, but decided against it.

The balance of critical opinion on *The Mint* was certainly in its favour, but he was not prepared to sit down and tackle another original work. His idea was that 'a book should burst out of a man, against his will.'[5] He felt no such inspiration, and was in any case finding it hard to give time to the *Odyssey* even though the publishers were pressing for delivery. They now asked him to complete the translation by the spring of 1931. He wrote 'I can manage that if only I work at it desperately . . . I am so tired of the smug Odysseus and his priggish son and sly wife. A horrible family.'[6]

During 1930 absurd rumours had continued to appear in the continental press. According to a German newspaper Lawrence was up to his old tricks in Kurdistan. 'Confessions' produced in Russian courts spoke of his collusion with anti-Soviet elements in London during 1927, when he was, in fact, in India. At home, he was the *bête noire* of anti-imperialists and die-hards alike.

Two tragic events then brought about a great change in his RAF work. In October 1930 Lord Thomson was on board the R101 airship when it crashed near Beauvais in France. Thomson's successor allowed Lawrence to play a much fuller role in the Air Force and to mix again with whoever he chose. Then in February 1931 something happened which affected Lawrence directly, and determined how he would spend his last years in the RAF. An Iris III flying boat crashed near Plymouth and he was in one of the first boats to reach the scene. He had watched helplessly as the crew drowned because the RAF tender was too slow to reach them in time. The experience was more bitter bcause he now shared ownership of a private speedboat, the *Biscuit*, with Sydney Smith.

The crash and subsequent inquest strengthened the hand of those within the Air Force who wanted faster seaplane tenders. A prototype, the *RAF 200* had been ordered and was sent for trials at Plymouth and Hythe. Although Lawrence was not formally

3. T. E. Lawrence to E. Thurtle, 13.3.1930, *Letters*, p. 685.
4. F. L. Lucas to T. E. Lawrence, 18.3.1929.
5. T. E. Lawrence to F. N. Doubleday, 27.1.1931.
6. T. E. Lawrence to Miss L. M. P. Black, 25.11.1930.

qualified as a mechanic or coxswain, his experience with the *Biscuit* won him a place in the four-man trials crew.

Boat testing left no time for the *Odyssey*, since he was fully occupied from 7 am until 10 pm. Days out on the water in continuous salt spray left his eyes in no state to tackle Homer. Finally, as the translation was long overdue, he decided to spend his August leave finishing it. He went to his old London retreat in the attic at Barton Street, and worked on it intensely.

When writing to literary friends he often dismissed the translation as a 'pot-boiler' but this is belied by the amount of time and care he put into it. It would have been against his nature to do such work badly. In the event his *Odyssey*, first published in 1932, has proved to be one of the most successful and enduring of English renderings.

Lawrence refused to begin another literary project of his own, scorning Buchan's suggestion that he should write a life of Alexander the Great. He claimed that people only wrote literature when unhappy, and that he was quite content. However, he was always willing to read other people's manuscripts and to offer constructive critic-ism. On one occasion after giving this kind of help he was persuaded to write an introduction. This was to *Arabia Felix*, by Bertram Thomas, who had succeeded in crossing the notorious 'Empty Quarter' of Arabia. At one time Lawrence had wanted the RAF to fly over this unexplored desert in an airship; he had been delighted with Thomas' achievement, urging friends in Whitehall to recommend a knighthood.

During the spring of 1932 he was busy supervising the commissioning of 200 class launches. He returned to Hythe in May to work on eight dinghies and two high-speed armoured boats. This left him 'dog-tired' and unable to keep up with a mounting backlog of correspondence. In July he was sent to Bridlington in Yorkshire where the RAF had sea-bombing ranges. His task was to fit up the two new armoured boats for target-towing work.

The amount of travelling his job now involved was not particularly to his taste. He knew that his work was valuable but regretted the loss of his secure and agreeable base at RAF Mount Batten and the weekend visits to friends. Plymouth had lost its attraction because Sydney Smith had been transferred to a new command at Manston in Kent. He wrote to Smith's wife: 'Since life is all growing roots and tearing them up every time I reach a new station, I vow that I will not put down roots, to save pain – but the things grow in the dark, all unknowing.'[7]

His reputation, however, was yet again to be a nuisance. He had maintained that the new RAF craft needed and deserved wider publicity. Despite instructions to keep a low profile, he had made sure that influential journalists were aware of the develop-

T. E. Lawrence and Clare Sydney Smith in the Biscuit, *Plymouth Sound*
By an unknown photographer, 1930
(no. 301)

7. T. E. Lawrence to C. Sydney Smith, 27.10.1931, *The Golden Reign*, p. 126.

ments, encouraging them to attend press days and see the boats on trial. It was not long before some reporters began to focus their stories on 'Lawrence of Arabia' rather than the new boats. The *News Chronicle* and *Sunday Chronicle* suggested that he was solely responsible for their introduction.

The Air Ministry remained intensely sensitive about press coverage of Lawrence in the RAF. These latest reports on his influence were patently exaggerated, and caused so much irritation that he was relieved of his work on high-speed boats and sent back to Plymouth in September 1932 for 'normal duties'. He was very disappointed.

Back at Mount Batten he took up the massive correspondence he had so neglected, and agreed to edit for Cape the Middle Eastern war memoirs of an anonymous Scotsman. However, he had no liking for 'normal duties' and was increasingly galled that the RAF should so squander his talents and knowledge of marine craft. Mount Batten was less agreeable without Sydney Smith, who was followed by a succession of temporary COs. In March 1933, seeing no prospect of a return to work on boats, he decided to apply for a discharge. The application was approved, and a date set for his release : 6 April 1933. At the last minute, however, the Air Ministry changed its mind ; Lawrence was offered a transfer to a technical establishment at Felixstowe, with a general brief to help supervise the construction of new boats. This would again involve much travelling, and when away from his station he was to wear civilian clothes.

The work of replacing the ageing service fleet with modern and efficient vessels was extremely important, and the new job was even more responsible than his earlier work had been. He decided to stay on, and was a little dismayed to find that his first task, at Cowes in the Isle of Wight, was to oversee the construction of 'five stupid pinnaces of Admiralty design . . . Thousands are thrown away upon them.'[8] There were as yet no new types large enough to supersede these fifty-six foot boats. From Cowes Lawrence moved back to Hythe where he oversaw more engine tests and construction. Another batch of 200 class tenders was passing through the yard.

During the summer of 1933 Basil Liddell Hart submitted to Lawrence the typescript of a new biography. Cape had suggested this project as early as 1929, and Lawrence had given guarded support on the grounds that the author was a serious student of military history and irregular warfare. The work was of much higher quality than the earlier book by Graves, and Lawrence had helped Liddell Hart considerably.

Lawrence continued to receive suggestions for writing projects of his own, but was giving all his mind to RAF work which now absorbed him as few other things had done. For the time being he could not begin anything new, and even his letters became short and scrappy. At the back of his mind, however, another book was taking shape. In December he told Charlotte Shaw that it would be called *Confession of Faith*. Beginning with *The Mint*, it would bring his RAF experiences up to date, and include a discussion of 'our entry into the reserved element', the air. He thought it might take a long time ; and, as the end of his twelve-year enlistment was only a few months away, he could settle down afterwards to write it at Clouds Hill.

That winter he found himself in trouble with the authorities yet again when the *British Legion Journal* printed three chapters from *The Mint* which had been copied and sold to them by a journalist. Lawrence was particularly annoyed, as he had promised Trenchard that *The Mint* would not be published. Fortunately the chapters concerned were from the last part of the book, and did not cause serious offence.

In November 1934 Lawrence moved to Bridlington. His last RAF task was to supervise the overhaul of ten fast target boats used on the bombing ranges. This was demanding work, but as his retirement approached he realised how much he would regret leaving the force : he would 'feel unutterably lost without my blue covering.'[9] Despite all the vicissitudes of his service career, the RAF had given him security, with freedom to follow his own interests. Moreover, for the past four years he had been engaged in something which suited his talents and was clearly worthwhile (the value of his work would be shown in the Second World War, when 14,000 British and Allied lives were rescued from the sea by high-speed service craft).

Lawrence left Bridlington and the RAF at the end of February 1935. He was forty-six. He cycled down to his cottage in Dorset, but was horrified to find the place

Clouds Hill
Photograph by Malcolm Brown
(no. 329 vi)

8. T. E. Lawrence to T. B. Marson, 22.6.1933.
9. T. E. Lawrence to F. Rodd, 23.11.1934,
Letters, p. 829.

besieged by pressmen who wanted to know what Lawrence of Arabia would do next. Appeals to the Press Association and photographic agencies did something to rid him of the problem, though freelance reporters and photographers were very persistent. They so irritated him that he 'banged one in the eye'; finally, at the end of March, they left him alone.

Now that he had time on his hands offers of all kinds began to flood in. He could have taken a directorship, a job in publishing, or even one in the City. The publisher Peter Davies wanted him to edit some fragments left by Frederic Manning, who had just died. Ralph Isham suggested a life of Mahommed. There was also an opening for Lawrence in the reorganisation of national defence; Churchill, Nancy Astor and Ernest Thurtle all thought that the job was his if he would take it.

For the immediate future, however, he was determined to try and live quietly in his cottage on the few shillings a week that came from his investments. Clouds Hill suited him perfectly; he had no commitments and no family responsibilities, and could please himself. His mother and elder brother, Bob, were still in China working as missionaries (much to his disapproval), though they soon had to leave because of the civil war. His youngest brother Arnold had become an archaeologist.

He busied himself arranging Clouds Hill to his taste, and tried to adjust to the idea of infinite leisure. He had given his speedboat, the *Biscuit*, to a new owner, and doubted whether he could afford to keep his motor cycle. But he was remarkably fit, and passed some of his time travelling and sightseeing in the south of England on a push-bike.

Once more he was thinking of writing and printing. He had asked John Buchan to read *The Mint*, saying that if the verdict was favourable he might be persuaded to start something new. Buchan reassured him, but for the moment Lawrence could not find the right project. Cape was willing to provide translating or editing work whenever he wanted it, but this was not what he was looking for. Instead he decided to resurrect the plans he had cherished since his student days to print fine books, and he took steps to install a small press in a shed near the cottage. He wanted to produce a private edition of *The Mint*, which he had now revised in detail. He had a frontispiece printed for the book: a recent sketch of himself in RAF uniform by Augustus John.

Friends began to visit, and some stayed with him at the cottage. Jock Chambers, who had been at Farnborough, came for a week. E. M. Forster arranged to come too. Then on Monday 13 May 1935 Lawrence rode his motor cycle to the Post Office to send off a parcel of books and a telegram to Henry Williamson. On the way back he came over the brow of a hill to find two boys on bicycles in his path. He swerved to avoid them, but knocked one down, and then crashed. He was taken to Bovington Military Hospital with severe head injuries. He never regained consciousness, and six days later he died.

293
T.E. LAWRENCE DISEMBARKING FROM
THE SS *RAJPUTANA*
Press photograph (2 February 1929)

Lawrence arrived in Plymouth on 2 February
1929. Trenchard had arranged for him to be
taken off the ship unobtrusively by Wing
Commander Sydney Smith.

Unfortunately the press had expected
some such manoeuvre, and Lawrence was
photographed and filmed as he descended a
ladder from a side door in the *Rajputana* into
a waiting naval launch.

The attempted secrecy added more fuel to
press speculation about Lawrence's
activities. The next day he was in London,
and newspapers reported that he 'managed to
disappear . . . He went to great pains to
shake off the pursuing crowd of Press men
who wanted to interview him.'[1]

'There followed a taxicab chase lasting
nearly an hour, and "Aircraftman Shaw"
failed to elude his pursuers.'[2]

Eventually the row settled down, but not
before his effigy had been publicly burnt by
Communists on Tower Hill.

1. *Illustrated Sunday Graphic*, 3.2.1929.
2. *Observer*, 3.2.1929.

294
T.E. LAWRENCE
By Augustus John, 1929

Lawrence wrote on the back of this portrait:
'Painted in the morning and afternoon of an
August day in 1929 at Freiern,
Fordingbridge, while I was going to Solent,
for the Schneider Cup. TES' (for the
Schneider cup see no. 300).

Augustus John gave him the painting,
saying 'My only condition is that you sit
again, for your face as you say is a good
wearer and should be periodically recorded.
I wish I could say the same of mine.'[1]

The Visitors of the Ashmolean Museum,
Oxford (A726)

1. A. John to T. E. Lawrence, 3.9.1929.

Oil on canvas, 66 × 50
Inscribed on reverse.
Provenance: Given by A. W. Lawrence, 1946.
Literature: *Biographers* (Liddell Hart), p.34; *Grosvenor*,
no.13.

295

PERSONAL CHEQUE SIGNED 'J.H. ROSS', 6 FEBRUARY 1929

In the summer of 1922 Lawrence opened a bank account with the Lombard Street branch of Martins Bank, where his friend Robin Buxton (wartime commander in the Imperial Camel Corps) was now Manager. The account went under Lawrence's RAF name, 'John Hume Ross'.

Although Lawrence dropped this pseudonym when he was dismissed from the Air Force in January 1923, and subsequently re-enlisted as Thomas Edward Shaw (a name he adopted by deed poll in 1927) he never changed the name of this bank account.

He inadvertently began to endorse this 1929 cheque drawn for cash with his real name. Having written 'T E S', however, he realised his mistake, crossed it out and initialled it 'JHR'. He then signed 'J. H. Ross' in full to endorse the cheque.

At the time, just after his return from India, he was staying in London at 14 Barton Street (see no. 207), trying to evade the press. He probably drew this substantial cheque to cover his living expenses and buy second-hand books. That day, 6 February, he also met H.S. Ede of the Tate Gallery for lunch.

J. M. Wilson

Printed cheque completed in ink, 8.5 × 19.5

296

T.E. LAWRENCE
By Augustus John, ? c.1929

This drawing is not associable with any of those recorded by Lawrence himself nor with any of the drawings included in John's various exhibitions. Most commentators tend to link it with the August 1929 sittings (see no. 294) but it could equally well have been done in 1923 (see no. 266). It is one of the most powerful and sober of John's images of Lawrence.

National Portrait Gallery (NPG 2910)

Charcoal, 33.7 × 26
Signed bl. : *John*
Provenance : Given by T. E. Lawrence to Eric Kennington and by him to the NPG, 1937.
Literature : *Grosvenor*, no. 14.

297
T. E. LAWRENCE
By Sir Charles Wheeler, 1929

At the request of Herbert Baker (see no.
206) Sir Charles Wheeler executed this
bronze head of Lawrence. Wheeler recalled
the work for the bust in his autobiography:
'There was only one sitting, but that was of
five hours' duration. It was on a cold
November day in 1929. He would not sit but
stood the whole time – like a rock . . . His
chin was large, but not so prominent as John
portrayed it and there was a marked ridge of
the frontal bone of his forehead running
parallel to his eyebrows . . . to help me with
the modelling of his shoulders he divested
himself of his shirt and stood naked to the
waist . . . Then I noticed what few can have
seen, large white weals round the thorax
made by the lashes of the whips before he was
thrown by the Turks in a blood tub for
dead.'[1]

The marks described by Wheeler are
depicted on the back of the bust, but it seems
more likely that these were battle wounds
rather than scars from the Deraa episode.

Mrs Peng Wilkinson

1. C. Wheeler, *High Relief*, 1968, pp. 104-5.

Bronze on hexagonal base, unique cast, 52.1 h.
Inscribed on back: *C.W. Nov 6 1929*
Provenance: The artist, sold Christies, 4 June 1971
(104).
Literature: *Grosvenor*, no. 54.

298
T.E. LAWRENCE
By Sir Charles Wheeler, 1929

An idealised sculpture, carved in 1929
shortly after Wheeler's study from life (see
no. 297). There were no sittings.

National Portrait Gallery (NPG 5016)

Hopton Wood stone, 28.6 h.
Inscribed on back: *T.E.L. Scholar/C.W. Sc./1929*
Provenance: Given by Lady Muriel Wheeler, 1975.
Literature: *Grosvenor*, no. 55.

299
T. E. LAWRENCE WITH WING COMMANDER SYDNEY SMITH AT THURLESTONE
Photograph by ?Clare Sydney Smith (1930)

When Lawrence returned from India in
January 1929 he was met at Plymouth by
Wing Commander Sydney Smith. The two
already knew and liked one another, having
met during the Cairo Conference in 1921 and
later at Cranwell.

In due course Lawrence was posted to
Sydney Smith's station, RAF Cattewater near
Plymouth. Their relationship proved to be a
very happy one. Lawrence belonged to the
small headquarters section and as Smith's
personal clerk he drafted a good deal of the
station's correspondence. He was frequently
a guest in the Smiths' home.

Bodleian Library (MS.Res.c.54)

Literature: *The Golden Reign*, ill. fp. 118.

300
T.E. LAWRENCE AT THE SCHNEIDER TROPHY AIR RACE
By James Jarché (7 September 1929)

Lawrence's commander at RAF Cattewater,
Sydney Smith, was heavily involved in the
organisation of the international Schneider
Cup seaplane races held over the Solent in
September 1929. Lawrence had assisted him
with this work, acting as his personal
secretary, for several months previously.

The Air Ministry realised that Lawrence's presence at the event might attract press attention, and had asked that there should be no photographs. James Jarché, the leading photographer at the *Daily Herald* who took this picture, gave the following excuse: 'We all promised. Aircraftman Shaw was to be immune to our attentions. So he was, for a time. But he was a tremendous temptation to us. To begin with, he was always about with people who were themselves notable in Society and the Air Force . . . Suddenly there was a cough, not quite loud enough to cover the sharp, metallic click as a shutter fell . . . Promises were thrown to the winds now. Our word was worthless as soon as one of us had broken it, and if one man was going to have that picture, we all were. So Aircraftman Shaw was photographed from all angles. The photographs appeared all over the world.'[1]

There is some doubt as to the accuracy of Jarché's account, since no photograph of Lawrence was published in the British press and no other photographs of him taken during the Schneider Trophy are recorded.

Daily Herald Archive, National Museum of Photography, Film and Television (E323)

1. J. Jarché, *People I have shot*, 1934, pp. 227-8.

301
T. E. LAWRENCE AND CLARE SYDNEY SMITH IN THE *BISCUIT*, PLYMOUTH SOUND
By an unknown photographer (1930)

During the Schneider Trophy races in 1929 Lawrence spent much of his time on the private yacht which acted as a floating headquarters. The yacht belonged to Major Colin Cooper, and was equipped with a small American 'Biscayne Baby' speedboat manufactured by the Purdy Boat Co.

The speedboat was used as a ferry during the event and Lawrence greatly enjoyed driving it. The engine, however, badly needed attention and was renowned for giving trouble. When Lawrence offered to strip it down and service it Major Cooper decided to give the boat to Lawrence and Sydney Smith. During the following winter it was completely overhauled at Cattewater, and subsequently Lawrence spent many happy hours in it exploring the rivers and creeks of South Devon. He was often accompanied, as in this photograph, by Mrs Sydney Smith.

The launch, which was renamed the *Biscuit*, made Lawrence seriously interested in speedboats. Its planing-hull design was much faster than the conventional displacement-hull tenders used by the RAF at Cattewater. With encouragement from Lawrence, Sydney Smith began pressing the Air Ministry to introduce the faster types.

J. M. Wilson

Literature: *The Golden Reign*, ill. fp. 119.

302
MODEL OF POWER BOAT, THE *BISCUIT*

A model of the power boat the *Biscuit* (see no. 301) which Lawrence kept at Clouds Hill.

The National Trust, Clouds Hill
Painted wood, 8 × 26

303
T. E. LAWRENCE WITH CLARE SYDNEY SMITH (right), HER SISTER LILY AND MRS GALPIN
Photograph by Sydney Smith (1930)

Taken at Thurlestone, where Lawrence spent a few days' leave as the guest of Sydney Smith's family during the summer of 1930. From left to right: Lawrence, Mrs. Galpin (a friend of the Smiths'), Mrs. Smith's sister Lily, and Clare Sydney Smith.

The photograph was reproduced in Mrs Sydney Smith's biographical account of her friendship with Lawrence, *The Golden Reign*, as 'The Judgement of Paris'.

Bodleian Library (MS.Res.c.54)
Literature: *The Golden Reign*, p. 118, ill.

304

T. E. LAWRENCE ON HIS BROUGH
SUPERIOR MOTORCYCLE, UL 656,
TALKING TO GEORGE BROUGH
By an unknown photographer (October
1930)

Shortly after his return from India in January
1929, Lawrence was offered a new Brough
superior: 'Some anonymous person or
persons bought and sent me a very large and
apolaustic Brough . . . So large a present
(valued at three years of my pay) pauperises
me a bit, in my own sight, for accepting it.'[1]
He refused to take the motorcycle as a gift,
and after consulting Robin Buxton, his
banker, he paid for it himself. The
'anonymous person' behind the scheme was
Charlotte Shaw, as Lawrence could easily
guess. She was consoled by the fact that
Brough had given a substantial discount on
the purchase price.

Lawrence was delighted with the new
Brough: 'Speed is a wonderful thing . . . I
had a good run up to London (235 miles) . . .
averaged over 40: and touched 94 at times.
A nobly running bike.'[2] He kept this
motorcycle until March 1932.

George Brough wrote of Lawrence in
1937: 'In the several runs I took with him
. . . T.E.L. was most considerate to every
other road user. I never saw him take a single
risk nor put any other rider or driver to the
slightest inconvenience – but when the road
was clear ahead, it required a very good and
experienced rider to keep anywhere near
T.E.L.'[3]

This photograph was taken at Brough's
Haydn Road works in Nottingham, where
Lawrence left his motorcycle for servicing
during the last week in September. George
Brough is seen leaning on sticks because he
had been injured shortly before while taking
part in a motorcycle race.

Bodleian Library (MS. Res.c.54)

1. T. E. Lawrence to E. M. Forster, 5.2.1929,
Letters, p. 641.
2. T. E. Lawrence to F. L. Lucas, 26.3.1929,
Letters p. 647.
3. *Friends*, p. 565.

305

ADVERTISEMENT FOR BROUGH
MOTORCYCLES, *c*.1929

On 27 September 1926, shortly before
leaving England on what he thought would be
a five years posting in India, Lawrence sent
George Brough the letter which is
reproduced in this advertisement, together
with the following note: 'I am very much in
your debt for four years solid pleasure.
Would the enclosed be of any use to you?
. . . I don't mind your showing it to people
(or sticking it up on your stand, if that is a
practice at Olympia) but I'd rather you did
not print it in a newspaper till after
December 15, when I'll have gone abroad
. . . What I really meant it for is best thanks,
for a hundred thousand jolly miles.'[1]

Ironically, the advertisement exhibited
comes from a Brough Catalogue issued in
1929, or possibly 1930, after Lawrence's
return to England.

See also no. 274.

J. M. Wilson

1. T. E. Lawrence to G. Brough, 27.9.1926,
Letters, p. 499.

Printed sheet, 14.8 × 22.3
(illustrated p. 86)

306

*TOO TRUE TO BE GOOD: A POLITICAL
EXTRAVAGANZA*
From *Three Plays* by George Bernard Shaw,
London, 1934 (published with *Village Wooing*
and *On the Rocks*)

Shaw wrote *Too True to be Good* in the spring
of 1931. In the second and third acts he
incorporated a character, 'Private Napoleon
Alexander Trotsky Meek', very obviously

based on Lawrence. Private Meek is an
extraordinary character who occupies every
function in the army unit run by one Colonel
Tallboys, and who in the end effectively
assumes command. Lawrence and Shaw
discussed the play while it was in draft, and
Lawrence made a number of suggestions for
improving Meek's lines. A few days later he
wrote: 'A point about Pte. Meek occurred
to me last night . . . He wouldn't have told
the Colonel that he was his *intelligence officer*.
He might have said ''I do the Intelligence
work'' or more likely ''I am also your
Intelligence Staff, Sir''. . . to which the
Colonel would have responded by dwelling
on the Staff, probably, and forgetting the
Intelligence. The Meeks of the world are shy
of describing themselves as officers . . .

'Rifles at the ready: stand by with the
maroons: sights up to 2000: over their
heads, no hitting: contact. Charge your
magazines (or cut-outs open, if magazines
were already charged). Ten rounds rapid
fire. . . something like that.

'Meek wouldn't have said illiterate. . . at
least he doesn't. His difficulty is having not
passed the educational exam. for promotion.
He would probably have said that he hadn't
got his educational certificate. ''Not
educationally qualified'' is written on my
half-yearly return for promotion!

'These squalid accuracies should not
affect G.B.S. He must write so that the
audiences will comprehend.'[1]

The wording Lawrence suggested in these
and other notes on the play was adopted by
Shaw virtually unchanged. The actor chosen
by Shaw for the production, Walter Hudd,
was cast in the part because of a physical
resemblance to Lawrence. After seeing him
play the role at Birmingham, Lawrence
wrote reassuringly: 'I thought you did the
part admirably. You looked decent (I am
always as correct as I can be, regimentally
speaking) and I only wish nature had let me
look half as smart and efficient as yourself.
Only I get more gaiety out of my position.
It's comic really, and I often see that,
whereas you looked grim.'[2]

J. M. Wilson

1. T. E. Lawrence to C. F. Shaw, 26.6.1931.
2. T. E. Lawrence to W. Hudd, 3.9.1932, *Letters*,
pp.741-2.

Printed book, 282 pp., 20.7
(not illustrated)

307
JAMES HANLEY
By Sydney Earnshaw Greenwood, c.1930-5

James Hanley (1901-85) first met Lawrence in 1930. The following year he sent a copy of his new novel *Boy*. Lawrence wrote: 'it holds me terribly. I hate it, and am fascinated by it: and yet I laugh when I think of it after a while . . . There is a cold and yet not-at-all-quiet ferocity about your writing, which gives me more "kick" almost than anyone's.'[1]

Hanley sent Lawrence subsequent novels for criticism while they were still in draft. Lawrence greatly appreciated his work, although the subject matter was often almost unpublishable. In 1935 *Boy* was prosecuted for indecency and its publishers were taken to court. Lawrence found this prosecution 'monstrous',[2] and persuaded E. M. Forster to defend the book in court, but the publishers were fined £400.

This portrait of Hanley was painted by Sydney Greenwood, the uncle of Hanley's publisher Cecil Greenwood.

National Portrait Gallery (NPG 5231)
1. T. E. Lawrence to James Hanley, 27.6.1931.
2. T. E. Lawrence to C. J. Greenwood, 5.4.1935, *Letters*, p. 864.

Oil on canvas, 48.3 × 38.1
Signed tr.: *Greenwood*
Provenance: Purchased from the sitter through Bertram Rota Limited, 1978.

308
NANCY, VISCOUNTESS ASTOR
By John Singer Sargent, 1923

In 1919 Viscountess Astor (1879-1964) was the first woman to be elected to the British Parliament; she remained a Conservative member of the House of Commons until 1945. She and her husband entertained lavishly at their family home, amidst what Lawrence called 'little Cliveden's modest splendour'.[1]

He must have met her first during the early 1920s, and she subscribed to *Seven Pillars of Wisdom*, writing to him: 'I am one of the people who are very wealthy and would like a copy of your book, but I don't promise to read it!'.[2] He seems to have viewed her with a certain caution, since he wrote in 1928: 'I like her, you know, though the love of possessing myself kept me well out of her way always. Lionel Curtis said we were like Venus and Adonis. Which is really funny, to one who knows the facts of both cases.'[3]

On his return from India in 1929 Lawrence came into contact with her again, through the Shaws, and he also met her several times while he was serving at Plymouth (she was MP for one of the Plymouth constituencies). They became affectionate friends, and a streak of humour appears in his letters to her which had been absent from his correspondence for many years. He found her company exhausting, and

once wrote: 'I had been a bit carried about by that whirlwind . . . I like her: and admire her, even more: but, for living beside, commend me to some vegetable.'[4] More than forty of his letters to her survive, all dating from the last years of his life.

National Portrait Gallery (NPG 2885)
1. T. E. Lawrence to Mrs L. Curtis, 1.8.1933.
2. N. Astor to T. E. Lawrence, 20.3.1924.
3. T. E. Lawrence to C. F. Shaw, 18.1.1928.
4. T. E. Lawrence to C. F. Shaw, 1.5.1929.

Chalk, 55.9 × 38.1
Signed and dated b.: *John S. Sargent. 1923*
Provenance: Given by The Hon. Michael Astor, 1972.
Literature: D. McKibbin, *Sargent's Boston*, Boston, 1956, p. 82.

309
CORRESPONDENCE BETWEEN LADY ASTOR AND T. E. LAWRENCE
Plymouth, 4-6 July 1931

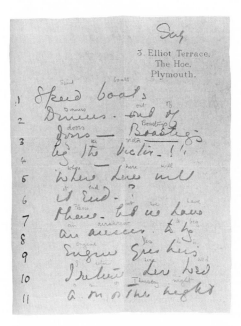

Lawrence was often baffled by Nancy Astor's almost illegible handwriting. On this occasion he wrote out his own interpretation of her letter in the gaps between the lines, and replied to each point in so far as it made sense. He then sent her both the illegible letter and his reply.

University of Reading
(i) Autograph letter from Lady Astor to T. E. Lawrence, ? 4 July 1931, 18 × 14 (ii) autograph letter from T. E. Lawrence to Lady Astor, 6 July 1931, 33 × 20.3 (iii) envelope addressed to Lady Astor by T. E. Lawrence, 9.5 × 12
Provenance: Given by the Astor Trustees.

310

BRUCE ROGERS

Photograph by Howard Coster, 1930
Vintage print

Bruce Rogers was one of the leading typographers and book designers between the wars. Although an American, he spent a substantial part of his working life in England.

In 1927 he was looking for someone to translate Homer's *Odyssey* for a finely printed edition; by chance, he was lent a proof of Lawrence's *Seven Pillars*, and he rapidly decided that here was 'a man who could make Homer live again – a man of action who was also a scholar and who could write swift and graphic English.'[1] Rogers approached Lawrence through a mutual acquaintance, Ralph Isham, and offered £800 if he would take on the translation, which could be anonymous.

Lawrence was delighted by the offer, and agreed to do the translation over a two-year period. He began work on it in May 1928.

Lawrence said of Rogers: 'I have for years admired him from ground level, and have even been able at intervals to buy books of his production . . . he's the ideal of all those who have tried to produce books'.[2] After their first meeting in September 1929, Rogers wrote that Lawrence was 'small and quiet and self-contained and extremely modest. His letters were so interesting that I own I was almost regretful when I heard that he was coming back to London – but he's a great success personally.'[3]

National Portrait Gallery (NPG X2353)

1. B. Rogers, Introduction to *Letters from T. E. Shaw to Bruce Rogers*, Mount Vernon, N. Y., 1933.
2. T. E. Lawrence to R. Isham, 2.1.1928.
3. B. Rogers to H. W. Kent, 12.2.1929.

19 × 23.4
Provenance: Acquired by the British Council Photographic Library, 1946; transferred to the Central Office of Information and thence to the National Portrait Gallery, 1974.
Literature: T. Pepper, *Howard Coster Celebrity Portraits*, New York, 1985, p.110.

311

SIR EMERY WALKER

Self-portrait photograph (c.1907)

Bruce Rogers arranged that Lawrence's rendering of the *Odyssey* should be produced by Emery Walker, one of the most distinguished English printers; he had worked with William Morris at the Kelmscott Press, and also co-founded the Doves Press.

Rogers wrote to Lawrence: 'Walker is my oldest friend in England and you may know that we published a book for the Grolier Club together in 1917 . . . They [Walker's firm] have acted as publishers for several books (chiefly on art) and are of course well-known as engravers and printers all over the world . . . Walker is now over 75 (though almost as vigorous as ever) and it would be a great pleasure to him to have his name on one more important book, before he stops printing for good – and in my eyes this will be the *most* important, except perhaps the Doves Bible – no, I won't except even that.'[1]

National Portrait Gallery (EW 1049/3)

1. B. Rogers to T. E. Lawrence, 3.8.1928.

312

AUTOGRAPH MANUSCRIPT OF T.E. LAWRENCE'S TRANSLATION OF *THE ODYSSEY OF HOMER*, 1931

In 1928, while working on Book I of this translation, Lawrence wrote: 'It has not dashed my pleasure in Homer. I like doing it.

Translating is an ingenious game, very exciting for a man who has no originalities of his own to express.'[1]

The work was to occupy much of his spare time during the next four years, although it suffered many interruptions. In 1931, when he began to work on high-speed launches for the RAF, the translation stood still for weeks at a time. The last section of the manuscript was completed on 15 August 1931, and he inscribed the final leaf 'For Sir Emery Walker, Knight – Wilfred Merton, Treasurer – Bruce Rogers, Printer – Miss Saunders, Scribe.

'This last page of my version of the *Odyssey* upon which I have spent almost as long as Odysseus and travelled further. . . which has furnished me with luxuries for five years and so wholly occupied my hours off duty that I have had no leisure to enjoy them. . . is affectionately, kindly, gratefully, gladly and with enormous relief and glee PRESENTED.'[2]

Charlotte Shaw had seen much of Lawrence's version in draft, and in December 1928 he had promised her this manuscript (from which the book had been typed out by Miss Saunders, referred to above). The gift was some recompense for the books, gramophone records, and food hampers she had sent him over the years.

The British Library Board (Add.MS 45930)

1. T. E. Lawrence to C. F. Shaw, 15.6.1928.
2. Manuscript leaf, now in the Harry Ransom Humanities Research Center, University of Texas, Austin.

Manuscript, leather bound, ff ii + 108 pp., 33
Provenance: Given by George Bernard Shaw, 1944.
(not illustrated)

313

T.E. LAWRENCE'S COPY OF *MINOR POEMS*

By Edmund Spenser, Ashendene Press, 1925

In December 1931 Lawrence wrote to K.W. Marshall, then working as an assistant at Zwemmer's bookshop in London: 'In the Zwemmer catalogue you sent me were two items that interested me. One was the Ashendene *Spenser's Minor Poems*. Probably it's sold. If not, will you send it me? They have paid me some money, and I could well celebrate.'[1] When Marshall replied that the Spenser was still available Lawrence wrote again: 'It is my habit to celebrate events in my life by presenting myself with books: and that splendid Spenser will just do to mark the ending of the *Odyssey* work. I only wish that I had been rich enough to get the Ashendene *Faery Queene* when it came out. Hornby's almost the best printer who ever lived.'[2]

For another of the books purchased to celebrate an important event in Lawrence's life see no. 48.

Private Collection

1. T. E. Lawrence to K. W. Marshall, 7.12.1931.
2. T. E. Lawrence to K. W. Marshall, 9.12.1931.

Printed book, 43.8
(not illustrated)

314

THE ODYSSEY OF HOMER
[Translated by T.E. Lawrence]; printed and published by Sir Emery Walker, Wilfred Merton and Bruce Rogers, 1932

Lawrence's translation of the *Odyssey* was published in England in November 1932 in a limited edition of 530 copies. No translator's name is given. The economics of this luxury edition had been calculated in 1928 before the Great Depression, but by 1932 the market for books priced at 12 guineas was much reduced. To make matters worse, Bruce Rogers had arranged with Oxford University Press to publish a popular edition in America. This trade printing, in which Lawrence was named as the translator, was extremely successful; as a result few of the English de luxe copies which Emery Walker

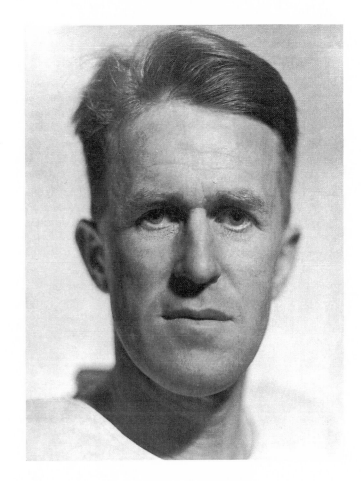

had reserved for the United States were sold.

The Bruce Rogers *The Odyssey of Homer* was set in Centaur, a typeface by Rogers, based on a 15th century original. The text is printed on a specially made grey paper, and the illustrations (twenty-six designs drawn after Homeric figures from Greek vase-paintings) are printed in black on roundels of gold leaf. The binding is full black Niger morocco.

Dr Lionel Dakers CBE

Printed book, 182 pp., 29.7

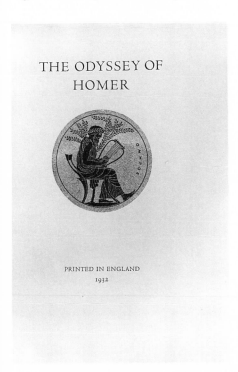

THE ODYSSEY OF HOMER

PRINTED IN ENGLAND
1932

315

T. E. LAWRENCE
Five photographs by Howard Coster, 1931
Vintage prints

Lawrence gave the following account of this series of photographs in a letter to Charlotte Shaw: 'On Friday I was on the embankment near the Temple . . . [when] a little bare-headed man rushed up and said "Colonel Lawrence?" Used to be, I replied. "I want to photograph you". But who are you, I asked. "My name is Howard Coster". A professional, I asked. "Yes, but this is for

myself. I don't want to sell it or show it. You and Gandhi are the two people I want to take". So I went along, for the joke of it, and he put me on a little chair, made me take my tunic off, and photographed me about a dozen times. A little shop in Essex Street. Rather a nice little stammering man, I thought. Works for Vogue! Had chased me for 5 minutes, afraid to speak!'[1]

Two weeks later, Coster sent Lawrence one of the photographs from the sitting as a gift; Lawrence mentioned it to his mother, writing: 'I think that it is very good, as a photograph.'[2]

National Portrait Gallery

1. T. E. Lawrence to C. F. Shaw, 14.10.1931.
2. T. E. Lawrence to his mother, 30.10.1931, *Home Letters*, p. 379.

(i) NPG X1967, 30.4 × 21.2, (ii) NPG X1969, 27.1 × 20.8 (iii) NPG X1968, 24.4 × 18.2 (iv) NPG X1970, 30.4 × 21.2 (v) NPG X3553 (print from original negative)
Provenance: Acquired by the British Council Photographic Library, 1946; transferred to the Central Office of Information and thence to the National Portrait Gallery, 1974.
Literature: T. Pepper, *Howard Coster Celebrity Portraits*, New York, 1985, pp. xiv, 107, ill. p. 12.

316
RAF 200 CLASS SEAPLANE TENDERS, SOUTHAMPTON
By an unknown photographer (1932)

A considerable number of small boats was operated by the RAF in connection with its seaplanes. They were used for ferrying crews, towing, refuelling and inspecting the aircraft, and for crash rescue.

In 1930 the first trials of a new 37½ foot planing-hull seaplane tender were carried out on Southampton Water. They were successful and it was decided that the boat should be sent to Sydney Smith's station (now renamed RAF Mount Batten) for evaluation service. It arrived in March 1931 and Lawrence was appointed to the four-man trials crew. He was involved in most aspects of running the boat but his special responsibility was writing reports. He continued to work on the development of this type for many months, providing liaison between the RAF and the British Power Boat Company who were soon instructed to build several more 200 Class launches. His clear thinking, combined with a thorough grasp of technical matters, helped to resolve many technical problems as these new craft were developed and improved.

J. M. Wilson

317
THE 200 CLASS SEAPLANE TENDER – PROVISIONAL ISSUE OF NOTES, 1932

In the spring of 1932 several of the new 200 Class launches were ready to go into service. Lawrence therefore wrote this operational manual for inexperienced crews. He thought that it would eventually be printed as an official Air Ministry publication, but the 200 Class was quickly superseded by larger vessels of similar type, and no printed edition of Lawrence's notes is recorded.

It is unusual for service manuals to be drafted by 'literary' writers; Lawrence's text is a masterpiece of clear technical description and explanation.

Private Collection

Bound duplicated typescript, 36.5 × 23
Literature: *The Golden Reign*, pp. 179-83.
(not illustrated)

318
'SERVICE LIFE BY LAWRENCE OF ARABIA'
British Legion Journal, November 1933

Lawrence was furious at this unauthorised publication of material from *The Mint*. He explained to a friend what had happened: 'An Irishman is lent the script by a friend of his to whom a friend of mine had without telling me lent it. . . ''Hot stuff'' says the Irishman and copies. . . how much of it? God knows. . . but the *Legion Journal* is then sent a précis of the last three chapters by him, and comes out with a mash of it as an article by me.

'Thunder from the Commissioner of Police [Trenchard]: from the Air Ministry. . . my head astonished but unbowed. The *Legion* apologises next month.'[1]

Lawrence clearly felt that the magazine had been at fault. A fortnight later he wrote: 'The *Legion Journal* is like its Editor – a nasty piece of goods. We will clean them off our hands and feet and forget them. I begin to sympathise with the non-combatants of the late war.'[2]

P. C. & B. A. Metcalfe

1. T. E. Lawrence to R. de la Bère, 26.11.1933, *Letters*, p. 780.
2. T. E. Lawrence to G. W. Howard, 11.12.1933.

Magazine, 27
(not illustrated)

319
CAPTAIN BASIL LIDDELL HART
By Eric Kennington, 1943

Liddell Hart (1895-1970) first contacted Lawrence in 1927, when, as military editor of the *Encyclopaedia Britannica*, he wanted to commission an essay on guerilla warfare. Lawrence agreed to allow Liddell Hart to edit an article from his writings on the subject in *Seven Pillars* and elsewhere. During the years that followed Liddell Hart corresponded occasionally with Lawrence, and sent copies of his military studies for criticism.

In 1929 Liddell Hart was approached by Jonathan Cape and asked to write a new study of Lawrence's career from the military point of view. Lawrence, who had been disappointed by the inadequacy of Robert Graves' biography, cautiously agreed.

In 1934, after the biography had been finished, Liddell Hart dedicated a volume of military essays, *The Ghost of Napoleon*: 'To T. E. Lawrence, who trod this road before 1914'.

Kennington presumably met Liddell Hart through Lawrence but would in any case have come across him during his work as an official war artist from 1939-45. A different version of this portrait is also in the possession of the sitter's family.

Lady Liddell Hart

Pastel, 66.6 × 54
Signed and dated bl.: *EHK 43*
Provenance: By descent.

Lawrence and many of the people associated with his career to write brief comments in her husband's book.

On the first page Lawrence wrote: 'T.E. Shaw puts his autograph on this first page for Mrs. Liddell Hart, at her request (very forcibly conveyed) . . . It will be sad if posterity is deluded by its fondness for colour into believing that he did, deliberately, one tenth of what this book ascribes to him. Chance, the help of others, the fatuity of enemies – to these what merits there may have been.'

Adrian Liddell Hart

Printed book, 466 pp., 22.5
Provenance: By descent.

321
T.E. LAWRENCE WITH B.H. LIDDELL HART AT THE BRITISH POWER BOAT CO. YARD, HYTHE
By an unknown photographer, 2 June 1934
Vintage print

On 2 June 1934 Liddell Hart went to see Lawrence at the British Power Boat Co. His purpose was to discuss an invitation he had received to write the script for a projected film of *Revolt in the Desert*. During this visit Liddell Hart and his wife were taken out in one of the high speed RAF launches.

Several photographs were taken of Lawrence and Liddell Hart together. As Liddell Hart was very tall, Lawrence stood on a bollard.

Liddell Hart Centre for Military Archives, King's College London

23.4 × 15.8
Literature: *Biographers* (Liddell Hart), p. 216.

Bernard Shaw's inscription in
no. 320

320
'T. E. LAWRENCE' IN ARABIA AND AFTER
By Basil Liddell Hart, London, 1934
With autograph inscriptions by T. E. Lawrence, Field Marshal Lord Allenby, Stewart F. Newcombe, Lloyd George, J. C. Smuts, Air Marshal Lord Trenchard, Winston Churchill, Allan Dawnay, George Bernard Shaw, Lord Lloyd, Sir Henry McMahon, John Buchan, Nancy Astor, Ronald Storrs, Augustus John, H. G. Wells, Eric Kennington, W. F. Stirling and Alec Guinness.

When Liddell Hart's biography of Lawrence was published in 1934, this copy was specially bound up with additional blank leaves. Jessie Liddell Hart then invited

322

T.E. LAWRENCE AT THE BRITISH POWER BOAT CO. YARD, HYTHE
British Power Boat Company photograph
(?1932 or 1934)

This photograph, taken at the British Power Boat Company's yard shows a group of visitors and an armoured target launch alongside. Lawrence, with his back to the camera, is standing on the left of the pontoon.

He was closely involved in the development of these boats, which were based on the RAF 200 Class design; he had experimented with moving targets in Plymouth Sound towing specially designed naval fog buoys behind his own speedboat, the *Biscuit*. When towed at 20 knots a modified fog buoy produced a large and very visible effect.

Although 8½ lb practice bombs would be aimed at the splash targets there was clearly some risk to the launch and its crew. Armour protection was therefore designed and produced by Hadfields of Sheffield. The launches were equipped with an extra engine because of the additional weight.

J. M. Wilson

323

T.E. LAWRENCE WITH HUBERT SCOTT PAINE, AT ADMIRALTY HOUSE, DEVONPORT
By an unknown photographer (17 May 1934)

Having succeeded with the RAF 200 Class, Hubert Scott Paine, owner of the British Power Boat Co, was keen to sell high speed launches to the Royal Navy. Lawrence shared this ambition. The following letter to Sydney Smith explains the circumstances of this photograph: 'The Admiralty went on being mulish about Scott Paine's motor-boats, and I lost patience and thought it might be rather

a rag to force one down their throats. Also it would buck the Navy up to have a modern boat set against their primitive junks. So I pulled string after string, and all the bells rang, till finally Scott Paine and I were asked down to Plymouth to explain these new boats. The Admiral put us up at Mount Wise for two nights, and behaved like the whitest sort of man.'[1]

Lawrence and Scott Paine were well received by the C-in-C, Sir Eric Fullerton, and his wife. In gratitude Lawrence sent her a proof copy of L. M. Nesbitt's *Desert and Forest*, and wrote: 'Thanks to your kindness and the Admiral's, what should have been an awkward visit to Plymouth turned into an excellent time. I do hope the result (or one result) will be Naval help in proving or disproving the value of these new hulls of ours. I have a feeling that we are on the edge of a great development in ship-building. . . not cargo ships, but fighting and express-passenger ships! That would be a very good thing for the Navy, and for this country. It seems the only possible answer to the Air, so far as I can see.'[2]

Not long afterwards the C-in-C ordered a new Admiral's barge from Scott Paine, described by Lawrence as 'a great 45 foot thing, full of cabins and lavatories and chromium plate.'[3] This photograph was taken at Admiralty House, Mount Wise, after the new launch had been brought round the coast by Lawrence and Scott Paine from Southampton Water. It shows (left to right) Lawrence; Scott Paine; Commander A. E. Cooper, Secretary to the Naval C-in-C, Plymouth; and Chief Petty Officer J. H. Pead, Chief Coxswain to the C-in-C.

J. M. Wilson

1. T. E. Lawrence to Sydney Smith, 15.11.1934, *The Golden Reign*, p. 177.
2. T. E. Lawrence to Lady Fullerton, 17.8.1934.
3. T. E. Lawrence to Sydney Smith, 15.11.1934, *The Golden Reign*, p. 177.

324

T.E. LAWRENCE
By Augustus John, 1935

This charcoal sketch was made during Lawrence's last visit to John's studio on 22-3 January 1935. Lawrence wrote three days later: 'John is on the water wagon, and was well, strong and interesting. Worried somewhat at the difficulty he is finding in continuing a picture. Many good starts, but no second wind. However he set out on a small head and shoulders, and in four bouts (morning and afternoon, for two days) it became a little jewel of a portrait. He felt it full of sparkle, and to be lovely paint. He was quite cheered by the success, his first for weeks: and at the end of it he took up a block of drawing paper and did two black charcoal studies of me. Each was also an R.A.F. fashion plate, much better than that foul ''walking out'' diagram in the Drill Book. The first he said was good about the knees, but poor in the head. The second he called a good drawing and wrote on it 'John to Shaw' and gave it me. It goes down to my puttees, and we tied it at once on my back with a cord and it sat there, *en pillion*, till I reached Clouds Hill, my cottage. Thence I took it to Emery Walker's in London and told them to mount, frame, and photo it half-size . . . Alas, why have I not a face like Ivor Novello and a figure like Weismuller, so that John may have a real birthday whenever I

come?'[1] In another letter of the same day, Lawrence described it as: 'A fine swagger drawing: small head, thin body and big knees!'[2] John commented: 'If we had had a bit more time I'd have done some more fashion plates. Not that I don't like this one which is quite trim.'[3]

Lawrence had sent the study to Emery Walker to have 100 half-size collotypes made, for the frontispiece to a limited edition of *The Mint* which he hoped to print at Clouds Hill after he had left the RAF. He died, however, before a press could be installed.

The locations of the oil portrait and first charcoal sketch referred to above are not recorded.

The Visitors of the Ashmolean Museum, Oxford

1. T. E. Lawrence to G. W. Dunn, 26.1.1935.
2. T. E. Lawrence to C. F. Shaw, 26.1.1935.
3. A. John to T. E. Lawrence, undated (1935), *Letters to T.E. Lawrence*, ed. A.W. Lawrence, 1935, fp. 120.

Charcoal, 50.5 × 35.5
Signed and dated br.: *John/to/Shaw/1935*
Literature: *Letters*, p. 845; *Grosvenor*, no. 16.

325
WING COMMANDER REGINALD SIMS
By an unknown photographer (1931)

This photograph of Reginald Sims (1885-1972) was taken in Iraq in 1931. While he was there Sims made a collection of insect photographs which he later annotated and bound. It was through Lawrence's interest in these photographs that the two first became acquainted. They first met, however, in

November 1934 when Lawrence was working on armoured boats used as practice bombing targets at Bridlington. Sims, then a Flight Lieutenant, was stationed at RAF Catfoss where he was equipment officer. Afterwards Lawrence often spent weekends at the Sims' cottage in Hornsea.

In 1937 Sims wrote a collection of reminiscences about Lawrence called *The Sayings and Doings of T.E.*, which was privately printed in 1975.

The Family of Wing Commander R.G. Sims

326
T.E. LAWRENCE AT HORNSEA
Three photographs by Wing Commander Reginald Sims, February 1935
Vintage prints

(ii)

Reginald Sims was a keen amateur photographer, and these three photographs come from a series he took at Hornsea in February 1935. Sims and his wife were much impressed by Lawrence's appearance. He wrote in 1937: 'I was full of admiration and joy at the sheer beauty of his face . . . His face was roughened and red, or as he referred to it, sandblasted, but although we knew he was about forty-five or so, the vivid impression he gave us was of eternal youth, and very beautiful youth at that.'[1]

The Family of Wing Commander R.G. Sims

1. *Friends*, pp. 550-2.

(i) 16.9 × 11.8 (ii) 19.3 × 16.8 (iii) 19.3 × 16.6
Provenance: By descent.
((i) illustrated p. 207)

327
HEROES OF MODERN ADVENTURE
By T.E. Bridges and H. Hessell Tiltman, London, 1934

Heroes of Modern Adventure was one of a series of popular boys' works by Bridges and Tiltman. It contains nineteen essays on personalities ranging from Amundsen to Lindbergh. Chapter XIII, pp. 173-93, is on 'Lawrence of Arabia', and is loosely based on the biography by Lowell Thomas.

While visiting the Sims family at Hornsea in January 1935 Lawrence annotated this copy for John Sims, then aged eleven.

The Family of Wing Commander R.G. Sims

Printed book with numerous pencil annotations by T.E. Lawrence, pp. 174-93, 21.6
Literature: R. P. Graves, *Lawrence of Arabia and his World*, 1976, ill. p. 109.
(not illustrated)

(iii)

328
T.E. LAWRENCE AT BRIDLINGTON
Photograph by Ian Deheer, 26 February 1935
Vintage print

Lawrence left Bridlington on 26 February 1935, planning to travel south by bicycle and visit several of his friends. He arrived in Cambridge the following day, and met his brother Arnold.

Lawrence went on to Clouds Hill only to find it besieged with reporters, and left, still by bicycle, for London: 'Romsey on Sunday night; and London by 4 p.m. Monday: 75 miles that second day! Improving!'[1] During the following three weeks he cycled over much of southern England, using a Youth Hostel pass he had taken out in the name 'T. E. Smith'. After years of motorcycling he enjoyed touring again by bicycle: 'It is dull work when the wind is against: but in lanes, and sheltered places and in calms or before winds, wholly delightful. So quiet: one hears all the country noises. Cheap – very! not tiring, up to 60 or 70 miles a day, which is all that I achieve, with sightseeing.'[2]

The Family of Wing Commander R.G. Sims

1. T. E. Lawrence to P. Knowles 19.3.1935, *Letters* p. 862.
2. T. E. Lawrence to G. Brough 5.4.1935, *Letters* p. 867.

20.4 × 12.5
Provenance: Given by the photographer to R. G. Sims.

329
CLOUDS HILL
Photographs by Walton Adams (1935)

When Lawrence discovered Clouds Hill in 1923 it was almost derelict. However it was only about a mile from Bovington Camp where he was stationed, and it offered exactly the space and calm he would need to revise *Seven Pillars of Wisdom* for the projected subscription edition. He took a lease on it and began to put it in repair.

During the next two and a half years he spent almost all his off-duty hours at the cottage, working on the text of *Seven Pillars* and correcting proofs. He also bought a gramophone and played classical music to friends in the Tank Corps.

After he was transferred back into the RAF he moved to Cranwell, and subsequently to India. The cottage was leased out, but he decided to buy it: it was 'a magically beautiful place'.[1] From 1929 onwards he made a series of improvements. A great deal of work was done in 1933, when he wrote: 'I have lavished money these last three months upon the cottage, adding a water-supply, a bath, a boiler, bookshelves, a bathing pool (a tiny one, but splashable into): all the luxuries of the earth. Also I have thrown out of it the bed, the cooking range: and ignored the lack of drains. Give me the luxuries and I will do without the essentials.'[2] He intended to retire to Clouds Hill after leaving the RAF in 1935.

1. T. E. Lawrence to R. Graves, 28.6.1927, *Biographers* (Graves), p. 55.
2. T. E. Lawrence to T. B. Marson, 21.12.1933.

(i) The book room

During the spring of 1933 Lawrence had bookshelves built in the principal ground floor room, and brought the books he had stored with friends since leaving All Souls. Afterwards he wrote to his mother: 'The book-room is all finished except for its fender, which I have not yet designed. My books fill one of the two shelved walls: the one on which the dishes used to sit (north side). The opposite wall waits with empty shelves. Only a remnant of my books have survived their ten year exile: but all the Kelmscotts are present in good order . . .

'The book room window has two fixed side-panes, cemented into the stone frame, and a pivoting centre-pane, in a stainless steel frame. That gives enough light and air to suit me. The other furniture is the window-seat, an affair six feet away, built up of Bob's former bed and a big box-spring mattress: very comfortable and useful. I propose to move Mrs. Hardy's little stool down there, as a table; and the fender will complete it.'[1]

1. T. E. Lawrence to his mother, 25.9.1933, *Home Letters*, p. 380.

(ii) The book-room – fireplace wall

The fireplace was installed in September 1933, when Lawrence wrote that he 'lit its first fire in the book-room. No smoke, and little smell of smoke upstairs: while the draught seemed plenty. In fact it burned very brightly, and I enjoyed it for the night was wet, like my clothes.'[1]

1. T. E. Lawrence to his mother, 25.9.1933, *Home Letters*, p. 379.

(iii) The music room

Again in 1933, Lawrence wrote: 'What used to be the bedroom, upstairs, I am turning into a work-room, to hold a table and papers and ink and food and probably the gramophone and my clothes. That will make the upstairs sitting-room big enough to walk about in.'[1]

1. T. E. Lawrence to his mother, 25.9.1933, *Home Letters*, p. 380.

(iv) The music room – fireplace wall

During his time at Bovington Camp this was the only habitable room, and it did not change greatly. A letter of 1924 describes the room on an April afternoon: 'It's streaming with rain against the western window, and the trees are tossing: — not as if they were playing, but wearily, as though this fourth day of the wintry weather was too much against their longing to turn green: and inside it is calm as ever . . . Palmer . . . is waiting for the *Rosenkavalier* waltz to end.

After it he wants a little bit of Mozart as played by the Lener. Palmer gets drunk on music . . . Meanwhile I'm out over by the very wet window (but on its dry side) writing to you. There'll be tea when I've finished the letter (see how short it will be!) and more and more animal contentment after that: till we wind up, when the dark comes, with a movement out of a Bach thing for two violins. We always finish with that, if the time is dark enough.'[1]

Note the candlesticks presented to Lawrence in 1935 (see no. 333).

1. T. E. Lawrence to C. F. Shaw, 30.4.1924.

(v) The bathroom

In July 1933 Lawrence decided to install a water supply to the cottage from a nearby spring. The next month he wrote: 'Cottag all a ruin now, with the new water-works in progress! Soon I shall have my very own bath! The first I have ever owned in exclusiveness. A milestone in life.'[1] Three weeks later he wrote to Charlotte Shaw: 'Yesterday was a DAY. At 1.45 p.m. water, driven by the smallest ram ever installed anywhere, began to flow into my cottage at Clouds Hill. The pipes are a hundred yards long: the ram was turned on at 10 a.m. without public ceremony: it worked steadily for hour after hour: and at 1.45, as I have said, the water arrived at its destination. The single, oldest and only inhabitant of Clouds Hill took off his R.A.F. cap with a simple gesture (to avoid knocking it against the roof-beam) and collected the first pint in a pint mug. It arrived in four minutes, and the S.O. and O inhabitant then drank it. The taste was of red lead and galvanised iron: but the quality was wet, indubitably'.[2] A bath and hot-water boiler were added later that year. Lawrence had his first hot bath at Clouds Hill shortly after Christmas.

1. T. E. Lawrence to R. V. Buxton, 12.8.1933.
2. T. E. Lawrence to C. F. Shaw, 31.8.1933.

(vi) Exterior, from the back (Photograph by Malcolm Brown)

'My cottage is a gem of gems – in the eyes of its owner. You see, I've almost made it, from the roots up. It is as ugly as my sins, black, angular, small, unstable: very like its creator. Yet I love it.'[1]

1. T. E. Lawrence to Lady Astor, 15.1.1934.

J. M. Wilson (i-v)
Malcolm Brown (vi)

(illustrated p. 210)

331

COLUMBIA 'GRAFONOLA'
GRAMOPHONE
*c.*1928

Lawrence's interest in classical music seems
to have begun after the war, and although he
had later to depend almost entirely on
gramophone records he had been for a time
a regular concert-goer. During a visit to
London in 1926 he wrote to Charlotte Shaw:
'I'm just in from Queen's Hall, where they
play now every night. The first night it was
Honeggers railway effort: then I heard Ethel
Smythe, in command of the crowd for the
Wreckers overture: tonight it was a
Symphony of Mozart. I suppose you sniff a
little at these Proms. There are very few
exquisite people in the dear seats: at least
few I recognise. But up in the gallery the
noise is very good, after a diet of boxed
music for so many years. I have a seat there,
almost of my own: No 12. It is right back
against the wall, and faces nothing. The edge
of the balcony stands like a wave-edge out
into the air over the music, and mixes it
well, before letting it come over to me. So
I think that it is the best seat for hearing in
the place: and it is quite the worst seat for
seeing: that is how I am able to get it nearly
every night. In 1920 and 1921 and 1922 I was
there a hundred times. Sir Henry Wood is
invisible from it, and that gladdens me, for
he is slightly ridiculous (all Anglo-Saxons
become ridiculous when they become
prominent) and his swaying figure would
otherwise tend to mix itself into the music.
And I can't see the ladies who sing, or play
violins, and I can't see the bows that mount
up and down with the notes. That mechanism
of drill is hateful in a soldier's eyes.'[1]

During the 1920s and 1930s he used good
gramophones (some given to him by the
Shaws) and built up a large collection of
records: 'Wireless is a very false-toned
caricature of music, I think. Gramophone is
my stand-by, and a magnificent stand-by,
surely.'[2] He was very particular about the
quality of his gramophones. In 1929 he
described his latest as 'a super-box, like a
W/T set inside, with an exquisite smoothness
and fullness of tone.'[3]

330
WILLIAM ROBERTS AND HIS FAMILY AT
CLOUDS HILL
Photographs by ?William and Sarah Roberts
(*c.*1930)
(i) William Roberts in the garden
(ii) Sarah Roberts by the Jidda doors
(iii) William and John Roberts in the
doorway

These three photographs of the artist
William Roberts and his family are the only
ones known to have been taken at Clouds Hill
before Lawrence's death. Lawrence lent his
cottage to the Roberts family for several
summer holidays.

William Roberts (1895-1980) was first
put in touch with Lawrence in 1920 by Colin
Gill, who knew that Lawrence was looking
for more artists to work on illustrations to
Seven Pillars. Roberts subsequently
contributed several portraits and a large
number of tailpiece drawings to the book.
He also painted an oil portrait of Lawrence

in 1922, at the sitter's own suggestion (see
no. 257).

Writing of the principal illustrators to
Seven Pillars, Lawrence said: 'John, Roberts
and Kennington are three extraordinary
draughtsmen. John so gracious, Roberts so
powerful, Kennington so alive. Roberts first,
I think, for pure line.'[1]

For the Jidda doors, see no. 204.

Private Collection

1. T. E. Lawrence to S. C. Cockerell, 15.3.1927.

One friend recalled that 'Beethoven, Mozart and Bach were the composers to whom he most frequently turned. Mozart, as he would say, was for his delight, and Beethoven for ''excursions of the spirit'' . . . He had a great affection for Delius . . . Haydn he thought ''restful'''.[4] Absent from this list is Elgar, whose work Lawrence deeply admired.

The National Trust, Clouds Hill

1. T. E. Lawrence to C. F. Shaw, 24.8.1926.
2. T. E. Lawrence to G. W. Dunn, 15.12.1932, *Letters*, p. 757.
3. T. E. Lawrence to Haford, 18.4.1929.
4. *Friends*, p. 337-8.

33.5 × 47 × 54.5

332
T. E. LAWRENCE'S TYPEWRITER
Royal 5, Royal Typewriter Company, New York, USA

While Lawrence was serving at the RAF Depot in Karachi his superiors suddenly realised the value of his literary skills. At first he worked in the engine repair shop, and the station Adjutant was surprised when 'a definite polish, not to say ornateness, developed in such minutes as arrived from that source . . . reports upon coldly routine subjects developed into reasoned expositions of the pros and cons of every side issue'.[1] After a few months Lawrence was asked to spend part of his time working in the station office, and he taught himself to type: 'there is a typewriter on the next table, and I aim to fill up the next few months of my leisure in learning how to knock it about. Typing

might, in the circumstances, be a useful accomplishment.'[2] For practice he typed out a draft of *The Mint* (see no. 283) in his free time. He later typed his translation of the *Odyssey*, although he wrote the final text by hand.

Typing proved a valuable skill and from 1928 onwards he carried out an increasing amount of clerical work in the RAF. Successive commanding officers were happy to delegate the task of dealing with official correspondence, and were usually delighted with the result.

As a keen typographer Lawrence was horrified by the ugliness of the fixed character-spacing on the typewriters then available, and he very rarely typed personal letters.

The National Trust, Clouds Hill

1. *Friends*, p. 402.
2. T. E. Lawrence to F. N. Doubleday, 25.8.1927.

17.5 × 25.5 × 35
Provenance: T. E. Lawrence; given by A. W. Lawrence to Pat Knowles and by him to Clouds Hill.

333
CANDLESTICK FROM CLOUDS HILL

By the time Lawrence retired from the RAF he had worked for several years with Flight-Lieutenants Beauforte-Greenwood and Norrington. As Beauforte-Greenwood recalled: 'A few days before he left he agreed to accept a personal memento of our association, and chose stainless steel candlesticks. My colleague, Flight-Lieutenant H. Norrington, and I presented him with a pair of these'.[1] They were given to Lawrence during a lunch at Hythe on 24

April 1935. On 5 May, two weeks before his death, Lawrence wrote a letter of thanks for this practical gift (there was no electricity at Clouds Hill): 'They look lovely . . . in exact keeping with their upper room. By day they sit on a brown oak mantel-shelf and a stainless steel fender. By night they move to my writing table (as at present) or to my reading chair. They clean easily; stand solidly and feel good. I only wish that they had not been possible – in other words that our association had not ended.'[2]

The National Trust, Clouds Hill

1. *Friends*, p. 571.
2. T. E. Lawrence to Beauforte-Greenwood and Norrington, 5.5.1935.

Steel, 23.5 h., 34.5 w.
Inscribed on base:
A SOUVENIR OF A VERY HAPPY PARTNERSHIP/1930–35/ FROM B.G. AND NORRY

334
BOOTS BELONGING TO T. E. LAWRENCE

A pair of standard issue RAF boots found at Clouds Hill after Lawrence's death.

Private Collection

Black leather, service type, 29.5 long

335
A YOUNG SOLDIER (PORTRAIT OF
T.E. LAWRENCE ?)
By Henry Scott Tuke, 1922

In 1935 this oil painting was found among Lawrence's possessions. It has been suggested that it is a portrait of Lawrence during the brief period that he spent as a boy soldier in the Royal Garrison Artillery in 1905. However, Tuke kept a detailed register of his paintings, and this one, described as 'Picture of "Gray"',[1] was painted in 1922. It was originally purchased by one R.F.C. Scott, and a marginal note in Tuke's register states that when Scott died it was bought, together with another of his pictures, for £5 by 'Gray'. Since Lawrence is known to have owned both these pictures (he gave the other one to Mrs Sydney Smith) there is some conjecture that he may have been the 'Gray' of the portrait.

A letter from Lawrence to another artist, Elsie Falcon, may throw some light on the mystery. She had asked Lawrence to sit for a portrait, and he replied: 'As for you drawing me . . . if you are like the artist who said "Do sit: I really can't afford a proper model" . . . then by all means. He worked what was left of his study of me into a beach picture after, giving me a new head, several sizes smaller. Apparently I am shaped rather like a tadpole.'[2]

The National Trust, Clouds Hill

1. *The Registers of Henry Scott Tuke*, annotated by B. D. Price, Falmouth, 1983.
2. T. E. Lawrence to Elsie Falcon, undated.

Oil on canvas, 43.2 × 53.6
Signed and dated br.: *H. S. TUKE 1922* (?)
Provenance: In T. E. Lawrence's possession by 1935.
Literature: *Grosvenor*, no. 53; E. Cooper, *H. S. Tuke*, 1987, ill. p. 47.

336
FREDERIC MANNING
By Sir William Rothenstein, 1921

Frederic Manning (1882-1935), an Australian, served as a private on the Western Front. He was an accomplished writer, and Lawrence had read his collection of essays, *Scenes and Portraits*, before the war.

He was drawn by Sir William Rothenstein in 1921. As Rothenstein recalled, 'since I had drawn so many poets, he had sought me out. He was an attractive youth, a little precious and frail, looking wise for his years. I found him to be very intelligent; he came almost daily, then he disappeared . . . he believed his father would pay for the drawing I did of him, and for other extravagances; not so his father.'[1]

In 1930 Manning published anonymously *Her Privates We*, an account of his war experiences. Lawrence guessed that Manning had written the book, saying: 'the preface gives it away. It is pure *Scenes and Portraits*'.[2] He was deeply impressed with the new book, and told Manning: 'You . . . have produced love-poems of a sort, and your [book] is the most wonderful, because there is no strain anywhere in the writing.'[3]

In November that year Manning published an enlarged edition of *Scenes and Portraits*. He dedicated one of the new essays, 'Apologia Dei', 'To T. E. Shaw'.

Lawrence corresponded regularly with Manning during the 1930s, and intended to visit him after leaving the RAF in March 1935. Manning died, however, days before the visit was due. Lawrence wrote to Peter

Davies, Manning's publisher: ' the books are so much more intense than ever he was, and his dying doesn't, cannot, affect them. Therefore what has died really? Our hopes of having more from him − but that is greed. The writing of them was such pain − and pains − to him . . . He had done enough . . . Yet his going takes away a person of great kindness, exquisite and pathetic. It means one rare thing the less in our setting. You will be very sad.'[4]

National Portrait Gallery (NPG 4417)

1. Sir W. Rothenstein, *Men and Memories*, II, 1932, p. 26.
2. T. E. Lawrence to F. Manning, 25.2.1930, *Letters*, p. 682.
3. ibid.
4. T. E. Lawrence to P. Davies, 28.2.1935, *Letters*, p. 859.

Chalk, 39.4 × 29.2
Signed and dated r.: *W. R. 1921*
Provenance: Purchased from Elkin Mathews Ltd, 1964.
Literature: J. Rothenstein, *The Portrait Drawings of William Rothenstein, 1889-1925*, 1926, p. 66, no. 570.

337
TWO CORRESPONDENCE CARDS: 'TO TELL YOU THAT IN FUTURE I SHALL WRITE VERY FEW LETTERS'
T. E. Lawrence to Lady Astor, 5 May 1935, 8 May 1935

Lawrence had these cards printed in the spring of 1935 and enclosed one of them with almost all the letters he wrote.

The note of 8 May is a reply to an invitation from Nancy Astor to visit Cliveden.

University of Reading
Printed cards, autograph letters on reverse, both 8.9 × 11.3
Provenance: Given by the Astor Trustees.
Literature: (8.5.35), *Letters*, no. 582; M. Brown & J. Cave, *A Touch of Genius*, 1988, pp. 214, ill., 215.

To tell you that in future I shall write very few letters.
T. E. S.

Heny Williamson, correcting proofs of The Pathway, at Georgeham, August 1928.

338
HENRY WILLIAMSON
By Powys Evans, 1928

Henry Williamson (1895-1977) was a prolific and talented writer. He is probably best known for *Tarka the Otter*, and it was this novel that led to his friendship with Lawrence. On first reading the book, Lawrence sent a long and detailed criticism to Edward Garnett who forwarded it to Williamson. Many of Lawrence's specific comments were incorporated in the fourth printing, which carries a note: 'Slightly revised, following suggestions of T.E.L'. From then until 1935 Williamson corresponded frequently with Lawrence about his work, and in 1935 Williamson dedicated his novel *Salar the Salmon* to Lawrence and to V.M. Yeates, the author of *Winged Victory*.

By the late 1930s Williamson had become a convinced fascist, and in *T. E. Lawrence by his Friends*, published two years after Lawrence's death, he claimed that he had written just before Lawrence's death proposing arrangements for a meeting between Lawrence and Hitler: 'He replied immediately by telegram, asking me to come the next day, wet or fine'[1] (see no. 339). In reality the text of Williamson's letter of 10 May contains no reference whatsoever to Hitler or to any political matter. Williamson's claim must therefore be dismissed as political propaganda for a party whose cause he personally espoused. It seems very unlikely that he would have concocted the story if he had been able to foresee the

events of the following years.

The Fascist party in Britain was constantly seeking to recruit famous names to its ranks, and Lawrence was approached directly and indirectly on at least two occasions during the 1930s. The advances were rejected.

National Portrait Gallery (NPG 5110)

1. *Friends*, p. 455.

Pen and ink, 29.2 × 23.8
Inscribed b.: *Henry Williamson, correcting proofs of The Pathway,/at Georgeham, August 1928.*; followed by device inscribed *HW*
Provenance: Purchased Phillips, 7 September 1974 (11) by R. N. Ricks; given by him, 1976.

339
TELEGRAM FROM T.E.LAWRENCE TO HENRY WILLIAMSON
13 May 1935

On 10 May 1935, a Friday, Henry Williamson wrote telling Lawrence that he planned to go to London on the following Tuesday, and asking whether he could call in at Clouds Hill; he wanted to lend Lawrence the typescript of *Winged Victory*, a novel by V.M. Yeates who had died not long before, and said he would call again a few days later to collect it. He ended: 'I'll call in anyway on Tuesday unless rainy day'.[1]

By the time he received this letter it was too late to send a reply by post, and on Monday 13 May Lawrence left Clouds Hill on his Brough for Bovington Camp, a mile distant, where he sent a parcel to A.E. Chambers (see no. 340) and this telegram to Henry Williamson. His fatal accident took place on the way back.

Henry Williamson Literary Estate

1. H. Williamson to T. E. Lawrence, 10.5.1935.

Post Office telegram form completed in pencil, 13.7 × 21
Provenance: By descent.
Literature: *Letters*, no. 583.

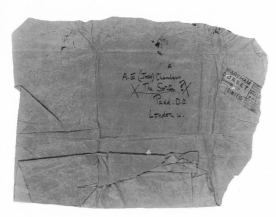

340
BROWN PAPER WRAPPER FOR PARCEL
ADDRESSED TO JOCK CHAMBERS
Wareham, 13 May 1935

On 13 May 1935, the day of his fatal
accident, Lawrence posted this parcel to
'Jock' Chambers, a friend whom he had first
met at the RAF School of Photography,
Farnborough, in 1922. Chambers had
received relatively little education but was
highly intelligent, and Lawrence frequently
sent him good books to read.

For some years Chambers had been
working as a sorting clerk at the Paddington
District sorting office in London. It amused
Lawrence, when writing to him, to concoct
absurd addresses.

The Curators of the Bodleian Library,
Oxford (Dep.c.282)

Single irregular sheet of brown paper, 59.5 × 48.8
Inscribed: *To A. E. (Jock) Chambers/The Sorter/Padd D. O./
London and W.*
Provenance: A. E. Chambers; purchased.

341
T. E. LAWRENCE ON HIS LAST BROUGH
SUPERIOR MOTORCYCLE, GW 2275, AT
CLOUDS HILL
By an unknown photographer (1935)

This photograph of Lawrence riding his
motorcycle in civilian clothes is believed to
have been taken shortly before his death,
possibly by one of the freelance photographers
who troubled him at Clouds Hill.

Liddell Hart Centre for Military Archives,
King's College London

342
T. E. LAWRENCE'S BROUGH SUPERIOR
SS 100 MOTORCYCLE, GW 2275

Lawrence registered this motorcycle, his
seventh Brough, on 27 February 1932. Soon
afterwards he wrote to George Brough: 'It
is the silkiest thing I have ever ridden . . .
at 50 [m.p.h.] she is a dream. Just popples
along so mildly that I can count the revs . . .
I think this is going to be a very excellent
bike. The crowds that gape at her, just now,
will stop looking after she gets dirty . . . I
am grateful to you and everybody for the care
taken to make her perfect.'[1]

He kept it for longer than his other
motorcycles, and although he hoped to
acquire a new model which was being
developed in 1935, he was in no great hurry.
In April 1935 he wrote to Brough: 'The old
bike goes so well that I do not greatly long
for its successor.'[2]

On 13 May 1935 he was returning from
Bovington Camp to Clouds Hill on this
motorcycle when he suddenly came upon
two boy cyclists in a dip in the road. It
appears that he was not travelling fast at the

time, but he had to swerve to avoid them and knocked one of them down. He himself was flung off the Brough and sustained severe brain injuries. Six days later he died, without having regained consciousness.

The motorcycle was returned to the Brough Works some weeks afterwards. It was not greatly damaged, and after repairs was sold to a new owner in September 1935.

J. M. Weekly

1. T. E. Lawrence to G. Brough, 5.3.1932, *Letters*, p. 738-9.
2. T. E. Lawrence to G. Brough, 5.4.1935, *Letters*, p. 867.

Motorcycle, 112 h. × 236 l.
Provenance: Supplied to T. E. Lawrence, 3 March 1932; sold (ex works) to King & Harper, Cambridge, 30 August 1935; re-discovered by L. Perrin, Portsmouth, c.1958; sold to present owner, 1977.
Literature: Brough Superior Club, 'A series of letters from T. E. Lawrence to George Brough and notes on the identity and use of Lawrence's Brough Superiors', (ed. M. Leatherdale), privately printed, December 1987; *Toyota Today*, Spring 1988, ill.

343
T. E. LAWRENCE'S MOTORCYCLE AT BOVINGTON CAMP AFTER HIS FATAL ACCIDENT
By an unknown photographer (21 May 1935)

BBC Hulton Picture Library

WHAT 50 YEARS ON STAGE HAS TAUGHT ME—MARIE TEMPEST

DAILY SKETCH

TOO BIG FOR WEALTH AND GLORY
Lawrence the Soldier Dies to Live for Ever

344
NEWSPAPER CUTTINGS RELATING TO T.E. LAWRENCE'S ACCIDENT AND DEATH

After Lawrence's motorcycle accident on 13 May press reporters besieged the military hospital at Bovington Camp where he lay in a coma. Their only source of information was a short bulletin on Lawrence's condition given twice daily; to prevent inaccurate gossip, the soldiers at the Camp were forbidden to speak to journalists. A guard was put on Clouds Hill to protect Lawrence's valuable belongings from thieves or souvenir hunters.

The result was an irritating lack of news, and as the days passed some of the stories filed from Bovington were closer to fiction than fact. Great play was made of the official 'secrecy': it was suggested, for example, that there were classified government documents at the cottage. Ironically, these contemporary reports from frustrated pressmen have been cited again and again, over the years, as evidence that there really was something secret at Clouds Hill.

After Lawrence's death, the press looked for further material consistent with the Lawrence legend. The *Daily Telegraph* was one of the first to raise the 'Mystery of a black car'.[1] Most newspapers reported glamorous stories about Lawrence's role in the Arab Revolt: 'Rode 300 Miles Alone In Raid On Damascus';[2] 'Elusive as "The Scarlet Pimpernel"'.[3] One even asked: 'Is Lawrence of Arabia Alive?'[4] *The Times*, however, published a long obituary, an article on *Revolt in the Desert* by Liddell Hart, and several appreciations, including one from Winston Churchill: 'In Colonel Lawrence we have lost one of the greatest beings of our time. I had the honour of his friendship. I knew him well. I hoped to see him quit his retirement and take a commanding part in facing the dangers which now threaten the country. No such blow has befallen the Empire for many years as his untimely death. The personal sorrow which all who knew him will feel is deepened by the national impoverishment.'[5]

J. M. Wilson

1. *Daily Telegraph*, 22.5.1935.
2. *Daily Herald*, 20.5.1935.
3. *Daily Mirror*, 20.5.1935.
4. *Sunday Review*, 22.6.1935.
5. *The Times*, 20.5.1935.

345

FORM OF SERVICE FOR T.E. LAWRENCE'S FUNERAL, 21 MAY 1935

Lawrence did not hold conventional religious beliefs. He told Liddell Hart a year before his death that 'he had been brought up in a conventional religion, [but] he had discarded it, and did not notice its loss. Theological speculation and meditation were good as an intellectual exercise, but one could not get anywhere by such abstractions.'[1]

The funeral service arranged by A. W. Lawrence, his younger brother, was extremely simple. Psalm 121 was followed by the hymn 'Jesu, Lover of my soul, Let me to Thy Bosom fly' and, after prayers, by the *Nunc Dimittis*. There was no sermon or address of any kind.

787573 Arthur Russell

1. *Biographers* (Liddell Hart), p. 209.

Folded sheet, 17.8 × 11.5
(not illustrated)

346

THE FUNERAL OF T. E. LAWRENCE AT MORETON, DORSET
Two photographs by an unknown press photographer (21 May 1935)

(i) Lawrence's coffin being carried from the church

(ii) The procession to the graveyard

After the service the coffin was taken to the new graveyard at Moreton, a few hundred yards from the church. Among the mourners present were Lady Astor, Winston Churchill, Lionel Curtis, Mrs Thomas Hardy, Augustus John, Lord Lloyd, Siegfried Sassoon, General Wavell and Earl Winterton. Neither Lord Allenby nor Lord Trenchard were able to attend, nor the Shaws, who were travelling overseas.

The six pall bearers were selected to represent different aspects of Lawrence's career. They were (clockwise from left) Sgt. Bradbury, Colonel Stewart Newcombe, Pat Knowles, Eric Kennington, Arthur Russell, and Sir Ronald Storrs. Lawrence's youngest brother, Arnold, and his wife are immediately behind the bier. His mother and elder brother Bob were not present, since they were at that time travelling home from missionary work in China.

Liddell Hart Centre for Military Archives, King's College London

347

T. E. LAWRENCE'S GRAVE AT MORETON
By unknown photographers

(i) A temporary fence around the plot, August 1936

(ii) The tombstone, 1939

The tombstone and inscription were chosen by Lawrence's mother and elder brother, and reflect their strong religious convictions. The smaller stone at the foot of the grave carries the emblem and motto of Oxford University: an open book and the words *Dominus illuminatio mea* from the 27th Psalm.

Liddell Hart Centre for Military Archives, King's College London

348
SARAH LAWRENCE'S PRINTED
ACKNOWLEDGEMENT FOR LETTERS
OF CONDOLENCE
July 1935

Mrs. Lawrence would like to thank you for your kind expression of sympathy, and to say that she values very highly those tokens of affection for her dear son.

She is unable to answer all letters personally, but hopes you will accept these few lines of appreciation of your kind thoughts and words.

July, 1935.

P T O.

After Lawrence's death his mother received a great many letters of condolence, many of them from people she did not know. She had only just returned from China, and could not possibly cope with such a volume of correspondence. Instead she had this acknowledgement printed.

On the reverse is a note from M. R. Lawrence, the eldest brother, to a distant acquaintance from wartime days.

P.C. & B.A. Metcalfe

Printed card with letter from Dr M. R. Lawrence on reverse, 14.2 × 21.5

349
SARAH LAWRENCE
By an unknown photographer, c. 1940
Vintage print

Sarah Lawrence in her eightieth year; she died in November 1959, aged ninety-eight.

Lawrence's relationship with his mother was never easy, and although his post-war

letters often show concern for her welfare, he found it best to keep his direct contacts with her to a minimum. In 1927 he wrote to Charlotte Shaw: 'I have a terror of her knowing anything about my feelings, or convictions, or way of life. If she knew they would be damaged: violated: no longer mine. You see, she would not hesitate to understand them: and I do not understand them, and do not want to . . . And now two of my brothers are dead, and Arnie (the youngest) and I have left her, and avoid her as our first rule of existence . . . We are so helpless: we feel we would never give any

other human being the pain she gives us, by her impossible demands: and yet we give her the pain, because we cannot turn on love to her in our letters, like a water-tap . . . Knowledge of her will prevent my ever making any woman a mother, and the cause of children. I think she suspects this: but she does not know that the inner conflict, which makes me a standing civil war, is the inevitable issue of the discordant natures of herself and my father, and the inflammation of strength and weakness which followed the uprooting of their lives and principles. They should not have borne children.'[1]

In another letter to Charlotte Shaw, who had met Sarah Lawrence, he again discussed this difficult relationship: 'Probably she is exactly like me; otherwise we wouldn't so hanker after one another, whenever we are wise enough to keep apart. Her letters are things I dread, and she always asks for more of mine (I try and write monthly: but we haven't a subject we dare be intimate upon: so they are spavined things) and hates them when they come, as they do, ever so rarely. I think I'm afraid of letting her get, ever so little, inside the circle of my integrity: and she is always hammering and rapping to come in. A very dominant person.'[2]

Mrs Valerie Gatty, niece of the artist
Sonia Mervyn

1. T. E. Lawrence to C. F. Shaw, 14.4.1927.
2. T. E. Lawrence to C. F. Shaw, 8.5.1928.

21.7 × 16
Provenance: Given to Sonia Mervyn by the sitter.

LEGACY

By the time Lawrence died, the mythical figure created by Lowell Thomas had already endured for fifteen years, during twelve of which Lawrence himself had done his best to escape from it. As a result there were, in a sense, two quite distinct Lawrences in existence: the man and the legend.

This distinction has survived down to the present day, for example in two strains of biographical literature, one romantic and sensational after the example of Lowell Thomas, and the other striving towards accuracy.

The career of the mythical Lawrence has been dramatic: it touched its nadir in the biographies by Richard Aldington and Suleiman Mousa, and may have reached its zenith in David Lean's memorable film.

The other biographical tradition has been more cautious. Its starting point was perhaps Liddell Hart's study of the Arab Campaigns (see no. 320), and it drew much strength from the posthumous editions of Lawrence's works and letters. More recently there has been considerable progress as contemporary archives have at last become available. Lawrence has now been adopted as a subject for academic research: a welcome development, since in the final assessment his achievements must be set in their proper historical context.

The closing section of this exhibition illustrates the extraordinary variety of 'Lawrenciana' that has been produced since 1935: plays and films; children's books; biographies; ephemera; translations, and finely printed editions of his works. The sheer range of these materials is astonishing, and only a tiny fraction can be shown here.

This diversity must reflect Lawrence's complex character as well as his practical and intellectual achievements. Few notable careers have been so varied: at different times he was historian, archaeologist, photographer, Intelligence officer, guerilla leader, diplomat, writer, serviceman and mechanic.

But while these exhibits owe part of their existence to Lawrence, they have all been individually and deliberately created. They are the product of differing attitudes and intentions; each one a reaction to some perception of Lawrence the man or Lawrence the legend.

Recumbent effigy of T. E. Lawrence at St.
Martin's Church, Wareham
By Eric Kennington, 1939
(see no. 350)

350
RECUMBENT EFFIGY OF
T. E. LAWRENCE
By Eric Kennington, 1939/54

Eric Kennington began carving an effigy in
1935, at the suggestion of Lawrence's family.
It was completed four years later, and in
September 1939 it was placed in St. Martin's
Church, Wareham. Kennington explained
the thinking behind the effigy as follows: 'A
year before [Lawrence's] death, he and I
talked about the English recumbent effigies of
1200-1600 . . . A plan to make a great book
on these sculptural effigies was stopped by his
death in 1935, so I carved his memorial . . .
[in] an attempt to continue the broken
tradition of our early "image-makers".'[1]
Kennington modelled the face using
photographs, his own earlier bust (see no.
275), and also from memory. Beside
Lawrence's head are the three books he
carried during the Arab Revolt: *The Oxford
Book of English Verse*, *Morte d'Arthur*, and the
Greek Anthology. Beneath his feet is an
example of Hittite sculpture, recalling his
archaeological work at Carchemish.

This cement cast was made in 1954 and
entirely re-worked by the sculptor.

The Trustees of the Tate Gallery (TG 6230)

1. Eric Kennington, quoted in M. Chamot, D. Farr &
M. Butlin, *The Modern British Paintings, Drawings and
Sculpture I*, Tate Gallery, 1964, pp. 356-7.

Ciment fondu, 59.7 × 209.5 × 87.6
Provenance: Purchased from the artist, 1954.
Literature: R. Storrs in E. Kennington, *Drawing the RAF*,
1942, p. 46; *Grosvenor*, nos. 33-5.

351
T. E. LAWRENCE
By Herbert Gurschner, 1934

Although this portrait was painted during
Lawrence's lifetime there is no reference to
Gurschner in Lawrence's recorded correspondence, and it seems unlikely that there
were any sittings. The picture was
commissioned by Desmond Chapman-Huston,
a distant relative of Lawrence's on his
father's side, as the frontispiece for a
projected book: *Ned, An intimate study of
Lawrence of Ireland and Arabia*. This was never
published.

Herbert Gurschner (1901-75) was an
Austrian-born religious painter and print-
maker. The religious influence is evident in
this depiction of Lawrence, which was
probably based on photographs.

The National Gallery of Ireland

Oil on canvas, 97 × 76
Signed br.: *GURSCHNER-TIROL/LONDON*
Provenance: Commissioned by Major D. Chapman-
Huston; given by him, 1950.
Literature: A. Stewart, *Fifty Irish Portraits*, National
Gallery of Ireland, Dublin, 1984, p. 50, ill.; *Grosvenor*,
no. 41.
Exhibitions: Dublin, National Gallery of Ireland, *W. B.
Yeats*, 1965 (167 – as D. H. Lawrence).

352

THE UNVEILING OF THE MEMORIAL TO T. E. LAWRENCE AT ST PAUL'S

(i) Form of service
(ii) An address by the Viscount Halifax
(iii) Ticket for the service

In 1935 a committee was formed to raise money for a memorial to Lawrence, and an appeal was launched in the names of Lord Allenby, Sir Herbert Baker, Winston Churchill, Lionel Curtis, Augustus John, G. B. Shaw and Sir Evelyn Wrench. Appeal leaflets were distributed in copies of Jonathan Cape's edition of *Seven Pillars of Wisdom*.

Part of the money raised was to pay for the installation of a bronze cast of Eric Kennington's 1926 bust (see no. 275) in the crypt of St Paul's Cathedral. The bust itself was given by Eric Kennington and was unveiled on 29 January 1936 by Viscount Halifax, then Chancellor of Oxford University.

A memorial service was held after the unveiling. Lawrence's mother and two surviving brothers were present, as were many of Lawrence's friends including Lord Lloyd, R. V. Buxton, Lord Winterton, Sir Ronald Storrs, Sir Henry McMahon, Lord Trenchard, Winston Churchill, Lord and Lady Astor, Sir Herbert Baker and Lionel Curtis.

This was the only national memorial service for Lawrence; it took place on the day after the state funeral of King George V.

J. M. Wilson

(i) Printed pamphlet, 21.2 × 13.8 (ii) printed pamphlet, 21.3 × 14.1 (iii) printed card, 10.1 × 12.6

(not illustrated)

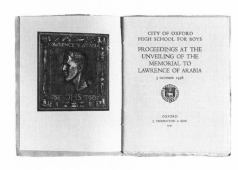

353

PROCEEDINGS AT THE UNVEILING OF THE MEMORIAL TO LAWRENCE OF ARABIA, CITY OF OXFORD HIGH SCHOOL FOR BOYS, 3 OCTOBER 1936
(Published) Oxford, 1937

A further memorial to Lawrence was installed, in October 1936, at his old school. The bronze plaque by Eric Kennington was unveiled by Winston Churchill.

The address given by Churchill was widely reported in the press. He spoke of 'that touch of genius which every one recognises and no one can define', and concluded with a resounding tribute: 'King George the Fifth wrote to Lawrence's brother, "His name will live in history." Can we doubt that that is true? It will live in English letters; it will live in the traditions of the Royal Air Force; it will live in the annals of war and in the legends of Arabia. It will also live here in his old school, for ever proclaimed and honoured by the monument we have to-day unveiled.'[1]

The border of the plaque shows objects associated with the different aspects of Lawrence's life: a saint, a knight, and castles; a dagger and an *agal*; Clouds Hill, books, and a speedboat.

J. M. Wilson

1. Reprinted in *Home Letters*, pp. xiii-xvi.

Printed pamphlet, 22.8
Literature: *Grosvenor*, no. 36.

354

LAWRENCE OF ARABIA MEMORIAL MEDAL
By Eric Kennington, 1935

This medal was struck by the Royal Mint for the Royal Central Asian Society (subsequently renamed the Royal Society for Asian Affairs).

The Society's 'Lawrence of Arabia Memorial Medal' is awarded for work of outstanding merit for the British Empire and for distinction in exploration, research or literature. The first award, in 1936, was to Glubb Pasha 'For pacification in the North Arabian Desert'. Other recipients include Colonel Peake Pasha (1940) 'For services in Transjordan'; Brigadier Orde C. Wingate (1943) 'For the first Chindit Expedition'; Sir John Hunt (1953) and Chris Bonnington (1985), both for the conquest of Everest; Sir Max Mallowan (1969) and Professor Seton Lloyd (1971) for services to archaeology; Wilfred Thesiger (1955) for his work and travel among the Arabs, and Miss Elizabeth Monroe (1980) for services to Arab studies. The most recent recipient was Sandy Gall in 1987, 'for his intrepid and hazardous seeking after the truth in Afghanistan following the intervention of the Soviet Union in the affairs of that country with all the misery which it had entailed for the Afghan people.'

Sandy Gall CBE

Silver, 5 diameter
Obverse: head of T. E. Lawrence, *LAWRENCE OF ARABIA*; reverse: ram's horns on sunburst, *LAWRENCE MEMORIAL/MEDAL CORNUA LEVAT/SUPER TERRAS*
Provenance: Presented to the lender, 1987.
Literature: R. Storrs in E. Kennington, *Drawing the RAF*, 1942, p. 27; *Grosvenor*, no. 31.

355
REVOLT IN THE DESERT
By William Roberts, 1952

Roberts retained a high regard for Lawrence.
He produced this monumental study in 1952.
Lawrence is seen in the lower right hand
corner accompanied by a troop of Bedouin
tribesmen. In contrast to the vorticist works
in *Seven Pillars*, the painting is executed in
the highly idiosyncratic style of Roberts'
later years.

Southampton City Art Gallery (7/1958)

Oil on canvas, 244.7 × 144.8
Signed br. : *William/Roberts*
Provenance : Purchased from RA by Ernest Cooper,
1952 ; purchased by present owner, 1958.
Literature : W. Roberts, *Paintings 1917-1958*, (privately
printed) 1960, p. 52 ; *Grosvenor*, no. 47.
Exhibitions : RA, 1952 (564) ; Arts Council, *William
Roberts ARA*, 1965 (86).

356

ROSS – A DRAMATIC PORTRAIT

By Terence Rattigan

(i) Published text, London, 1960

The opening scene of Terence Rattigan's *Ross* takes place in the RAF recruits' depot at Uxbridge, and the play goes on to present an interpretation of Lawrence's post-war motivation through a sequence of retrospective scenes set during the Arab Revolt. The play was successful both in London and New York, and has been revived several times.

   The dust jacket photograph of Sir Alec Guinness in the title role is by Angus McBean.

J. M. Wilson

Printed book, 224 pp., 19.1

(ii) Programme for a charity performance, Theatre Royal, Haymarket, 18 May 1960

Ross opened at the Theatre Royal, Haymarket, on 12 May 1960, with Alec Guinness in the title role. This charity performance in aid of the Family Welfare Association was given during the following week.

(ii) P.C. & B.A. Metcalfe

Printed pamphlet, 28.7 × 22

357

LAWRENCE OF ARABIA

Feature film directed by David Lean, screenplay by Robert Bolt; Columbia Pictures, 1962

Promotional pamphlets and stills

David Lean's *Lawrence of Arabia* followed *The Bridge on the River Kwai*. A remarkably talented cast was assembled, including Peter O'Toole in the title role, Alec Guinness, Anthony Quinn, Jack Hawkins, Anthony Quayle, Claude Rains, Donald Wolfit and Omar Sharif. It was made on location in Jordan, Spain and Morocco.

   The film was a resounding success, not least for its superb desert sequences. It won seven Oscars: for best picture, best direction, best cinematography in colour, best music score, best sound, best art direction in colour, and best editing. The script was severely criticised for its representation of Lawrence's personality, but the popular image it created has spread all over the world.

John Kobal

P. C. & B. A. Metcalfe

Literature: H. Kent, *Single Bed for Three*, 1963.

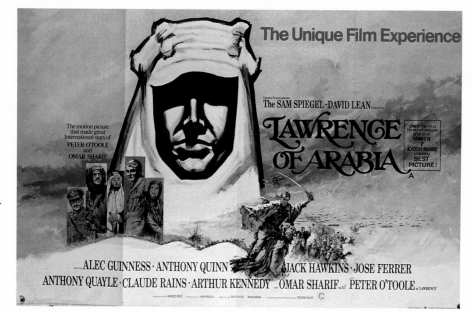

358

SOME FOREIGN LANGUAGE EDITIONS OF T. E. LAWRENCE'S WORKS

FRENCH

(i) *Les Sept Pilliers de la Sagesse*, Paris, 1936

(ii) *La Matrice*, (*The Mint*) Paris, 1955

Lawrence's determined opposition to French imperial ambitions in Syria seems if anything to have fuelled popular interest. *Revolt in the Desert* went through five impressions between 1928 and 1935, and *Seven Pillars of Wisdom* has remained almost continuously in print ever since; it has also been published in a pocket format.

The Mint has been reprinted in both 'Livres de Poche' and a series called 'L'Imaginaire'. Gallimard also published an edition of Lawrence's *Letters* and *The Essential T. E. Lawrence*.

DANISH

(iii) *Oprøret i Ørkenen* (*Revolt in the Desert*), Copenhagen, 1929

(iv) *Mønten* (*The Mint*), Copenhagen, 1956

Revolt in the Desert was published in Danish, Finnish, Norwegian, and Swedish. When the full text of *Seven Pillars* and *The Mint* became available they too were translated into Danish and Swedish.

ESTONIAN

(v) *Seitse Tarkuse Sammast* (*Seven Pillars of Wisdom*), Tartu, 1939

This first volume of an Estonian translation of *Seven Pillars* was published immediately before the war. No copy of a second volume is recorded in United Kingdom collections.

(i) – (v) J. M. Wilson

GERMAN

(vi) *Die Seiben Säulen der Weisheit*, Leipzig, 1936

Revolt in the Desert proved extremely popular in Germany and was reprinted many times. *Seven Pillars* has also been very successful, and was followed by editions of the *Letters*, *The Mint* and *The Essential T. E. Lawrence*.

P. C. & B. A. Metcalfe

JAPANESE

(vii) *Seven Pillars of Wisdom*, Tokyo, 1988

This appears to be the only Japanese translation of a work by T.E. Lawrence.

Heibonsha Publishers Co. Ltd

359

SOME PRIVATE PRESS AND OTHER EDITIONS OF WORKS BY T.E. LAWRENCE

Lawrence had a lifelong interest in fine printing, and made friends with some of the leading printers of his day. Since his death there have been many private press editions of his works, in addition to the specially bound limited editions issued by commercial publishers.

(i) *The Diary of T. E. Lawrence MCMXI*, Corvinus Press, 1937 (203 copies)

Lawrence knew and corresponded with Lord Carlow, proprietor of the Corvinus Press. Five texts by Lawrence and one about him were later printed in Corvinus editions: *The Diary of T.E. Lawrence MCMXI*; *An Essay on Flecker*; *A Letter from T.E. Lawrence to his Mother*; *Letters from T.E. Shaw to Viscount Carlow*; *Two Arabic Folk Tales*, and *Lawrence of Arabia* (the text of speeches by B.H. Liddell Hart and Sir Ronald Storrs).

P. C. & B. A. Metcalfe

(ii) *More Letters from T.E. Shaw to Bruce Rogers*, privately printed by Bruce Rogers at the Printing House of William Edwin Rudge, 1936 (300 copies)

After publication of Lawrence's *Odyssey* translation (see no. 314) Bruce Rogers suggested that it would be appropriate to print a small edition of Lawrence's letters written to him about the project. This was completed in 1933 as *Letters from T. E. Shaw to Bruce Rogers*. Following Lawrence's death this supplementary volume was issued.

J. M. Wilson

(iii) *Crusader Castles*, London, Golden Cockerel Press, 1936, 2 volumes (1,000 copies)

During the 1930s the Golden Cockerel Press was the most successful commercial private press in England. Its books were illustrated by many of the leading artists of the time. Four Lawrence titles were issued: *Crusader Castles* (two volumes); *Men in Print*; *Secret Despatches from Arabia*, and *Shaw-Ede*.

P. C. & B. A. Metcalfe

(iv) *From a Letter of T. E. Lawrence*, Verona, Officina Bodoni, printed for the Double Crown Club 150th dinner, 11 June 1959 (about 75 copies)

Giovanni Mardersteig's Officina Bodoni was, for a considerable period, one of the most famous private presses in the world. This leaflet was not published, but was produced as a keepsake for members of the Double Crown Club, a British society dedicated to fine printing.

J. M. Wilson

(v) *Minorities*, ed. J.M. Wilson, London, Cape, 1971 (125 copies)
T. E. Lawrence's commonplace book

Minorities was published by Jonathan Cape in 1971. This special extra-illustrated edition was issued by Cape in association with the London rare-book specialists Bertram Rota. In the past, Cape had also issued limited editions of *Revolt in the Desert*, *Seven Pillars of Wisdom*, and *The Mint*.

J. M. Wilson

(vi) *The Odyssey of Homer*, New York, Limited Editions Club, 1981 (2,000 copies)

For many years the Limited Editions Club has published handsome books, printed by leading presses and finely illustrated. Lawrence's introduction was included in its edition of C.M. Doughty's *Travels in Arabia Deserta* (1953). The Limited Editions Club *The Odyssey of Homer* was illustrated by Barry Moser and printed at the Hampshire Typothetae.

Dr Lionel Dakers CBE

(vii) *T.E. Lawrence: Letters to E.T. Leeds*, ed. J.M. Wilson, The Whittington Press, 1988 (20 copies)

The Whittington Press is the largest British Private Press currently in operation. Its editions are published in standard and 'special' forms. 650 copies of this edition were issued in buckram, 80 in full Nigerian goatskin, and twenty in this special binding designed by Richard Kennedy.

J. M. Wilson

360
HEAD PIECE FOR THE CORVINUS PRESS
DIARY OF T. E. LAWRENCE MCMXI
By Eric Kennington, 1937

This woodcut was used to illustrate two books printed by Lord Carlow at the Corvinus Press: *The Diary of T. E. Lawrence, MCMXI* (see no. 359 i) and *Two Arabic Folk Tales*. In the former it was used at the head of the text, printed in black on a gilt ground. In *Two Arabic Folk Tales* it is printed in two parts at the head and foot of the title page.

The Family of the Artist

Two-colour print (photo-lithograph), 9.3 × 12.3
Provenance: By descent.
Literature: As above; *Two Arabic Folk Tales*, Corvinus Press, 1927; *Grosvenor*, no. 37.

361
SOME BIOGRAPHIES OF
T. E. LAWRENCE

(i) R. H. Kiernan, *Lawrence of Arabia*, London, 1935

In the wake of Liddell Hart's *'T. E. Lawrence' In Arabia and After* (1934, see no. 320) three authors set to work on shorter popular studies: Charles Edmonds, R. H. Kiernan, and Edward Robinson. They could not have foreseen that demand for such biographies would be greatly increased in 1935 by Lawrence's death and the publication of *Seven Pillars of Wisdom*. Their books were each reprinted several times, but Kiernan's *Lawrence of Arabia* proved to be the most successful. There were thirteen impressions between 1935 and 1951.

(ii) *T. E. Lawrence by his Friends*, ed. A. W. Lawrence, London, 1937

After Lawrence's death, his younger brother and Literary Executor, A. W. Lawrence, considered authorising an official biography in addition to David Garnett's *Letters of T.E. Lawrence*. Instead he decided to publish this collection of 79 essays by people who had known Lawrence well at different stages of his life. In its original form *T. E. Lawrence by his Friends* ran to five impressions. It was also printed in America and Germany. An abridged English edition was published in 1954.

(iii) Clare Sydney Smith, *The Golden Reign – the story of my friendship with Lawrence of Arabia*, London, 1940

A great many of those who met or worked with Lawrence recorded their impressions of him in autobiographies. Clare Sydney Smith was the wife of Lawrence's commanding officer at Mount Batten, and *The Golden Reign* is one of the most important sources of information for this period. It contains fifty otherwise unpublished letters to Wing Commander Sydney Smith and his wife. There have been three editions, but only the first is extensively illustrated.

(iv) Yoshio Nakano, *Arabia no Lawrensu*, Tokyo, 1971

This first Japanese biography of Lawrence was originally published in 1940, and has been reprinted at least nine times.

(v) Richard Aldington, *Lawrence L'Imposteur*, Paris, 1954

In retrospect, Richard Aldington's debunking biography seems to have been an inevitable reaction to the twenty-year accumulation of uncritical adulation which had built up since Lawrence's death. The book might, however, have been more valuable and successful if it had not been written in so venomous a tone. Today, its interest is mainly literary, since the documentary sources now available dispose of the contentious issues Aldington discussed.

This French version preceded the English publication, and news of it caused a furore in the British press, greatly increasing popular demand for the edition published by Collins in 1955.

(vi) Jean Beraud Villars, *Le Colonel Lawrence*, Paris, 1955

For many years this biography (translated into English in 1958) was the best short account of Lawrence's life. It was, however, written from a French political viewpoint, and it repeated a number of convictions about Lawrence which had been widely held

in France for many years. It was therefore the first biography published in English to contain the allegation that Lawrence was involved in espionage activities before the First World War.

(vii) Anthony Nutting, *Lawrence of Arabia – the Man and the Motive*, London, 1961

Anthony Nutting acted as a principal adviser to Sam Spiegel during production of the *Lawrence of Arabia* film. His book was published in time to catch the wave of popular interest generated by the film, and as a result it sold extremely well.

(viii) Victoria Ocampo, *338171 T.E. (Lawrence of Arabia)*, London, 1963

Lawrence's life has intrigued many intellectuals, and has provoked several very thoughtful studies, notably by André Malraux and Victoria Ocampo. Her *338171 T.E.* was written in French and originally published in Argentina in 1942. This English translation by David Garnett was published in 1963. In his introduction A. W. Lawrence stated that the book gave 'the most profound and the best balanced of all portraits of my brother.'

(ix) Suleiman Mousa, *T. E. Lawrence: An Arab View*, Oxford, 1966

First published in Arabic in 1962, this highly critical account of Lawrence's role in the Arab Revolt came as something of a surprise to British readers. It was written, however, without access to the British and French archives of the First World War. When these became available they failed to substantiate Mousa's case against Lawrence and other European officers serving in the Arab Revolt.

(x) Philip Knightley and Colin Simpson, *The Secret Lives of Lawrence of Arabia*, London, 1969

In 1968 the *Sunday Times* acquired sensational information to the effect that Lawrence had periodically subjected himself to severe beatings during the post-war years. This was used in a series of articles on Lawrence, which were followed a year later by a full-length biography. The marketing of the book was remarkable: translation rights were sold at the Frankfurt Book Fair in 1968, even though little of the book had at that stage

been written. It was translated into more languages than any other Lawrence biography.

(xi) John E. Mack, *A Prince of our Disorder, the Life of T. E. Lawrence*, London, 1976

John E. Mack, a professor of Psychiatry at Harvard Medical School, spent ten years researching this study of Lawrence. It is likely to remain of enduring importance and interest for its informed examination of Lawrence's motivation and attitudes.

(xii) Konrad Morsey, *T. E. Lawrence und der arabische Aufstand 1916/18*, Osnabrück, 1976

It is perhaps ironic that the first serious study of Lawrence's wartime role using British and German documents should have been carried out by a German scholar. Morsey's book remains one of the most thorough and important investigations into Lawrence's part in the Arab Revolt.

(xiii) Maurice Larès, *T. E. Lawrence, la France et les Français*, Paris, 1980

This book was drawn from a 1,200-page thesis for the French *Doctorat d'Etat*. It is the most substantial piece of academic work undertaken on Lawrence to date. As the title implies, it examines every aspect of the relationship between Lawrence, France, and French opinion.

(xiv) *The T. E. Lawrence Puzzle*, ed. Stephen E. Tabachnick, University of Georgia Press, 1984

The T. E. Lawrence Puzzle contains fifteen essays about different aspects of Lawrence's career by academic writers from America, Britain, France, Germany, and Israel.

J. M. Wilson

362
CHILDREN'S LITERATURE RELATING TO T. E. LAWRENCE

Lawrence's adventures with the Arabs have been a popular subject for children's books for many years. The titles below are only a small selection from this very wide field of publishing.

(i) Lowell Thomas, *The Boys' Life of Colonel Lawrence*, New York, 1927 (also published in England)

(ii) *Boys' Magazine*, 12 January 1929 (includes free tin badge)

(iii) Gurney Slade, *In Lawrence's Bodyguard*, London, 1931

Gurney Slade wrote two other children's novels about Lawrence: *Led by Lawrence* and *Lawrence in the Blue*.

(i)–(iii) P. C. & B. A. Metcalfe

(iv) Rowland Walker, 'Lawrence of Arabia' in *The Wonder Book of Daring Deeds*, London, 1937

J. M. Wilson

(v) Robert Graves, *Lawrence and the Arabs*, Children's Edition, London, 1938

P. C. & B. A. Metcalfe

(vi) Major J. T. Gorman, *With Lawrence to Damascus*, (Great Exploits), Oxford, 1940

J. M. Wilson

(vii) James Cadell, *The Young Lawrence of Arabia*, London, 1960

(viii) Kenneth Allen, *Lawrence of Arabia*, (Macdonald Adventures), London, 1978

(vii–viii) P. C. & B. A. Metcalfe

363
LAWRENCE OF ARABIA: POSTHUMOUS EPHEMERA

Lawrence has been the subject of a wide range of ephemeral and exotic publications. Jane Sherwood's *Post-Mortem Journal* contains a record of the medium's messages from beyond the grave; Beatrice Epstein's article in *Prediction* is an astrological analysis.

Comic strip books are much more popular in Europe than in England: examples shown here originate in Spain, Italy and France. The Italian version includes a glamorous female character.

(i) Jane Sherwood, *Post-Mortem Journal* – *communications from T. E. Lawrence through the mediumship of Jane Sherwood*, London, 1964

J. M. Wilson

(ii) Beatrice Epstein, 'T. E. Lawrence, an astrological profile', in *Prediction*, April 1963

P. C. & B. A. Metcalfe

(iii) Mitchell's cigarette card: *A Gallery of 1935, no. 49: Lawrence of Arabia*

(iv) Brooke Bond tea card: *Famous People, no. 37: T. E. Lawrence*

(v) Comic strip book: Elliot Dooley, *Lawrence van Arabië*, Amsterdam, 1974 (Originally published in Spain, 1963)

(vi) Comic strip book: F. Tacconi, *L'Homme du Desert*, Montreal, 1979 (originally published Milan, 1976)

(iii)–(vi) J. M. Wilson

(vii) Comic strip book: Combelle, *Lawrence d'Arabie, ou le mirage du désert*, 1983

Private collection

1888

16 August : born Tremadoc, Wales

1896

Family settles at 2 Polstead Road,
Oxford, having lived briefly in Scotland,
France and the New Forest.
September : enrols at City of Oxford High
School for Boys

1907

July : leaves school
October : goes up to Jesus College,
Oxford

1908

Summer : bicycle tour in France

1909

Summer : walking tour in Syria

1910

July : awarded First Class Honours in
Modern History, partly on merits of
thesis on medieval military architecture
December : travels to Jebail

1911

March : begins work as archaeologist at
Carchemish

1913

Summer : brings Dahoum and Hamoudi to
Oxford

1914

January–February : Sinai Survey
June : spring season at Carchemish ends
October : joins Geographical Section,
War Office
December : sent to Cairo Intelligence
Department

1915

May : Frank Lawrence killed
October : Will Lawrence reported
missing

1916

March–May : sent to Mesopotamia
End April : fall of Kut
5 June : Arab Revolt begins
October : to Hejaz, meets Feisal

1917

January : capture of Wejh
March : Wadi Ais
May : starts for Akaba
June : secret northern journey behind
Turkish lines in Syria
6 July : capture of Akaba

Early July : crosses Sinai to Egypt, meets
Allenby for first time
November : Azrak ; captured and tortured
at Deraa
11 December : joins official allied entry
into Jerusalem

1918

January : Tafileh
April : Waheida
August : Azrak
September : Tafas
1 October : enters Damascus
4 October : leaves Damascus for England
11 November : Armistice
December : with Feisal in Britain

1919

January : to Paris for Peace Conference
April : father dies
Starts work on Seven Pillars
14 August : first Lowell Thomas
travelogue at Covent Garden
November : elected to All Souls
Loses MS of Seven Pillars

1920

September : finishes second version of
Seven Pillars
December : joins Middle East
Department, Colonial Office

1921

March : Cairo Conference
July–September : negotiates with Hussein
and Abdullah

1922

Redrafts Seven Pillars
July : resigns from Colonial Office
August : enlists in RAF as John Hume
Ross, sent to RAF Training Depot,
Uxbridge
Writes 'Uxbridge Notes'
November : transferred to RAF School of
Photography, Farnborough
27 December : Daily Express reveals
enlistment

1923

Discharged from RAF
March : enlists in Tank Corps as T.E.
Shaw, sent to Bovington Camp
Summer : rents Clouds Hill

1924

With Lawrence in Arabia by Lowell Thomas
published in USA

1925

June : threatens suicide
July : transferred to RAF, sent to RAF
College, Cranwell

1926

December : subscribers' Seven Pillars issued
Posted to RAF Depot, Drigh Road,
Karachi

1927

March : Revolt in the Desert published
Summer : starts revising the 'Uxbridge
Notes' for The Mint
Lawrence and the Arabs by Robert Graves
published

1928

March : finishes The Mint
May : transferred to RAF Depot at
Miranshah
Autumn : begins work on translation of the
Odyssey
September–December : press speculation
links Lawrence with unrest in Afghanistan

1929

January : sent back to England
March : transferred to RAF Cattewater
(later RAF Mount Batten)
September : works with Sydney Smith on
Schneider Trophy

1930–5

Works on high speeed seaplane tenders
and armoured target towing vessels for
RAF at Plymouth, Hythe and Bridlington

1932

Completes provisional issue of notes for
200 class seaplane tender
The Odyssey of Homer translation published
First performance of Too True to be Good
by G.B. Shaw

1934

'T.E. Lawrence' In Arabia and After by Basil
Liddell Hart published

1935

February : leaves RAF
13 May : crashes motorcycle on returning
from Bovington to Clouds Hill
19 May : dies without regaining
consciousness

The exhibition organisers would like to thank the following for permission to publish copyright material in the following catalogue entries and essays:
Edward Arnold 215
Lady Astor's Literary Executors: Sir John Astor and Sir Edward Ford 308
Mr Bruce Burroughs 310, 311
Jonathan Cape Ltd 17, 21, 22, 88, 96, 157, 171, 176, 191, 198, 202, 207, 232, 236, 239, 241, 264, 275, 304, 326, 332, 333, 338, The War n.1, n.7, n.17
Century Hutchinson Limited 117
Winston S. Churchill Esq. MP 245, *Seven Pillars of Wisdom* n.20
Collins Publishers 258
The Daily Telegraph 191, 344
The Edward Garnett Estate 214
The Glasgow Herald 178
The Hamlyn Publishing Group 297
William Heinemann Ltd 197, International Diplomacy n.6, 264, 286
The Principal and Fellows, Jesus College, Oxford 65
The Augustus John Estate 264, 294
A.W. Lawrence, the Trustees of the Seven Pillars of Wisdom Trust and the T.E. Lawrence Letters Trust 7, 19, 21, 23, 30, 31, 34, 38, 39, 40, 48, 49, 50, 52, 53, 54, 62, 64, 65, 67, 68, 80, 81, 83, 84, 85, 88, 90, 91, 98, 99, 102, 108, 109, 117, 120, 122, 125, 126, 127, 133, 136, 146, 160, 172, 180, 182, 184, 185, 186, 190, 191, 193, 197, 198, 204, 205, 209, 211, 215, 218, 221, 224, 230, 231, 232, 233, 236, 237, 238, 239, 240, 242, 243, 244, 245, 248, 252, 254, 255, 256, 257, 259, 260, 261, 262, 263, 264, 265, 266, 268, 270, 272, 273, 274, 276, 278, 279, 280, 281, 284, 285, 306, 307, 308, 310, 312, 313, 315, 318, 323, 324, 329, 330, 331, 332, 333, 334, 335, 345, 349, Youth n.1, n.2, Carchemish n.1, n.2, n.3, n.4, n.11, The War n.12, n.14, n.20, International Diplomacy n.3, n.5, n.7, n.8, n.11, n.,12, Seven Pillars of Wisdom n.3, n.4, n.6, n.9, n.10, n.12, n.14, n.15, n.17, In The Ranks n.2, n.7, n.8, n.10, n.12, n.14, n.16, n.18
Methuen & Co. Ltd 301
John Murray (Publishers) 84
The Trustees of the Paul Nash Estate 239
Oxford University Press 144
The Palestine Exploration Fund 72
Crown-copyright material in the Public Record Office is reproduced by permission of the Controller of Her Majesty's Stationery Office 98, 100, 105, 121, 123, 129, 132, 166, The War n.8, 203, n.4
The Bernard Shaw Estate The War n.10
The Sunday Times 194
Tate Gallery, London 350.
A.P. Watt Ltd on behalf of the Rt. Hon. Lord Tweedsmuir of Elsfield CBE 271

Photographic Acknowledgements

Photographs, manuscripts and documents from the Reserve Collection in the Bodleian Library are among a collection of biographical materials given by Lawrence's literary executor, his brother A.W. Lawrence, and embargoed until the year 2000. The exhibition organisers are particularly grateful to A.W. Lawrence and the Trustees of the Seven Pillars of Wisdom Trust for their permission to show these in the current exhibition and to reproduce them in this catalogue. (See nos. 8, 10, 15, 149, 201, 269, 274, 292, 299, 300, 304.)

Photographs from the Department of Western Asiatic Antiquities at the British Museum are from papers relating to the excavations at Carchemish 1911–14 and are reproduced by permission of the Trustees of the British Museum. The negative numbers are given at the foot of each entry. (See nos. 52(i)–(iv), 53(i)–(iii), 68(i)–(iv).)

Photographs from Lawrence's own collection of albums given to the Imperial War Museum are reproduced with the permission of the Trustees of the Imperial War Museum. Negative numbers are given at the foot of each entry. (See nos. 92, 94, 100(i)–(iv), 117(i)–(vii), 123(i)–(vii), 130, 132(i)–(ix), 133(i)–(iv), 143, 150, 156(i)–(iv), 159, 183, 202, 234.)

The exhibition organisers would also like to thank the following for making copyright photographs available in the following catalogue entries. All other photographs were provided by owners of the exhibits, or the sources given in the catalogue:
By gracious permission of Her Majesty The Queen 244; Vivien John 115; The Kobal Collection 357; by kind permission of Mrs Felix Man 273; Charles Pocklington Associates 342; the reproduction of the head of Hypnos (39) is copyright of the Trustees of the British Museum. Many of the exhibits have been photographed by Barnes & Webster, Frank Thurston and Eileen Tweedy.